A WOMAN'S CHALLENGING JOURNEY FROM
DENIED DREAMS TO SELF-DISCOVERY

RIVERS
Rock Me
HOME

LILAH L. LEWIS

Rivers Rock Me Home

Copyright 2023 to Lilah L. Lewis

Cover design and formatting by Let's Get Booked:

www.letsgetbooked.com

Dedicated to those who seek to adjust

and move forward

PART ONE:

Home

"Truth is stranger than fiction, but it is because fiction is obliged to stick to possibilities; truth isn't."

Mark Twain

PROLOGUE

Rivers

Spanking didn't work. Time out didn't work. Shaming didn't work. Reasoning didn't work. Star charts didn't work. Stella Ann's parents struggled to manage her strong will, sassy attitude, independent manner, and impulsive behavior. It was a constant battle.

"I met with Stella Ann's teachers today about moving her out of the split second and third-grade class. When we received the list of students in the split class, I knew it would be a disaster for her to be in a large class. I asked if she could be moved to the fourth grade. The challenge would keep her busy, but the teachers told me Stella Ann was too young," Lou said.

"We had no forewarning she would be placed in the split class. Being the busy-body-want-to-help kind of kid she is, we knew she would be in trouble constantly," Burt replied.

"So, Burt, now what?"

"We make ourselves as visible as possible at the school to keep an eye on Stella Ann's mischief. We need to determine if constant punishment is warranted. It is unreasonable for her to miss every recess and receive hand paddling. Following through with more involvement will depend mostly on you, Lou."

"I am willing to do anything to help Stella Ann stay out of trouble. I will volunteer in the library and cafeteria and offer to be the room mother for the class of all 36 kids."

Even with her parents' best efforts, Stella Ann stayed in trouble. She wasn't a bully or mean. She was impulsive, would not stay in her seat, blurted out answers to questions, talked too much, was the class clown, and assigned herself as Miss Take Care of Everyone. She always finished her work early, got excellent grades, and proceeded to help the other kids finish their work. She felt lucky she still had the feeling in her left hand from all the hand paddling she received from her teacher. Mrs. Davis could make even one lick with her paddle sting for an hour afterward.

"Young lady, if I am called to this school again, you may never leave your room until you are an old lady. Stella Ann, I need to work to keep our family going. I can't keep coming here to negotiate your punishment. Stop your constant chatter, and for goodness sake, stop bothering other kids. I am on the verge of signing a waiver for you to be paddled by the principal," Burt lectured as they left the principal's office.

"I want to help my classmates and the teacher, and I get in trouble for trying to be nice. I don't like this school, Daddy. I want to go home to Columbia, where I have friends," eight-year-old Stella Ann replied.

She was not alone in that sentiment. Although the move to Nashville had originally promised to be a positive step forward for the family, it was a disastrous decision.

When school ended, they moved back to Columbia, which was beneficial to the whole family. Stella Ann was challenged in her class, and the only change in her behavior was that she cried. Ron, her older brother, was quickly included in the circle of friends he left two years before. Lou was close to her family, and Burt had a new job he liked.

Burt and Lou decided the best thing they could do was to keep Stella Ann busy. Putting a tennis racket in her hand proved to be positive for her. They had her on the tennis court as much as time and opportunity allowed.

Stella Ann challenged others and needed to be challenged.

"Why can't I go to the rodeo carnival, too?" Stella Ann almost screamed at the breakfast table. "Ron gets to do everything, and I always have to stay at home." She usually didn't mind staying home, but the rodeo carnival was the event of the year in their small town.

Burt replied, "Stella Ann, you are only twelve. It is not a safe place for young girls at night. We will take you and a friend to the carnival on Saturday afternoon before the rodeo starts."

"Daddy, you always say I can be anything and do anything if I work hard, but then you tell me I can't go to a carnival because I am a girl. I don't understand."

"Someday you will. I still believe you can do and be anything you want. You have many rivers to cross and bridges to burn before you are considered grown. Stella Ann, you are not going to the carnival with a group of kids older than you. We are not going to discuss this again."

Defiantly, Stella Ann said, "I can't wait to get out of this boring town. I want more. I want to be more and do more. When I graduate, I will leave, have some freedom, make my own decisions, and only come back to visit." Burt did not respond to her immature, temper-tantrum babble.

Her daddy was right. She had rivers to cross, bridges to burn, rocks to skip, and hours of riverbank counseling to seek before she returned to her hometown for good. Thirty years of living in marital turmoil and scandal explained her constant exhaustion. Her despair and determination pushed her to find the peace she desired and rightfully deserved. It was time to think of herself for a change.

Rivers, as a metaphor for Stella Ann's life, provided the perfect flow and balance between rage and serenity. For her, rivers reflected unsolicited turbulence, self-created chaos, temporary stagnation, and earned calmness.

River rocks, whether smooth and round or sharp and angular, guarded nature's secrets, showed evidence of water rages and conducted ripples of sweet music. River rocks held stories in solid confidence until the end of time unlike the messages of dancing rivers which encouraged constant movement.

Stella Ann crossed four significant physical rivers often. The Duck River surrounded her hometown, was shallow in places, and flooded the area during heavy rainstorms. It burst onto the lower field of her family's place. The river crept slowly to her parents' house and settled at the apple and pear trees near a small barn. Encroaching water forced the movement of their small menagerie of horses and cows to higher ground. The Duck

River shouted home to Stella Ann; it changed over time yet maintained a consistent presence. She sighed a deep breath of relief when she traveled home and saw the road signs that identified the Duck River. She was safe.

The Cumberland River was a distinct landmark in Nashville, a partner hometown for Stella Ann. Her family made necessary trips to Nashville to shop, go to movies, have a rare restaurant meal, and visit relatives. The Cumberland River had a dominant presence in the area. They crossed the Cumberland River to travel to the only home they had ever known, Columbia. They cringed to think their trips home were visits. They lived in Nashville for two years, but it never seemed like home to them. When they crossed the Cumberland River on the Shelby Park ferry, the novelty appeased Stella Ann and her brother during their return trips to Nashville. It only happened if there was extra money in her Daddy's pocket to pay the fare. The other option was to drive over the Shelby Street bridge.

The Life and Casualty building was a landmark in Nashville, and Stella Ann's grandfather worked there. He took her to the top to a lookout balcony where she saw the Cumberland River winding its way around the city. For a quarter, she looked through a telescopic contraption and saw the river up close. She never knew how prominent the Cumberland River was until she was an adult and saw the river from an airplane.

To Stella Ann, the Tennessee River followed her everywhere. She daydreamed, made plans, and solved life's problems as she sat on the banks of the Tennessee River in Knoxville. She crossed it when she traveled back and forth between Chattanooga and Nashville. The bridge she traveled across the Tennessee River to visit her college roommate in West Tennessee scared her, and as she crossed it, she gripped her steering wheel so tightly her hands cramped. The Tennessee River, at that juncture, rivaled the Mississippi River.

She sat on a park bench on the bank that overlooked the Tennessee River in downtown Chattanooga when she needed to be alone or to sort out her life. To be close to such natural beauty and strength made her problems shrink in size. Eating at one of the restaurants along the river and watching the sun set was a huge treat. One treasured event in Chattanooga was the Sunset Symphony on the Fourth of July. Stella Ann swelled with pride to be in a city with diverse and polished musical talent, which was present in most areas of Tennessee. The celebratory fireworks from a barge on the river were magnificent. The crowd behaved, had genuine fun, and expressed gratitude for their country.

Then there was the Mississippi River. It was powerful and majestic as its muddy waters churned forward, outlining the western border of the state. Stella Ann was twenty years old when she saw the Mississippi River for the first time. She thought it odd the Tennessee/Arkansas boundaries landed in the middle of the river. The drive across the Tennessee/Arkansas bridge was an adventure. One never forgot the river was in charge and flowed with the authority of a king over his kingdom.

Stella Ann crossed the rivers of her life via many bridges. Some bridges grew to be landmarks of comfort and other bridges were burned to preserve her self-respect and inner peace. Rivers of raw, sad emotion shrouded her for years, but rivers of mercy and laughter sustained her and gave her hope and strength. She didn't know how she would get there, but she knew she would return to the hometown she promised to leave and never return to decades before.

CHAPTER 1

Fear

Stella Ann repeatedly challenged her luck at the stop sign at the end of the road where her family lived. She pressed her foot all the way down on the gas pedal of her little white Volkswagen, looked to the left without stopping at the end of the road, and pulled out onto Highway 31 toward town. She had honed her driving and timing skills like those of a race car driver but knew she would eventually get caught if she didn't stop playing traffic and police roulette.

As she rushed to the football game, Stella Ann never realized she was being followed until she crossed the Duck River, a river that wove around Columbia and Maury County. Commanding blue lights flashed in her rearview mirror. She whispered a forbidden swear word as she pulled her car to the bumpy, narrow shoulder of the road. She took a deep breath, got her license out of her purse, and waited for the trooper to approach her car. When he asked to see her license, she was prepared to hand it over.

As he looked at her license, he mumbled a low-pitched sound of frustration. He returned it and asked, "Is your daddy Burt Langston?"

"Yes, sir," Stella Ann replied as she swallowed hard. Her heart raced as she wondered if she would get a speeding ticket requiring her to work extra hours at the flower shop to pay her daddy back.

"I clocked you at 35 miles an hour as you pulled onto the highway and ignored the stop sign. You sped up to 50 miles an hour as you approached the Duck River bridge. It is a 30-mile-an-hour speed zone all the way into town. I know your daddy. Your ticket is to tell your daddy you got pulled over. I will follow up with him about your driving. Stop at stop signs, slow down, and pay attention to your rearview mirror."

"Yes, sir," Stella Ann replied. "And I promise I won't do it again." Both knew she would. The officer let her go without an official monetary ticket, which would have been better for her than the punishment of telling her daddy. She decided she might as well go to the game. It could be the last game she would get to attend for a few weeks.

She watched the officer depart into the distance and continued her drive to the football game. Her mind raced, thinking of what would likely happen when she returned home. She was sure her daddy had already heard about her state trooper encounter on the police radio he kept in their family room and never shut down.

She knew she was in trouble, and a parent/child standoff would happen when she got home. The dead silence always seemed like hours but would only be minutes. After a few minutes, Burt would clear his throat and say, "Have you got something you want to tell us, young lady?" The question confirmed he knew what had happened, and her confession would bubble out as she endured the hardline parental wrath of her father. Grounded was a concept Stella Ann knew well. Despite the consequences of her fast driving and other impulsive teenaged antics, her sixteenth year proved to be one of the best years of her life.

Stella Ann waited at the stoplight that controlled traffic at the intersection of Carter's Creek Pike and Columbia Highway. She silently scanned the changes which had evolved in the area during the thirty years she was away. Her recognition of the small historic town where she grew up was clouded by incomprehensible change. Now concrete buildings, manufacturing plants, and new roads replaced working farms that once peppered the land. Commercial signs and lights illuminated the night sky in all directions when a few years earlier two stoplights controlled Main Street.

There had been a farm with a beautiful white two-story clapboard house, white fence, and horses grazing in the field near the intersection. As a child and young teen, she attended birthday parties and hayrides there. She got her first kiss at that farm.

Bradford, her future boyfriend, led her to the fence next to the horse barn, and the full moon glowed with a smile. Bradford was polite and asked if he could kiss her. She nervously nodded her head yes. Her body and mind exploded with silent fireworks and beautiful inner music. Cupid worked his magic. Commercial establishments and a fire station now stand where horses grazed and where she and Bradford kissed for the first time. They were thirteen years old.

The light was long to accommodate heavy traffic, and she let her memories help her consume the time. A few miles north, outside the city limits of the small town of Spring Hill, was a fish place and a hamburger joint. Years before, those establishments sat in the dark. Now, they glowed from the commercial lights illuminating the area.

The traffic light wasn't at Carter's Creek Pike and Highway 31 when she left Columbia thirty years earlier, but neither was Saturn Parkway and other new construction. Progress laced with good intentions played a nasty trick on her hometown and other small towns in the beautiful state of Tennessee.

The light turned green, and the driver behind her honked in a continuous and impatient hurry. Stella Ann thought to herself the driver must be a transplant, a Yankee. Original residents of the area would never think to be so rude. The abrasive noise of the horn brought her back from her short mental vacation. She looked down at Cash, her fluffy little spaniel, who sat in the passenger seat. They were on their way to check on her mother and run errands. With each visit, Lou successfully talked Stella Ann into leaving Cash with her for a few hours. Lou and Cash were best buddies, but at 94, Mama was not interested in a fulltime dog. Cash's visits and play sessions were enough for Lou.

"Anybody home? Mama, we are here. How are you today? Stella Ann hollered as she went through the kitchen. Lou was in her typical place, her comfortable chair in the family room where she could see out the picture window. Hollering was necessary because her mama was deaf in one ear and losing hearing in the other.

"In here!" Mama replied. She was reading the paper as her TV blasted. Mama always read the paper cover to cover and back again. She was an avid reader, and the family kept her supplied with books, magazines, and newspapers.

"Come here, baby boy," she said as she looked at Cash wagging his fluffy tail with anticipation. I know you want your treats and cold water. I can't resist spoiling you when you look at me with your big brown eyes. You are a sweet boy. We will get your snacks in a minute." She treated Cash like he was a child, and he loved every minute of it.

As she looked at Stella Ann, she half stated and half asked, "You are going to leave him with me, aren't you? We haven't had a play day in a long time."

"Of course, Mama, I will leave him with you for a couple of hours."

"Stella Ann, I put several articles on the kitchen table you need to read. One article is about the election. There is an obituary of someone who was in your class, and the last one is about books and writing. It was a very good read, and it might help you when you write your book. You should set up a schedule and set a goal to have it written by your next birthday."

Stella Ann thought to herself, "Won't she ever stop telling me what I need to read and what to do?" She concluded the answer was no because it is what mothers do regardless of their child's age.

She continued her inner thoughts as her mama continued to chatter.

"Mama is remarkable for her age. She looks and acts much younger than her calendar years. She lives in the home she and Daddy built sixty years earlier. She takes care of herself and the place and watches the neighborhood. Mama toggles between being a concerned neighbor and a nosey old lady. She watches the neighborhood and mentally documents each car in the neighbors' driveways as well as the passengers in each. Tom, her favorite radio celebrity, and information buddy, keeps her attention peeled toward city and county functions. She doesn't miss a show. She treasures Thursday mornings when he invites guests on his radio show. Mama believed if Tom said something was so, it was the gospel truth."

"Ok, Mama, I'll get those articles when I come to get Cash. To answer your question about the book, I have it outlined. Hopefully, I will break through the obstacle of fear I have harbored for years when I finally sit down to focus and write. I will be back in a couple of hours to get Cash. You two have fun."

She approached her car, stopped, and hung her arm over the opened driver's side door. She looked toward the back field. She thought about all the nature walks, horseback rides, and creek excursions she took as a kid. The park that swarmed with kids daily was not on the other side of the creek when she was a kid. It was an empty unused field. For a rare and risky adventure, she and her brother climbed a wobbly wire fence at the creek to access a historic campsite used by Union soldiers during the Civil War. They picked up mini balls and rusted treasures there.

Stella Ann Langston Taber was a newly retired teacher at 65, yet by her son's standards she was forever twelve years old. He often said she would never grow up, and they laughed about it. In her mind, time was of the essence to accomplish her goal, yet she was the world's worst procrastinator. She felt her creative ideas had to marinate to come to full fruition. Sometimes her ideas turned sour and faded, and she moved on to something else. Poetry and song writing had been an exciting venture at one time, but prose was her present passion. If she could only focus for more than a split second, she could make her book happen.

She liked to remember the good old days when people knew each other and took care of each other. Families were local and supportive, and friends were loyal. Progress was a fact of life. A lot happened in her life and in her hometown while she was gone. Some good, others not.

Most people born and raised in Columbia said the complexion of the town had improved, but the people had changed. Many original Columbia residents claimed frustration and bewilderment because no one on Main Street knew them anymore. The original families who had sustained Columbia dwindled each year.

It seemed Columbia was on a fast track to merge with Spring Hill,

Franklin, Brentwood, and Nashville. All of those towns had become landing places for many people from other parts of the country and the world. People with deep family roots in small southern towns called the invaders Yankees regardless of where they were from.

Lou instilled a love and fascination with the written word in Stella Ann before she could hold a book. Lou and Burt provided their children with regular visits to the library, especially during the summer. They owned one car, so Burt would take them to the library after lunch and pick them up on his way home from work. If it was a pretty day, they would walk home.

Stella Ann was never ready to leave the library. She remembered the creaky floor and the smell of the old Maury County Library. She loved to sit in the little chairs in the children's room as she decided which two books she wanted to take home. She tolerated the familiar musty smell of the worn books and inhaled the crisp paper and ink smell of the new books. Her competitive spirit led her to want to be the first one to write her name on the library card to check out a new book. The librarian was a very nice old lady with gray hair pulled back in a bun. She wore black lace up jalopy looking shoes which made a clomping sound on the wooden floors. She always wore a black cardigan and day dress belted right under her bosom.

Her mama read to her every day, and as she got older encouraged her to read, write, draw, or color. A new "Little Golden Book" was a well-guarded treasure, and a new box of Crayola crayons, the 64 count with a sharpener, was like a birthday surprise over and over to Stella Ann. Paper doll books appeared if she was sick, and she spent hours on the gray and green living room rug cutting them out and playing with them. Her grandmother would save magazines for her and Lou, and each month one included a paper doll called Betsy. Betsy always had the prettiest clothes. Her mother taught her books were to be handled with care and never thrown away or abused. Lou also taught her kids books and toys were to be shared. Stella Ann did not care for the sharing rule.

By the time Stella Ann was nine years old, she could not get enough of the written word. Her favorite author was Carol Ryrie Brink who wrote

Caddie Woodlawn. She also loved history and biography books, especially those about Andrew and Rachel Jackson and Abraham Lincoln. Despite her short attention span and constant activity level, books intrigued her. She spent hours in her room reading. Stella Ann had no concept of time when she sat in the hall by the bookshelf. She was mesmerized with the vast information housed in the red leather-bound World Book Encyclopedia set Lou insisted they provide for their children. It took Lou and Burt years to pay off such an expensive investment.

Stella Ann kept a diary from the time she was nine years old. Her first diary from Lou was a red five-year diary with a brass lock and tiny key. It held the dreams of childhood as well as the names of the four children she would like to have someday. There was an entry about the death of President and Mrs. Kennedy's new baby shortly after birth. The loss of the Kennedy baby was covered on TV and made a profound impact on Stella Ann. She promised herself someday she would name one of her children after baby Kennedy.

Some years held only a few entries in her diary; other years the pages exploded with entries and spilled over into the next year's space. Life and loss of focus got in her way, and she neglected her diary, but she always came back to her writing. The joy and freedom she equated with writing were interrupted when her diaries and her innermost thoughts were discovered and shared. Her pen became idle; her words silenced. She later taught others to write and to enjoy the creative freedom and beauty of the written word. As a teacher, she fiercely guarded the creative and personal written words of her students.

As an adult, each time Stella Ann tried to write she would become overwhelmed. The daily routines of life became burdensome, and she would lose focus. She watched her life instead of participating in it with the freedom she desired. She was fearless as a child. As an adult she covered fear with isolation, lies, stories, excuses, jokes, and laughter.

When she gave herself the freedom to write about ideas swirling in her head, fear stopped her after the first paragraph or two. Stella Ann read about seasoned authors who took years to write a book and understood the claim. She also understood authors who wrote only one book. It was an exhausting process and could be equally daunting and exhilarating.

Her thoughts ran rampant. "Would her "writer's block" episodes take over? Was the purpose of writing to help someone or to cleanse her own soul?" An honest answer included both.

Stella Ann decided to burst out of the trap of conventional English structure and write. She embraced the idea of author's privilege. She decided to let go of an intense fear which consumed most of her adult life. She stopped looking over her shoulder. It was liberating to take a breath of fresh air and move forward. The question in the back of her mind that haunted her was if the new energy and rush of adrenalin would last until she completed her book. She was notorious for dropping a project midway.

It was more than a story; it was a journey of forgiveness and revelation. It was a raw open wound begging to heal. The purpose of her writing screamed selfish and self-absorbed, but it cut deep into the very core of Stella Ann's soul and revealed the reasons for the angst she desired to bury. There were incidents for which she was to blame or shared the blame; other incidents originated from sources having nothing to do with her.

Stella Ann hated the victim's label and mentality. She wasn't a victim but a participant and codependent enabler. She desired to be a woman who figured life out regardless of her delayed and failed attempts. She possessed guts and a driven determination to fix things, especially her life. Her story would give credence to how she dug her way out of turmoil, scandal, and a haunting false narrative about her that cried for clarity. She was forced to accept some questions had no answer, and things needing closure remained an open but manageable wound. Stella Ann was ready for the challenge.

Stella Ann wondered if she would find herself again. The real Stella Ann was buried deep in the recesses of her reality, her story, her truth. She delved off into a desperate void along her way. "Would she reclaim and solidify her core values? Was she ready to meet the person she had become after spending years lost to someone else's dream? Was she ready for truth or would she find safety in fiction?"

There was more than one answer.

CHAPTER 2

Learn to Adjust

"No, Stella, you cannot go to The University of Tennessee. You have two options. You can go to Campbell University and play tennis for them or go to Clarkston State, a fine school where many of the kids from Columbia attend. If you don't like those options, young lady, then you can get a job in town and live at home," Burt said with authority as they sat at the breakfast table. He referred to her as a young lady when he expected her to listen and respect his authority. Stella Ann cringed then as well as when he called her Stella.

Breakfast was nonnegotiable. The family was required at the breakfast table no matter what. It was Burt's rule. The only excuse not to be at breakfast was illness. Lou made a full breakfast every morning of homemade biscuits, oats or cream of wheat, scrambled eggs, bacon or sausage, and fresh orange juice. A rare treat would be cold cereal or cinnamon rolls.

"But, Daddy, it makes more sense for me to go to a school where I will be happy," Stella Ann quipped back. "You immediately squelched my desire to go to Memphis State with some of my friends and now you won't even consider UT. You want to control every part of my life." Stella Ann knew she should not play the control card. It never served her well.

"You are exactly right. We will control every bit of your life until you are on your own. Raising you has been like being in a cage with a tiger every step of the way. It is our job as parents to make sure you are supported and safe. Now, young lady, you need to get to school." Burt was obviously flustered and bordered on angry. Stella Ann backed off. She realized further argument would get her nowhere with her daddy, and she shut down.

"You can get a good education at either of the schools you are offered, Stella, and the schools within your reach are excellent. Anywhere you go, young lady, you have to apply yourself and work hard," Burt replied with a tense voice. "You aren't always going to be happy, Stella. You've got to learn to adjust and make the best of life."

Lou sat buttering her biscuit and listened intently as she watched and listened to the verbal sparring match between her husband and daughter. It wasn't the first one nor the last.

Burt Langston was determined for his kids to get an education. It was something he valued but never had the opportunity to pursue. He went to Columbia Military Academy for ninth and tenth grades and then transferred to Central High School. He dropped out of school his senior year for a short tour in the Navy. Burt was a mechanic by trade and quickly moved into management. He worked long hard hours to provide for his family. He was a proud man, and his kids never knew their financial struggles. Money or sex was never mentioned in the family, and he rarely changed his mind once he dug in on a subject.

Stella Ann never missed an opportunity to sway her daddy. Her persistence could quickly tap his temper, but she didn't give up. She knew the discussion would be repeated many times. She had a year to convince him UT was the best place for her to get her higher education degree. She planned to make the best of her senior year in high school. It would be a bittersweet year for her and Bradford, her boyfriend since eighth grade.

She and Bradford developed a puppy love relationship in junior high school. When the junior high school kids met on Friday night at Chaffin's Downtown Cinema called the "Mouse House" by most young teens, they sat together. Most of the "couples" never watched the show; they talked, giggled, and made out. On Valentine's Day, Bradford gave Stella Ann a

21

pendant with her name on one side and his on the other. Stella Ann was ecstatic. She had never received a gift from a boy before. Her mother insisted it was too extravagant for her to keep and encouraged her to return it. Stella Ann kept it.

They were officially a "couple" for a short time. Their parents thought they were too young for a steady relationship, but they knew from their first kiss a spark existed between them. Their parents spared nothing to keep them apart. They resembled a modern-day Romeo and Juliet. Bradford went to Columbia Military Academy, and Stella Ann went to Central High School. There was a competitive spirit between them, and both finished at the top of their respective class by graduation. School events often collided with plans they made, and each felt obligated to support their own school. At the insistence of their parents, they broke up many times and dated others, but they were always drawn back to each other.

"Stella Ann, I guess it will be ok for you to call Bradford to see if the color of your corsage can be changed. I don't approve of girls calling boys, but your new dress makes it necessary," said Lou as she sighed. She taught Stella Ann not to call boys. It was a rule drilled into most girls; good Southern girls did not call boys. The beautiful pink and white dress Lou made her was a surprise, so the call was merely a formality.

Stella Ann's hand shook as she called the numbers to Bradford's house. He answered. Stella Ann was relieved she did not have to talk to either of his parents. They intimidated her, and she knew they did not like her. "Bradford, I have a request about the flowers for Saturday night. Mama made me a new dress for the prom today. I am not wearing the red and navy-blue dress from last year. My new dress is pink and white. Is it too late to change the color of my flowers from red to pink?"

"Stella Ann, it should not be a problem to switch the color of the flowers," Bradford replied. "It is only Tuesday, so there should be plenty of time to notify the florist. I will ask my mom to make the switch from red flowers to pink ones. I am looking forward to the prom Saturday night."

"Thank you, Bradford, I am looking forward to it also. Tell your parents they are invited to the senior presentation. I am on the prom queen court this year, and we will be presented at the end," she said. "See you Saturday night at 6:30, Bradford." She was uncomfortable that she had called him and quickly got off the phone.

A moment of prom day excitement for girls was when corsages, wristlets, or nosegays were delivered to their house before the dance. Lou answered the door and thanked the delivery boy for the box. With the white box in hand, Lou went to Stella Ann's room where she was primping for the big event. Lou had already put Stella Ann's hair up, which took forever with Stella Ann's long, dark, thick mane. Lou handed the box to Stella Ann to open and could tell something was wrong by Stella Ann's expression. Lou looked in the box and saw dried purple and brown flowers with a pea green and purple crumpled ribbon. If Bradford saw the flowers the florist sent, he would be embarrassed. Lou called the flower shop where Stella Ann worked to see if another corsage could be made before Bradford arrived.

"Mrs. Langston, I wish I could help you. We are hustling to get all the corsages made and delivered by prom time tonight. We could have used Stella Ann's help today, but I gave her this Saturday off a long time ago. It will be my treat if Stella Ann wants to come over and make a corsage or nosegay for herself. I am low on flowers, but anything would be better than dead flowers. Who is the lucky young man taking Stella Ann to the prom?" asked Mr. Farrell, the shop owner.

When Lou told him, he answered, "I am not surprised Norma Taber would pull a silly stunt to keep those kids from having a good time tonight. She did not like an arrangement we made for one of her parties, and I offered to make it right for her. She came in and made a loud, unreasonable scene laced with swear words I had never heard. Bring Stella Ann over, and she can make whatever she wants."

Stella Ann finished a sweet pink and white nosegay of miniature roses and baby's breath with pink and white satin ribbons in time to get home, finish her make-up, and put on her beautiful new dress. Hopefully, Bradford would never know what happened to the flowers. Stella Ann had no clue "Flower Gate" was only a few hours away. The gates of scorn and fury would be opened when Norma, Bradford's mom, saw the flowers Stella Ann was carrying.

It was fun to see her friends all dressed up for the prom. The girls' dresses were beautiful, and the boys cleaned up well and looked handsome in their tuxedos with ruffled shirts. Stella Ann and Bradford made a dashing couple. The junior class had done a tremendous job transforming the gym into an Italian café with a real fountain. Parents gathered in the hall to enter the gym for the presentation. Except for one, parents, teachers, and friends smiled and said complimentary things as each couple walked off the stage.

"Stella Ann, those are not the flowers I ordered," said Norma Taber with a look of anger and disdain.

Stella Ann responded, "There must have been a mix up with the flowers or the delivery. Can you describe what you ordered?"

"Well, I did not order those tacky flowers!" Norma barked angrily and walked off.

"What did Mom mean, Stella Ann?" Bradford asked.

"Can we talk about this later? I want to have fun tonight," Stella Ann answered. She took his hand and led him to the dance floor.

She had an early curfew, and her parents were always up when she came home. She was not allowed to go to the after-prom breakfast parties held into the early morning. Burt believed nothing good happened after midnight and set Stella Ann's senior curfew at 11:30 p.m. She was glad to get the extra 30 minutes with Bradford.

The phone rang as she shut the front door and walked toward the family room.

"Stella Ann, you might as well get the phone this time. We have answered it nonstop since we got home from the presentation," said Burt. "See who it is, and we will talk with you when you hang up."

"Hello?" said Stella Ann. The verbal venom which spewed from the other end of the phone was deafening.

"You ungrateful little hussy! Those were not the flowers Bradford sent you. I called my florist, and she described what they sent. You are trash. You are the worst kind of trash! We should have never let Bradford get involved with you. You were raised on the wrong side of the tracks. Didn't your parents teach you any manners?" Norma Taber was livid.

"Mrs. Taber, you are correct. The flowers I carried were different. I could not let Bradford be embarrassed by the flowers the florist delivered. They were dead and had the wrong color ribbon which was smushed and crumpled. The corsage looked like it was pulled out of the trash. I was able to go to the flower shop where I work and make a nosegay Bradford would be proud for me to carry. I am sorry if you are upset." Stella Ann poured fuel on Norma's already raging fire by mentioning the florist where she worked.

"A little teenage girl should not talk to an adult the way you have talked to me. If a boy sent my daughter a dog turd with a ribbon on it, I would make her wear it. You are the most spoiled little brat I have ever seen. Your parents have not done a good job raising you. Stella Ann, I will not allow you to destroy Bradford's dreams and reputation," Norma hissed back.

Choice swear words flew around her house on occasion, but Stella Ann had never heard anyone talk like Mrs. Taber. She tapped all the inner control she could to keep her temper from consuming her mouth. The verbal attack on her parents was more than she could stomach.

"You listen to me, Mrs. Taber, you can say whatever you want about me, but I will not allow you to disrespect my parents. I am hanging up the phone now. Goodbye."

The last thing Stella Ann heard before she hung up was, "You will not hang up on me." Stella Ann slammed the phone down hard.

She turned around to find her parents behind her. They knew Stella Ann could take care of herself, and the conversation they heard was confirmation.

"You handled that well, but you shouldn't have hung up on her, Stella Ann," Burt said. "Mrs. Taber has called here relentlessly since we got back from the presentation. Stella Ann, Bradford may be a nice boy, but your mama and I have decided you should not date him anymore. You two are going to college in a few months anyway. I am sorry Bradford's mama ruined your senior prom."

Stella Ann did not say a word and went to her bedroom. She knew "Flower Gate" would blow over, and she would be allowed to date Bradford through the summer. The key would be Bradford's reaction and if his mother apologized.

The phone rang shortly after the family got back from church the next day. It was Bradford. Burt answered and was hesitant to let Stella Ann speak with him, but what happened was not Bradford's fault. Burt felt it was unfair to hold him responsible for his mother's actions. Burt called Stella Ann to answer the phone.

"Stella Ann, I had fun with you last night. You looked pretty in your dress," said Bradford. "My mom told me what happened about the flowers, and you owe my mom an apology. She said we couldn't go out again until you apologize, Stella Ann."

What Bradford said took Stella Ann's breath away. She couldn't believe what she heard. Stella Ann knew Burt was on the extension in the kitchen and heard Bradford.

Burt intervened, "Bradford, I don't think you got the whole truth from your mother about what happened. I have heard enough about this flower nonsense. I do not want your mother to call this house again. I don't know what she planned to gain by ruining Stella Ann's prom, but she succeeded in making a fool of herself and of you. Stella Ann, hang up your end of the phone."

"Bradford," Burt continued, "you are not to call here again or bother my daughter. She is no longer allowed to date you. Honoring your mother is commendable and the right thing to do, but defending her abhorrent behavior and language is not the kind of boy I want my daughter to date. Goodbye, now." Burt hung up the telephone and continued with his Sunday dinner.

Stella Ann couldn't understand why something as beautiful as flowers had caused such turmoil. It was a long time before Bradford learned the truth. The incident provided a window into what her future could look like if she followed her heart instead of her head.

Her senior prom and "Flower Gate" triggered Stella Ann's first encounter with depression. She and Bradford didn't date during the summer. She was devastated and spent most of her time at home in her room; the rest of her time was spent working double shifts at Opryland, a music based theme park in Nashville.

In the fall, she started classes at Clarkston State University, a school about 75 miles north of Columbia. It was a good school with a beautiful campus, and Stella Ann made the best of it. She adjusted. She didn't go home every weekend like a lot of the students on campus. To Stella Ann, being alone was ok; being with the loud, obnoxious roommate she was assigned was awful. Stella Ann was relieved Wanda went home every weekend. Many of her high school classmates were in her dorm, so she often escaped to their rooms.

After Christmas, she moved to another floor of the dorm and lived with a sweet, pretty girl from Jackson, Tennessee. They became great friends and would laugh until their sides ached. They remained friends through the years and continued to laugh like they did in college when they talked on the phone.

Stella Ann had one date her freshman year, and it was to a football game. Her date was a fraternity boy, and he got roaring drunk before half time. Stella Ann had never been around drinking and was disgusted by her date's behavior. She claimed she had to go to the restroom, left the game, and walked across campus to her dorm. She never heard from him again.

"What a waste of time," Stella Ann thought. Any further prospects or desire to date was irrelevant to Stella Ann. She became the keeper of the basement door in her dorm. She slept on one of the green leather sofas in the rec room of the dorm on weekends. She opened the locked door and let girls who missed curfew into the building. She helped many girls avoid getting caught by their dorm mother.

"Please, Daddy, please let me go to Knoxville for the UT homecoming with my roommate. Bradford invited me to the game and fraternity party. Wanda's boyfriend is a sophomore, and her parents said she could go if I was allowed to go," Stella Ann negotiated.

Burt responded with an emphatic, "No, Stella Ann. It is not a good idea for two young girls to make a long bus trip alone."

"Daddy, Bradford said he would pick me up at the bus station. We checked on tickets, and they don't cost much. We could leave on Friday afternoon at 2:00 p.m. and get back Sunday by 6 p.m. Please, Daddy. "I will pay for my ticket from my summer savings," Stella Ann begged.

Burt softened his voice, "I don't know, Stella Ann. I don't approve of your association with that boy. It reeks of trouble to me. I need to talk about this with your mama, and don't get your hopes up."

"Daddy, Gail said I could stay with her because her roommate is going home for the weekend. Please, Daddy?" She and Gail had known each other since kindergarten.

"Stella Ann, go to bed. We will talk about this tomorrow. Good night, sleep tight."

Stella Ann hung up the phone and felt hopeful she would be allowed to make the trip. She went to bed happy.

Two weeks later, a Greyhound bus pulled into the Knoxville bus station from Nashville. Stella Ann and Wanda gathered their belongings and disembarked. Unlike a short bus trip with her two best friends to go shopping in Nashville, the trip to Knoxville was long. Patience was not a virtue attributed to Stella Ann. Wanda didn't shut her mouth the whole trip. She babbled and squealed nonstop about nothing.

Stella Ann was very excited about the weekend ahead. She cut her long dark hair into the latest shag hairstyle, and she felt confident and stylish in her new hot pants outfit and black patent leather knee boots. She felt grown up even though she looked twelve years old. All she wore at Clarkston State was blue jeans, a denim embroidered work shirt, and clogs. Her hair was always in pigtails. She hoped Bradford would be impressed with her new look and introduce her to all his friends.

But where was Bradford? Wanda had already been picked up by her boyfriend. Stella Ann got her luggage and walked to the station door. She saw a tall, dark figure walking toward her she didn't seem to recognize. The person wore brown jeans, flip flops, a striped poncho, love beads, and sported a mustache and very long dark hair.

"Hi, Stella Ann, how was the trip? I am sorry I am late. My friends and I started the weekend party routine early, and I lost track of time," he said.

It was Bradford. She barely recognized him. She felt a little foolish in her fashionable outfit and new hairstyle, and he had transformed into a hippy.

"Who are you? Do I know you?" she half teased. "I didn't recognize you at first, Bradford."

The last time she saw him he was a clean-cut young man with a nice haircut and wore a navy blazer, buttoned down collar shirt, tailored khaki slacks, and loafers. His clothes always came from the preppy Ivy Shoppe in West Nashville. He was a very handsome young man with dark hair, blue eyes, well chiseled muscles, and stood just under six feet. When he wore his military uniform in high school, Stella Ann admittedly swooned. Stella Ann had dark hair, fair skin, blue eyes and stood an average height of five feet, four inches. Together, he and Stella Ann complemented each other well.

She was embarrassed to walk with him to the car and felt a little guilty about it. He looked shaggy and ungroomed. She wondered if he knew how ridiculous he looked. He had gone to the weird side of college life, and it was obvious he had gained weight since he left for college.

"I will take you to Gail's dorm, so you can drop off your bags. I'll pick you up in about an hour," Bradford said as he opened the car door for her. She always appreciated his impeccable manners and thoughtful ways.

"Sure," Stella Ann said. "You can drop me off at the door, and I will meet you at the same place in an hour." Stella Ann didn't want Gail to see Bradford.

An hour turned into a couple of hours before he picked her up. Stella Ann didn't think much of it because Bradford was always late when they dated in high school. When he finally arrived, he acted strange and without remorse for his tardiness. They grabbed a hoagie sandwich at one of the many delis around campus and ate in Bradford's car. Then he took her to his fraternity house to meet some of his new friends. To Stella Ann, Bradford's fraternity brothers were creepy, drunk, or stoned. She had never been in an environment like the fraternity house but had seen actors behaving similarly in movies. They were only there a short while before Bradford took her back to Gail's dorm. Stella Ann was more than ready to leave and was glad to get some sleep. She was exhausted from the excitement of her adventure, the bus ride, and the newness of Bradford's campus life.

The next day, instead of attending the football game Stella Ann had looked forward to, they hung out with his friends and listened to strange heavy metal music in his ornately beaded dorm room. All he needed to add to the garish decor was a mirror ball. They ordered more hoagie sandwiches from the nearby deli. Stella Ann had never eaten a hoagie sandwich before this trip and was developing a taste for corned beef on white bread with provolone cheese and a kosher pickle.

It was a weekend filled with learning curves. Stella Ann was relieved to get back on the bus and return to Nashville. She had a lot to process, and the last thing she wanted to do was share any of it with her big-mouth roommate. Wanda would dominate the conversation anyway. Hopefully, she would see Stella Ann nod off and shut up.

Wanda's parents picked them up at the Nashville bus station and took them to Clarksville to school. Stella Ann was glad to get back. She called her parents and closed the door on the weekend. She was disappointed and confused.

Stella Ann and Bradford didn't see each other again until Christmas break. They exchanged gifts and went out to dinner in Nashville. Their favorite restaurants were McGregor's for the best steak and biscuits anywhere and Regal's for spaghetti and a romantic atmosphere. They liked to sit in the garden room where there were white twinkling lights all year. They were consistent about writing letters to each other, and their communication kept the relationship ignited, but Stella Ann quietly braced herself for another break up.

The next time she saw Bradford was in February in the Nashville newspaper. He was in a picture at the candy counter in the student center on the UT campus. He never ate candy, so Stella Ann was confused by the content of the picture. She barely recognized him. It was apparent he had gained more weight, much more than the freshman fifteen pounds most expected to gain. He looked like a blown-up dough boy, but at least he ditched the poncho and love beads.

She was in her room studying for midterms; it was a cold rainy day in early spring. The dorm mother called her to the lobby to greet a visitor. Bradford stood by the welcome desk.

"Would you mind going to the car to talk with me? I drove here on my way home from Knoxville. My family is going to Fort Lauderdale, Florida, tomorrow for spring break. I wanted to see you before I leave," he said.

Stella Ann was baffled but agreed to go to the car with him. It was raining which made the visit even more ominous.

"Bradford, what are you doing here? Do your parents know you are here?" Stella Ann asked.

"No, they don't. They would be furious with me," he replied.

"Bradford, what is it?" Stella Ann inquired.

"I am kind of nervous. I want to ask you something."

Stella Ann sat in the passenger seat quietly perplexed. Bradford pulled out a small black velvet box from his coat pocket and opened it.

"Stella Ann, I know the timing is not the best, and we have not dated steadily in a while, but will you marry me?" he asked.

Stella Ann didn't know what to say. It was an unexpected and randomly timed request. "Bradford, we are freshmen in college, different colleges. I am only 18 years old. As much as I want to get married someday, I can't agree to get married now. This is so quick. I need to think." Stella Ann rambled and couldn't stop.

Bradford said, "Look, Stella Ann, please take the ring and think about it. I have figured out the logistics and how we can make this work. We could get married this summer and live in the married student apartments on campus. I don't want to spend another year in different schools."

The proposal seemed fast, furious, and rushed to Stella Ann. She was the impulsive one of the two. She was baffled. She sensed there was another reason for Bradford's dash to the altar, and she wondered where he got the ring.

In their romantic, dreamy dating moments, they talked about marriage someday. Bradford stole her heart in the eighth grade, and she knew he was the only one for her. Stella Ann wanted their relationship to be appropriate and honor her religion before they took their relationship to the next level. They lived in the middle of the Bible Belt, and her family was grounded in fundamental beliefs. He pressured her a lot, and they argued a lot because of it. She loved Bradford and having sex was a big decision. She wanted to experience it with someone she loved and was committed to for life. It was important to her. An engagement ring would not change that boundary.

She was concerned about Bradford's motivation for popping the marriage question so soon and without including her in the plan. It was almost like he was desperate. She felt like she was a pawn to get what he wanted for his medical future. She knew his grades were terrible. Did he love her, or did he want her to help him with his grades or both?

Bradford had a convincing charm, but he never said he loved her. It was almost like Bradford was frantic and anxious. Romance engulfed Stella Ann, and she took the ring. They kissed, hugged, and said goodbye. She waved as she stood in the rain watching him pull out of the parking lot.

As she walked back to her dorm, she thought to herself, "What happened? It was not the marriage proposal Stella Ann dreamed about as a little girl. It was quick, cold, and calculated. Bradford dropped the ring off and left. It felt like he was checking off boxes. He wasn't there more than thirty minutes. "Dang! I just got engaged!" she said before she returned to her dorm.

She did not expect her marriage proposal to be so unremarkable, empty, and isolated. She wanted to share such a special moment with her family and friends, but that was never going to happen now. She didn't have a good look at the ring until she got back to her room. It was stunning, a marquise cut two carat solitaire in a gold setting. Her parents were not going to be happy with her at all. How would Stella Ann tell them? She decided a face-to-face conversation with her parents was necessary and made plans to go home the following weekend.

"Hell, no, young lady, you will not get married now!" Burt could be heard all the way to the town square. "You can give that ring right back to him."

Lou said, "Burt, calm down. Stella Ann, let me see the ring. Oh, my goodness! It is beautiful. Look at it, Burt."

"I don't need to look at it, Lou. It is going right back. You know how I feel about those people, and I don't want Stella to be part of the Taber family. Her life would be miserable. The boy didn't even ask for Stella's hand in marriage. No, there won't be a wedding!"

"Burt let's give this some time. This situation will work out like it is supposed to work out," said Lou, the steady optimist.

They were talking as if Stella Ann wasn't in the room. It was much like watching a tennis match.

She loved showing her ring to her girlfriends in the dorm and reveled in the myriad of questions about the wedding. Questions with no answer.

Stella Ann's next visit home was two weeks later. She learned from Lou that Dr. Taber made a visit to see her daddy.

Lou said, "Stella Ann, Dr. Taber and Norma do not want you and Bradford to get married so young either, but they do want their son to get into medical school. Dr. Taber proposed a scenario for your daddy to consider. It didn't go over very well with Burt. The atmosphere in the house was tense." Lou recounted the conversation for Stella Ann that transpired between Dr. Taber and Burt. "Dr. Taber said something like this, Stella Ann." Lou continued trying to sound like Dr. Taber.

"We understand Stella Ann is a very good student and maintains a high-grade point average. Norma and I would like to offer to pay for Stella Ann to transfer to UT Knoxville. We will pay for tuition, room and board, and books. You and Lou would only need to provide Stella Ann's clothes, a car, and spending money. The offer would be handled much like a scholarship. We are confident Stella Ann can help Bradford bring his grades up to a competitive level. Will you give it some thought? We would like to help the kids."

"Stella Ann, I thought Burt was going to punch Dr. Taber in the face. Your daddy was angry and insulted. I had never seen Burt get red faced with anger until Dr. Taber's visit. It took a long time for Burt to calm down," Lou recalled.

Lou recounted how Burt responded, "I don't have to give your big idea any thought, Hank. I will not sell my daughter into your crazy self-serving plot to benefit your son. My daughter is not for sale."

"Burt belted out a litany of curse words I can't repeat and told Hank to get his pompous behind out of his house. He said you were our daughter, and we would educate you the way we saw fit."

Stella Ann was glad she was not home when the conversation transpired. Later in the summer, Stella Ann tugged at Burt's heart strings again to let her go to UT.

Stella Ann got out of school for summer break before Bradford and started her job at Opryland. It was a fun place to work in the summer, but it was hard work. She was going to be hosting the horse show with her cousin, Mark, who was the announcer. Mark was tall, handsome, and had a fabulous voice. Stella Ann didn't see him much because he lived in Atlanta. Mark was going to live with their grandparents during the summer to be able to work at Opryland.

She and Bradford dated on the weekends, but their relationship was strained. Something about Bradford continued to seem off to Stella Ann. She rarely said the right thing when they were together. Bradford snapped at her relentlessly. She couldn't make sense of his behavior. He had gained even more weight since they got engaged. With each phone conversation and date, it became clear their engagement was not going to lead to marriage. By the middle of June, Stella Ann gave the ring back and called off the engagement.

Bradford said, "If you give the ring back, it will be a long time for you to get it again. You will have to work for it."

Stella Ann didn't understand what he meant by "work for it" and let it go. She silently promised herself hell would freeze over before she worked for a ring. There was no doubt she loved Bradford, but they had too much to accomplish before they got married. She was carried away by the romance of how things could be, not by how things would be in a real marriage.

She worked extra shifts at Opryland and signed up for night classes at UT Nashville. When she couldn't get extra hours at Opryland, she worked at a department store. Most nights, she did not get home until after midnight. Burt and Lou met her in Nashville often and followed her home. She secretly applied to UT Knoxville for the fall, just in case Burt changed his mind.

Many conversations took place over the summer between Burt, Lou, and Stella Ann about her transfer to UT Knoxville. The conversations were exhausting. By early August, Stella Ann got an acceptance letter to attend UT, and fall semester tuition at Clarkston State was looming. The decision deadline was immediate.

Burt called Stella Ann and Lou into the family room after dinner one hot summer evening in August for a family meeting.

"Stella, your mama and I have decided to let you transfer to UT Knoxville next quarter."

Stella Ann could barely contain her excitement. "Oh, Daddy, really? Do you mean it? I can transfer. You aren't going to change your mind, are you? I was getting nervous because tuition is due soon at both schools."

"Stella Ann, it might not be as easy as you think at this point. Your mama and I have set boundaries and rules for you. You must maintain a grade point average of 3.5 or better."

"Daddy, I can handle the GPA requirement with no problem."

"You are going to have to sign in and out of the dorm at night and on weekends like you did at Clarkston State."

"But, Daddy, girls aren't required to sign in and out at UT."

"Your mama and I read the literature the school sent here, and it is an option for parents to request it. We are going to request it, Stella Ann."

Lou added, "We want you to go through sorority rush and establish yourself with a group of friends."

Stella Ann had to pick her battles and agreed to sign in and out, and she had already signed up to go through rush.

"The last requirement, Stella Ann, is we are expecting you to pay for one quarter a year and to help each quarter with your books, sorority, and supplies."

She couldn't wait to tell Bradford she was going to UT even though their relationship had cooled down over the summer. They were working

35

and taking classes which left little time for dating.

A few weeks later, Stella Ann, Burt, and Lou attended UT new student orientation. The school was huge. Stella Ann was excited and grateful to be there. Lou was not as excited as she thought she would be for her daughter, and a tear or two rolled down her cheek. Burt tried to be a good sport about it all but sensed he was throwing his daughter to the wolves.

After a couple of days in Knoxville and numerous lists in hand, they returned home prepared to check off the lists of school, dorm, and personal items needing to be purchased. Stella Ann was back at UT within a month. Sorority rush was a week before classes started. She pledged a sorority suited to her interests and made several friends before classes started.

Moving day was stressful, busy, and exciting. It was hard and emotional saying goodbye to Burt and Lou. Tears flowed, and her mother seemed a wreck. Stella Ann watched as they drove out of sight then made her way back to her room. There were things to unpack, and she was ready to meet her roommate, Brenda, who was from a small town in west Tennessee.

They had only talked on the phone a couple of times over the summer, and Brenda was not going through sorority rush. It would be two weeks before Stella Ann would meet her roommate. She knew Brenda existed because all her things had been moved in and put away. Their paths didn't cross often because of class schedules, and Brenda was with her hometown friends a lot.

When they finally met, Stella Ann thought Brenda, a tall blonde with green eyes, was stunningly beautiful and proved to be a wild party girl with a longtime boyfriend. Brenda didn't talk much, which was going to be a challenge for Stella Ann. She smoked and drank coffee and could swear with an attitude that would shut anyone up. Stella Ann didn't drink coffee or smoke, but she had been known to blast a few naughty words. Neither had much patience, and while Stella Ann was scattered, Brenda was very neat and tidy. They rarely did anything together, and Brenda didn't stay in the dorm much. It allowed Stella Ann to focus on her studies. She had grades to maintain.

"No, I said, no, Bradford, stop," Stella Ann insisted. "I thought you understood I did not come here to be your bedmate. I will not stay at your fraternity house with you and keep your hands to yourself."

"Oh, Stella Ann, don't be such a cold fish and prude. "All the students here do it," he said in his most charming convincing voice.

Stella Ann got to her feet and walked across campus to her dorm. Bradford didn't try to stop her. She couldn't believe it. She had only been there a few weeks, and this was her welcome. "What had she done?" she thought. "Maybe she should have stayed at Clarkston State."

As she walked across campus in the dark, thoughts of her father sitting at the breakfast table commenting if a daughter of his got pregnant the boy would be looking down the barrel of his shotgun. She knew he was teasing, but he made his point. Her fundamental religious background kept her in fearful respect of her daddy and of God. Fear would manifest itself in other ways, but Stella Ann was oblivious to the signs.

It was a time of peace, love, and good vibes with massive doses of free spirit swarming in teenage minds. The adults responsible failed them in the navigation of free love. Many discovered free love was not free, including Stella Ann. In Stella Ann's protective home of fundamental religious values, words like alcohol and sex were not spoken. Alcoholic drinks of any kind were considered the juice of the devil, and drugs were only something a doctor prescribed when someone was sick. Smoking something other than a cigarette was unheard of, and few women smoked.

Until seventh grade, baby making and birthing was a mystery to Stella Ann. It wasn't until the health department nurse came to talk with the seventh graders that Stella Ann learned the details. It scared her to death and made her sick to her stomach. She was never doing that or so she said.

Years later, Stella Ann saw a similar reaction in her fifth-grade girl students during "the talk" sessions in the spring. Things had progressed enough by then the girls already knew the birth process, but they were completely grossed out by the menstrual cycle happening to them. Stella Ann felt their pain, and there was nothing they could do about it but accept the process and get prepared.

Those yearly rite of passage sessions would end in a barrage of laughter because the teachers could not hold it together during the question session. All straight-faced control flew out the window when the school nurse told the girls to get a mirror and look at their lady parts. It lightened the mood and eased the tension in the room. Stella Ann, in her menopausal stage of life, was the first to burst into laughter.

Bradford broke up with Stella Ann after the Tennessee/Alabama game. She had been at UT Knoxville for six weeks. She was on her own. It was embarrassing, and disappointing.

CHAPTER 3

Boundaries

Stella Ann called her friend, Gail, about the breakup. Gail was rock solid and always gave great advice. She understood Stella Ann. She told Stella Ann to give the breakup time, be patient, stop crying, and stick to her boundaries. Another friend heard about the breakup and called her offering his support. She and Sam had known each other since kindergarten. He had no agenda; he was a nice person and a genuine friend.

As the Christmas break approached, Stella Ann needed to secure a ride home since she didn't have her car on campus. Bradford promised Stella Ann early in the quarter she could ride in his car even though they had broken up. He said he wanted them to be friends. She knew Bradford used the "friend" card to his advantage. It was a tool from his charisma arsenal. A week before the end of the quarter, Stella Ann swallowed her pride and called Bradford.

"Bradford, I need a ride home for Christmas. Is the offer you made for me to ride home with you still valid?" Stella Ann asked.

"Hey, Stella Ann, how are you?" he said in a cool distant voice. "Some of my fraternity buddies are riding as far as Nashville with me, but there should be room for you," he replied. "I am leaving about five o'clock on Wednesday after my last class. I will pick you up at your dorm a little after five."

"Thank you, Bradford. I appreciate it. I will be sitting in the lobby looking for you." He wouldn't be hard to spot. His parents gave him a burnt orange chevy Chevelle car for high school graduation. He could be seen and heard for blocks.

At 4:00 p.m. the following Wednesday, Bradford called Stella Ann's room as she was leaving to wait for him in the lobby. "Hey, Stella Ann, another fraternity brother needs a ride to Nashville, and I am not going to have enough room in my car for you. I hope you can find a ride."

"No problem, Bradford. I am sure I can find someone on my floor going to Nashville."

She wouldn't let him know her despair, and she wouldn't find a ride. The floor was empty. Most girls left for home the day before. The dorm was closing at 10 p.m., and all students had to be out. There was nothing she could do but call her daddy.

"Take care and have a nice Christmas break," Bradford said flatly.

It was a signal she would not see him during the holidays. Why would she see him? They were no longer a couple. Plus, Stella Ann hated it when someone told her to take care. It seemed so empty and phony. Did they think she wouldn't take care? Stella Ann was angry.

"Daddy, I must be out of the dorm by 10 p.m., and my ride fell through. Can you come get me?" Stella Ann asked with a tense voice and holding back tears. It was a very difficult call to make. Her daddy was still at work but said he would be there before 10 p.m. Before they got off the phone, he told Stella Ann to call Lou and tell her the plan.

"Mama, Daddy is coming to get me and told me to call and let you know. He is leaving from work in a few minutes." Stella Ann said, fighting back tears.

"Stella Ann, call Gail and see if she needs a ride. I talked with her mother early in the week, and she said they were going to take off work to bring her home."

"OK, I will call as soon as we hang up," Stella Ann promised.

"Stella Ann, you all be careful driving home. It is a long drive, and I know you and your daddy will be tired. It was Bradford who left you without a ride, wasn't it?"

"Mama, how do you know so much? You are the smartest person I know. We will talk about this tomorrow. I love you."

"I love you too, Stella Ann. Be careful."

Burt hugged Stella Ann when he arrived and grabbed her luggage. He did not say a word about anything else. Burt put Stella Ann behind the wheel, so he could get some sleep. He decided that night he would allow Stella Ann to take her car to school after Christmas. He did not want her to be dependent on anyone, especially Bradford Taber. He taught her to be independent. He instilled in her she could be and do anything if she worked hard enough, and Stella Ann was a hard worker. He shut his eyes and tried to sleep despite Gail's constant chatter from the back seat.

The next day she reported for her job at the department store where she worked during the summer when she wasn't working at Opryland. She worked every hour the manager would give her up until 6 p.m. on Christmas Eve when the store closed. She got off in time for the Christmas Eve celebration at her grandparents' farm on Duck River Ridge. She always loved time with her mother's family.

Christmas Eve in the country was a scene right off a Norman Rockwell painting. At Granny's, there was laughter and excitement, and kids were everywhere. The food was abundant. Country ham, turkey, sweet potatoes with marshmallows, green beans, cranberry sauce, mashed potatoes, cornbread dressing, and yeast rolls lined the table. On the buffet would be fresh ambrosia, jam cake, coconut cake, pecan pie, fruit cake, cookies, and boiled custard in a pitcher. Next to the pitcher was always a small vinegar bottle with the "vanilla flavoring." The whiskey was referred to as vanilla flavoring and was only offered to the men. Christmas Eve was the only time any known alcohol appeared among her mother's relatives.

Stella Ann knew her granny had a secret. A big jug of Mogen David concord grape wine was kept in the pantry behind her aprons. Occasionally she would go in there and take a drink right out of the jug. She was a refined, well dressed, pretty lady, and to see her take a gulp of wine right from the bottle was hysterical. Stella Ann was bound by loyalty to never tell anyone about her granny's indulgence, but she determined others knew about it.

The men in the family sat in the dining room, and women and children sat in the kitchen. By Stella Ann's count, there were about forty people in the big old house for Christmas Eve. Every holiday her grandaddy cut a huge cedar tree from the steep hill behind the house and stood it in their living room. Ornaments made by grandchildren graced the tree, and multicolored lights with big bulbs flickered in a happy rhythm.

Her grandparents purchased all twenty-two grandchildren a gift, and the adults drew names. Granny let the grandchildren pick out something within her budget from a mail order catalogue, and squeals of delight rang out when presents were unwrapped. After the gift clean up, someone would break out singing a Christmas carol, and others joined in ending with "Silent Night" and a prayer. Stella Ann had a family life filled with love, fun, tasty food, and faith.

They went to her daddy's parents' house in town on Christmas Day. It was more subdued and formal, and the table was lined with fancy plates, silver flatware, and crystal glasses. There were only three grandchildren, and gifts were plentiful, but the atmosphere was stiff and formal. The only excitement or drama during Christmas at her daddy's family celebration was provided by Uncle Bill who was a party man. By Stella Ann's second year in college, she realized her Uncle Bill was an alcoholic who was totally uninhibited when he drank. She would never forget Christmas when he threw an electric beanpot his sister gave him to the basement all the while her grandmother was telling him to stop. He vacillated between funny and obnoxious.

Before Stella Ann returned to school, she learned from friends Bradford had moved on and had a new girlfriend. Stella Ann knew of her from pictures and events on campus. Her family was wealthy, and she was a beauty queen with several titles. It was interesting she was with Bradford because she preferred football players. The news stung Stella Ann and gave her the motivation to stay focused on her studies. Her car allowed her independence.

Burt and Lou never said a word about Bradford dumping Stella Ann. She used her stagnant love life as an opportunity to get to know her roommate better even though she would be gone for days at a time.

Brenda stayed with her hometown boyfriend a lot. She and Brenda became loyal friends. Brenda even taught Stella Ann how to smoke cigarettes and drink coffee.

The winter was long and dreary in Knoxville. The classes Stella Ann took during the winter quarter were challenging. She ended up in anthropology and art history. Freshman biology and writing composition at Clarkston State looked elementary comparatively. The only social life she had was with the girls on her dorm floor and her sorority sisters. She started a routine at Clarkston State letting late night daters in after curfew, and she became the keeper of the back door of her dorm at UT for after hour hamburger purchases. She held the back door open, so girls could run next door to a fast-food restaurant and get sacks of hamburgers after curfew. They could get a sack of twenty small burgers for $2.00 after 10 p.m. For every sack they purchased, Stella Ann got two burgers as her compensation for holding the door. She pulled a lot of all-nighters, and coffee and cigarettes kept her awake to study.

Spring break brought a retreat from all her studying and the dreary weather. She was ready to go home to rest and to sew a few new outfits for spring quarter. A spring break trip was foreign to her. She had only seen the ocean once on a trip with a friend's family when she was sixteen. Family vacations were usually a short drive away to a campground. She didn't have the money to spare for a trip but enjoyed hearing about the trips of her friends.

At the last minute, Brenda asked Stella Ann if she wanted to go to New Orleans with her to see her older married sister. Brenda's boyfriend was going on a cruise with his fraternity brothers, and Brenda did not want to spend spring break in west Tennessee. Stella Ann had never been to New Orleans. Air travel was something she had only seen on tv and in movies.

She thought convincing Burt and Lou to let her go to New Orleans was going to be a challenge. To her surprise they agreed to let her go, and Lou sent her spending money. The only request they had was that she not drink alcoholic beverages, and she assured them she would not drink. They had no clue smoking cigarettes had become her vice of choice.

Stella Ann had never seen anything like New Orleans. Looking out the airplane window, New Orleans appeared to be a dot surrounded by muddy water. She saw where the Mississippi River spilled into the Gulf of Mexico from her window seat. She was certain they would be sloshing in muddy water the whole time they were there.

The first thing they did after Brenda's sister picked them up at the airport was to go to the French Quarter for lunch. Brenda insisted they eat shrimp po'boys; a sandwich Stella Ann had never eaten. She had only eaten shrimp once or twice in her life at the Riverwalk Restaurant in Columbia. The first bite made her a fan of the sandwich, and she ate at least three shrimp po'boys during her visit. The antique shops, jazz music, food vendors, street artists, and array of people in the French Quarter were fascinating to Stella Ann. Brenda's sister lived about an hour east of New Orleans in Biloxi, Mississippi, and her husband was in the Navy. She promised they would return to the French Quarter before the trip was over.

Stella Ann was surprised when she got a call from Bradford after spring break. They hadn't spoken since he left her stranded at Christmas. It started out as a cordial formal conversation and merged into laughter. Bradford seemed much nicer than he was at Christmas.

Bradford asked Stella Ann if she would like to drive to the mountains for a picnic at Cades Cove, a beautiful area of the Smoky Mountains National Park. It was laced with meadows, wildlife, and streams, and had an atmosphere of serenity. It was only a 45-minute drive from school and was an enjoyable day trip for students to escape the routine of campus life. The national park gave Stella Ann a feeling of family nostalgia since her family visited the park as a rare vacation destination. On a trip when she was five years old, her grandmother bought her suede moccasins and a stuffed black bear in Cherokee, North Carolina. As Bradford waited for her answer, she took a deep breath, and her heart was pounding. Knowing she should use her head; her heart took over. She agreed to the picnic.

The trip to Cades Cove ignited a new romance and pleasant dialogue between them. They made no formal commitment to each other and agreed to let a relationship emerge naturally if it was meant to happen. No mention was ever made of his interval love interest. Stella Ann wanted to move forward and learn to trust him again. She could not deny her heart.

There was something about Bradford's demeanor which was confusing to her, and he had lost a lot of weight since they had last seen each other. He looked more like himself. Stella Ann loved his dark hair, blue eyes, and solid muscle tone, and he was just tall enough. He had started running and working out. His main sport in high school was football. He chose not to try out to play college sports. His focus was pre-med. Stella Ann played tennis from an early age and during high school. She gave up playing college tennis when she turned down her scholarship to play for Campbell University in Nashville.

Spring quarter was like a dream for Stella Ann. She and Bradford spent a lot of time together studying, listening to music, going to campus events, and enjoying the activities of his fraternity and her sorority. They rarely said a cross word to each other. She could not ignore the sliver of secrecy shrouding Bradford. Stella Ann could not put her finger on it. As the quarter was ending, romance and passion ramped up between them, and there came a point of no return. A point Stella Ann would struggle with for a long time. She couldn't tell anyone, and she for sure couldn't go to open confession at church. She convinced herself she was doomed to hell. Her emotions toggled between guilt and euphoria.

Stella Ann returned to her summer job at Opryland and requested another position. The stinky horse show was more than she could handle during the sweltering summer, and Mark, her cousin, decided to stay in Atlanta. She would miss him. He was fun and talented.

Luckily, she secured a day shift job as a hostess at the train station and gave tours using a microphone from the back of the train. She was excited about the position and loved the cute navy pin-striped bibbed shorts, red shirt, engineer hat, and red bandana she wore. She offered to work as many hours as possible. She needed the money for school, and when she could not work at Opryland, the department store always needed her.

Working was not a problem for Stella Ann. She enjoyed working, but boredom became an issue as the summer waned. Tennessee summers were unpredictable; hot and muggy one minute, chilly and raining the next. The steam from the train amplified the misery of Tennessee's summer humidity. To spice things up, she changed the tour script. Impulse management was a constant struggle for Stella Ann. She landed in trouble more times than she could remember for her mischievous antics.

"All aboard for Grinder's Switch! We will be pulling out of the station momentarily and ask that you stay seated during the tour." Stella Ann could say the whole spiel in her sleep without a mistake, but on occasion, mischief emerged.

The beginning of the tour detailed the history of the train. The steam engine was authentic. Then she would start the tour/show.

"If you look to the right, you will see buffalo grazing. The buffalo were donated to Opryland by the XXX family of XXX farms, famous for their Tennessee style sausage. It kind of makes you wonder what they make their sausage out of doesn't it?" There would be laughter, which was all Stella Ann needed to keep going.

"The General Andrew Jackson showboat is up ahead. You can call the Opryland guest services number or stop by the office at the front of the park to make reservations for the dinner party on board. I understand old Andrew was quite the party animal and could kick up a rowdy dance or two." More laughter pumped her act to a higher level. Audience reaction was especially important. She learned that in speech and drama classes in high school.

"The river flowing beside us is the Cumberland River. It runs from the Appalachian area through upper Middle Tennessee and up toward southern Kentucky. Today it is still used for shipping, pleasure boating, and skinny dipping. We are pulling into Grinder's Switch. Please stay seated until the train comes to a complete stop. Thank you for riding the train. Enjoy the rest of your day at Opryland and keep laughing."

Stella Ann pushed her luck when it came to mischief. She got away with her Opryland antics a few times, but when they stopped at the train station, she saw her boss rise from the front seat of the first car. She thought she was going to faint. He changed direction at the station entrance and made his way to the back of the train. She was in trouble.

"Langston, do you want to keep your job here?" he asked.

"Yes, sir, I do," she humbly replied.

"Then make sure you do not delve off the written script. Do you understand?"

"Yes, sir."

He turned around to leave and said, "I will have to admit your changes caused laughter and were clever. The guests were having a fun time, but you must maintain the integrity of the script. Our sponsors would not appreciate your jokes."

The next week she was assigned to work at the Wacky House where she stood upside down most of the day. It was her punishment and an attempt for her boss to get the message across to Stella Ann that he was in charge. She decided to behave and keep the mischief in check for the rest of the summer. She returned to the train station with a different attitude.

She and Bradford dated over the summer, but work schedules took up most of their time. Rare dates made for peace within their respective families.

Her fall class schedule was heavy because she made the decision to change her major. Her dean's list status provided an avenue for her faculty advisor to approve her extra class load. She and Brenda moved into an old dorm called Strong Hall, a charming homey building with an atmosphere of the once elegant, refined era of campus life. There was a wooden staircase in the entry, hardwood floors, antique furniture in the receiving area, and no air conditioning. The waiting list was always long for Strong Hall, so as juniors they felt fortunate to get a room.

Bradford decided to commit to his studies to pull his GPA up. Stella Ann knew her influence and competitive drive was good for him to improve his grades. They took a literature class and a physics class together. She helped him with the classics and writing. Math was his strength.

The study arrangement improved their grades as well as their love life. Things got heated and passionate between them. From the beginning, their physical attraction and chemistry were undeniable. They were powerful magnets when in the same proximity. Stella Ann harbored the

47

guilt of her actions, and it caused her a lot of stress. Stella Ann was aware her shame originated from her religious convictions and sheltered life. She was a pleaser by nature and intentionally sought to make her parents proud of her. Her despair and private tears were not eliminated through the justification of their origin. However, no amount of anguished inner turmoil stopped her from indulging in the guilty pleasures she and Bradford ignited.

She decided to talk with Brenda about her concerns. The first thing Brenda said was she needed to go to the student clinic and get on the pill. She wasn't expecting such a response, but she knew Brenda was right. She later learned the reason Brenda was mature about physical relations. She made an appointment, and Brenda offered to go with her for support.

The appointment wasn't bad, and she got birth control pills free on site. There was no reason her parents had to know. A few days after the appointment, the clinic nurse called to tell her she needed to come in for a consultation. She had a consultation, but the nurse insisted she return to the clinic immediately. Brenda was in class, so Stella Ann went alone. As soon as she checked in at the reception window, she was whisked downstairs to the basement of the clinic. It was poorly lit, damp, and cold down there. A middle-aged nurse in a white dress and starched hat led her behind a curtain and told her to sit on the metal examination table. Stella Ann had a strong urge to run.

A very stern looking doctor came in and sat down in front of her, crossing his legs.

"Well, little lady, it is a pity we must have this conversation, but you girls can't help yourselves around the football boys. You can't seem to keep your panties on. You are a cute little thing. I can understand how the boys get excited over you." To Stella Ann he looked like a mean army sergeant she had seen on a tv show.

Stella Ann, in a shaky voice replied, "What are you talking about? Where is the doctor I saw yesterday?"

Sternly, he said, "Dr. Pierce is not here today. He only volunteers here a couple days a week. I am the resident doctor at this clinic."

It was dark in the basement with a few treatment spaces divided off with curtains. To Stella Ann, it was creepy, ominous, and frightening. She almost started crying.

He said, "Little lady, how many football players have you slept with? I am going through this list of names on my clipboard, and if I name one you have had sex with say yes. We must protect these boys, and I don't expect you to lie. The truth always comes out once I talk with each player."

He succeeded in scaring Stella Ann to death, and the tears started flowing. The nurse came in and stood by the doctor.

"Sir," Stella Ann said. "You don't need to name anyone on your list. I don't know any of the players on the team. I have only been with my boyfriend."

"That's what they all say, little lady. Stop crying and let's get started." The nurse handed her a tissue. "I don't have much patience with situations like this," the doctor said. Stella Ann cried even more. The nurse leaned over and whispered something in his ear, and he left.

Later, the nurse came behind the curtain with two shots, put one in each hip, and told Stella Ann she needed to tell her boyfriend to come in and see the doctor. The nurse was kind, brought her a glass of water, and told Stella Ann to stay there a little longer to collect herself. She left the clinic confused and humiliated. Obviously the seventh grade coming of age talk did not cover the topic facing Stella Ann. No word suited her better at that moment than stupid.

The bank of the Tennessee River on the UT campus became Stella Ann's thinking place. It reminded her of the lower field at home that backed up to the Duck River. She had many conversations with herself while walking in the back field, and the riverbank of the Tennessee River offered her similar comfort. The predicament she was in this time did not seem to present many private solutions. She couldn't remember having cried so hard or feeling so alone, humiliated, and distressed.

When she got back to her dorm room she threw the pills in the trash, then called Bradford. It seemed like it took him forever to get to the phone which made her angry and disgusted. "I need you to come talk with me in person, Bradford. There is something important we need to discuss."

49

"I have a fraternity meeting in thirty minutes and can come afterward," he replied.

"No, this conversation cannot wait. Get over here now," Stella Ann screamed. Fear, desperation, and anger consumed her emotions.

He could sense tension in her voice and said he would be right over. "Meet me in the parking lot of Massey Hall," he said.

She was waiting in the parking lot when he arrived. She got in the car, sat there for a few seconds, and then looked at Bradford. She felt the temperature rise on her face and the anger darting in her blue eyes.

"I have a message for you from the student clinic. You are to see the doctor immediately. Your love interlude during our breakup has left you with a little present, and I have been the recipient of it also. Thank you very much, Bradford."

He sat there in defiant silence pressing his lips together. He tapped his steering wheel nervously and his blue eyes were darting from side to side. Then he said, "How do we know I am the culprit and not the guys you slept with while we were apart?" This was a side of Bradford she had never seen before.

"Bradford! You know you are the only one I have been with. Ever!" She got out of the car and leaned into the window, "Go to the doctor, Bradford, and leave me alone." She ran through the parking lot to her dorm. She felt like her life was over. Her lifelong dreams squashed. When she got back to the dorm, she flung herself onto her bed and cried. She cried a mad cry, a disappointed cry, a hurt cry, a painful cry, and fell asleep.

Brenda was a terrific support during her awful ordeal and went with her to the riverbank many times to chat. During those chats, Brenda told her she had a difficult decision to make when she was a senior in high school. She said she told her parents, and they helped her navigate her decision physically and emotionally. She encouraged Stella Ann to talk with Burt and Lou. It was something Stella Ann could not do. She would not be allowed to continue her education at UT. Too much was at stake.

Stella Ann did not see Bradford again until the winter quarter. He wooed her with his charm and contrition and appealed to her to help him study. His grades were not improving and were not competitive enough to apply to medical school. He had dreamed of becoming a doctor all his life. His plan was to return to Columbia and join his dad's practice. She agreed to help him from a distance, from across a table in a study room. She made it clear there would be nothing physical between them. As for Stella Ann, there was no relationship and would be no relationship. She was his tutor. Period.

By spring break, their relationship moved beyond tutor/student. Bradford made a significant improvement in his GPA, crossing the 3.0 mark. Romance blossomed between them again, but Stella Ann put the brakes on any physical relationship. They went home to Columbia for Easter weekend and had a dinner date at one of their favorite restaurants. On the drive to Nashville, Bradford asked Stella Ann to get something out of his glove compartment. She saw the small black velvet box that held the ring from their first engagement. She looked at Bradford confused and baffled. He told her to look in the box. It was the original engagement ring he had given her two years before.

"Stella Ann, if you don't say yes to getting engaged, you will never see this ring or me again," Bradford said.

Bradford did not understand a proposal was supposed to be tender and romantic with a profession of love and life forever. The concept of getting down on one knee was a joke to him, and asking her father for his blessing was not going to happen. It was like the first time he proposed but with a cold, distant, threatening edge added. Stella Ann thought he wavered between ignorance and arrogance when it came to proposals.

Stella Ann ignored his proposal style and said, "Yes, I will marry you. Let's set a date, so it will be concrete and something we can look forward to. Christmas is a beautiful time of hope and joy. Let's plan our wedding for Christmas break." She had no doubt she loved him. She had since they were in the eighth grade. She was the one rushing to the altar now, and she knew it was because of her faith and religious beliefs. She wanted their relationship to be right, but cruel reality dictated she would not get that wish.

Over dinner they set December 14 as a tentative wedding date. Neither mentioned parental reaction or approval. They talked about how happy they were and discussed wedding plans and possibilities.

It disappointed Stella Ann that Bradford had not asked Burt for her hand in marriage, and another important element was missing. Bradford never said he loved her.

Neither set of parents was excited or supportive of the engagement, but Stella Ann and Bradford made it clear they were going to get married with or without their parents' blessings. An engagement pool party was hosted by some of Norma's friends before she and Bradford left for the first summer school session at UT Knoxville. Burt and Lou were not invited. It hurt Stella Ann's feelings, but Burt and Lou were relieved. They didn't approve of the people or the wedding.

Forty years later, she found the dress she wore to their engagement party. Lou packed it away with other outfits she wore during her wedding festivities. The box showed up along with her wedding dress when cleaning out her mother's guest room closet. The dress looked like something a fashion doll would wear. It was a yellow checked gingham maxi sun dress with a white pique short sleeved jacket. It was nothing short of fabulous. Lou designed and made Stella Ann the most fashionable clothes with the best fabrics. In hindsight Stella Ann felt ashamed when she thought about the times she asked for a store-bought dress or outfit. For years, she wanted a department store dress and a birthday cake from Beck's Bakery. She never got either. They simply could not afford the splurge.

Guests at the pool party, the Taber's friends, drank a lot. Stella Ann felt like a misfit. The women cackled; everyone hugged and kissed. The men got in her personal space, wished her the best, and made inappropriate comments and gestures. She thought it was disgusting. Old people partying was an uncharted experience for Stella Ann. She might as well keep her mouth shut and tolerate it. This scene was going to be repeated often when she and Bradford got married.

During the first session of summer quarter, she shared an upstairs apartment with a girl named Cindy. She met her in an education class. Bradford stayed at the fraternity house. They needed to take more classes to graduate early and move to Chattanooga where Bradford planned to attend medical school, and summer school in Knoxville was the only answer. They would be back in Columbia by the end of July to help with wedding plans.

Her summer classes were intense. There was no time for anything except studying. To make matters more uncomfortable, the apartment had no air conditioning. Few places in Tennessee existed without air conditioning during the long humid summers. The Watergate hearings started and were televised. It was a stressful time in the country; people stayed glued to their tv sets to see if President Nixon was going to resign. Stella Ann went to class then watched the hearings as she ate lunch each day. She retreated to her room to study and read until she fell asleep. Stella Ann looked forward to her afternoon nap accompanied by her oscillating fan and Cindy's cat. A nap was a welcomed luxury during the sticky southern summer.

She and her temporary roommate watched the news and a summary of the hearings as they ate dinner. It was the only programming on the three tv channels. Bradford came over occasionally, but he was busy with fraternity work since he was president of his chapter. She and Bradford did not see each other much during the short session, but he did manage to drop his laundry off for her to wash each week. He saved the laundry money his parents gave him for their date nights.

After the summer session, wedding planning started with an intensity Stella Ann never imagined. Stella Ann had no idea how much work went into planning a wedding. Her wedding dress was the most important thing on her mind. She and Lou went shopping many times for dresses in Nashville and the surrounding cities. Most of the dresses were not available in a size small enough to fit her, and Lou thought all the dresses in their budget looked cheap. Stella Ann wanted Lou to make her dress, but Lou insisted she couldn't take on such a huge and expensive project.

Lou's mother died earlier in the year, and she was still grieving. Lou didn't think one ever stopped grieving over the loss of someone special. The grief became more distant but never less intense. It took a lot of energy for Lou to support Stella Ann in the wedding planning process. She was not in favor of the wedding, and she could not shake the overwhelming sadness she felt from losing her mother.

Their last stop was at a lovely little bridal shop in Green Hills, a nice shopping area in Nashville. Stella Ann tried on a dress that did not reflect one thing about her style or personality. She stood on the alteration pedestal and waited for a response from her mama. Then Lou said, "Stella Ann, take the dress off. We are going to Murfreesboro to Hancock Fabric to look at lace, fabric, and patterns. I understand they have more lace and wedding fabric than our Hancock's in Columbia. I am going to make your dress." The response was unexpected but made Stella Ann incredibly happy. She could not ditch the dress quickly enough.

Most of the time, Lou didn't need a dress pattern, but she knew making Stella Ann's wedding dress was going to be a huge project. She knew quality fabric and lace better than anyone, and she knew how to fit her daughter. Stella Ann was excited about her mama making her dress. This was what Lou needed to help her through her grief. Mama was back.

Norma invited Stella Ann and Lou to have lunch at her house the following week to discuss wedding plans. Lou already knew the role of the groom's mother because their son, Ronald, got married three years earlier. She stayed true to the saying, "wear beige and keep your mouth shut." She sensed Norma was going to defy all rules of wedding etiquette.

They were greeted at the Taber's door by Pearl, the family maid, and were ushered to a table in the party room looking out over a large pool with a slide. Norma was 39 years old and looked like royalty as she greeted them. She wore a tan and black designer pantsuit and had perfectly coiffed hair. The family diamonds dripped around her neck, wrists, and fingers, and she sported perfectly manicured red nails. The only item missing was a tiara. She could pull off sophistication if she didn't open her mouth.

Another lady named Willa Mae, the Taber's cook, served them a delicious lunch of shrimp salad, fresh fruit, petite yeast rolls, iced tea, and lemon pie for dessert. Before the first bite, Norma opened a notebook, and Stella Ann and Lou looked at each other. Lou told Stella Ann to listen and say as little as possible before they knocked on the front door.

Norma asked, "Have you selected your dress yet, Stella Ann?"

Stella Ann politely replied, "Yes, ma'am, we have been shopping several times, and I finally convinced Mama to make my dress."

"Oh, I see," Norma replied taking a deep breath.

She turned toward Lou and said with a twinge of sarcasm, "I am sure, Lou, you will do a lovely job. Stella Ann's clothes always look pretty, sweet, and girly."

It was no secret Norma had been smitten with Bradford's sexy, slutty, sequin slathered pageant queen during the time she and Bradford broke up. Her catty comments were Norma's way of indicating she did not like Stella Ann's style or anything about Stella Ann.

Stella Ann could see her mother tense and straighten her back. She politely replied, "Thank you. We purchased some lovely antique white Duchess satin, yards and yards of Alencon lace, and silk tulle for her train and veil. It will be a big job, but it will be prettier and fit her better than the dresses she tried on in the stores. Stella Ann picked out a design suited to her personality and style. It is identical to a dress she saw in a bridal magazine."

Norma asked Pearl to bring a dress from the hall closet. It was covered in a heavy garment bag from a fancy store in Belle Meade, an upscale area of Nashville. She took the garment out of the bag and said, "I was shopping last week and saw this dress for the bridesmaids, so I bought it to see what you think. It will look as good on my ten-year-old as it will the older bridesmaids. I thought it looked like a Southern belle."

It was a shiny blue sapphire polyester velvet off the shoulder number with a train. It looked cheap and too revealing for a winter wedding. The price tag was $150. It was too expensive by most standards.

Stella Ann was biting her tongue and thought to herself, "I wouldn't want my ten-year-old to wear that dress. Plus, it is way too much money for my friends to pay for a bridesmaid dress."

She took a deep breath and said, "The dress is lovely, but I had a different color and design in mind. I am leaning toward dresses of burgundy crepe back satin with a style from the 1940s. The dresses will flow as the girls walk down the aisle. I am not going for a Southern belle look."

Norma was not about to give up, "Well, Stella Ann, this dress comes in burgundy."

Norma was hell bent to turn Stella Ann's wedding into a Southern drama. This was a woman when casually asked if she could have anything she desired announced she wanted Rhett Butler, a character in a Southern novel. Of course, she brought down the house in laughter with her unbridled quick wit, but there was a lot of truth in her desire.

Lou changed the subject. "We are going to Nashville next week to talk with a caterer and baker. Would you like to talk to them about the groom's cake? They catered Ron and Jenny's wedding. The food was delicious, and the presentation was lovely. You are welcomed to join us and help pick out the wedding cake."

"What was Lou doing?" thought Stella Ann. "She didn't want to be anywhere near such an aggressive, snobby woman." In her youthful "in the present moment" innocence, Stella Ann failed to register the fact the difficult snobby woman sitting at the table with her was scheduled to be her mother-in-law in a few months.

Norma accepted the invitation. Their appointment was the following Tuesday.

It was imperative they make the best use of their time before Stella Ann and Bradford returned to school for fall quarter. Stella Ann had a sinking feeling Norma was going to sabotage their schedule. Nothing Stella Ann selected seemed to please Norma. She didn't like the cake design, the bridesmaids' dresses, the napkins, or the florist. At least Stella Ann won the battle of Norma wanting the men in the wedding party to wear top hats.

Before they finished dessert, Norma asked about a wedding photographer. Lou said, "Stella Ann has talked with a photographer in Murfreesboro who did the wedding of one of her high school friends. She loved the quality of the pictures and reserved the date for him to do the wedding. The bridal package was reasonable, and it included an engagement picture and a bridal portrait."

"Oh, that will not be necessary. We can get a much better package and better-quality pictures from the husband of one of my bridge club friends. In fact, he owes us some favors and will be happy to shoot the wedding free," Norma said.

"Why don't you use him for the rehearsal dinner?" Lou negotiated. "Stella Ann has her heart set on the photographer she has arranged."

"Absolutely not." Norma retorted. "My friend would be disappointed if her husband didn't shoot the wedding. I will call his studio tomorrow."

Lou thanked Norma for the lunch and politely excused them from the increasingly tense situation. Stella Ann drove. They remained still and silent until they got out of the driveway.

"We got blindsided, Stella Ann. Think long and hard before you go through with this wedding," Lou said. "There is plenty of time to call it off."

Lou thought the disastrous lunch meeting was a sign from God the wedding should not happen. Her gut instincts had never let her down. They were already snubbing their religion by agreeing for Stella Ann to get married in another church. Lou had never entered the door of another denomination and questioned whether her family would attend the ceremony. Their family had strict fundamental principles, no drinking, no dancing, and no musical instruments in the sanctuary.

Stella Ann said nothing to set Lou off into a disgusted rant. She was anxious to get back to Knoxville. Wedding planning was turning out to be a pain rather than the joy she dreamed it would be. With plans, parties, and deadlines, it was going to be necessary to come home almost every weekend. She braced herself for an extra busy fall.

Before she and Bradford returned to school, Norma and Hank invited them to dinner. They went to a new restaurant in Belle Meade with a fabulous salad bar and delicious steaks. The restaurant was like stepping into an elegant dining hall in an English castle, and they had their own private dining room. Bradford told her his parents had something important they wanted to discuss with them, but he did not know the topic. Dr. Taber started the meal with a champagne toast. Stella Ann had never had champagne before and thought it was tasty. Norma started talking.

"Hank and I have something important to share with you. We locked it away for an awfully long time to protect the family and to please Hank's mother. We knew the time would come when we would need to reveal the information because it directly affects you, Bradford, and ultimately Stella Ann. Legal paperwork needs to be finalized before you and Stella Ann return to school and before the wedding."

Hank took over. "When I married your mother, Bradford, she already had you. She married right out of high school. Her marriage to a man named Dean Bailey ended shortly after you were born. You and Norma lived with your grandparents, Grammie and Grandpa. We met at my uncle's oil business where she was working as a secretary, and I was a chemical engineer. I adopted you when we married. My parents were affluent and socially visible. They asked that we never mention your biological father or the adoption. We respected their request."

Norma said, "Hank adopted you, but the adoption was never finalized. Dean put a stipulation in the adoption papers you had to decide when you were twenty-one if you wanted your last name to be Taber or Bailey. We have a court date next week. You will stand before the judge to proclaim the name you want and sign the final adoption papers. It must be done before you and Stella Ann get married."

"Mom, I turned twenty-one months ago. Why didn't you tell me then? Why didn't you tell me years ago, so I could understand why Dad's family ostracized me?" Bradford questioned.

"You know now, Bradford. You and Stella Ann clear next Wednesday on your calendar. Our appointment with the judge is at eleven."

"Mom, do the little kids know about me?" He got no response and added, "I have been Bradford Taber all my life. Why would I change now?"

"Bradford, we will discuss details later. Let's have a nice dinner." Norma was ready to shut the discussion down.

Hank interjected, "Bradford, I have never thought of you any differently from our other children. You are my son. The younger kids do not know about your mom's previous marriage or your adoption. I see no reason for them to know now."

Hank could be empathetic and thoughtful. He had a thread of class engrained in him.

Stella Ann felt like she needed another glass or a whole bottle of champagne. She looked at Bradford and even though she had known him for years, she could not get a read about how he was taking the news. Bradford suspected something about his position in the family for a long time. Sometimes when they were alone, he would cry and tell Stella Ann he was different. He claimed he didn't fit in, and he was not like his siblings. Stella Ann listened intently and tried to reassure him of his status within his family and his parents' love for him. The only difference she could identify was Bradford's eyes were blue. If anything, he was treated as the favorite child in the family. Yep, she needed more champagne.

The next weekend, Stella Ann and Bradford decided to take a day trip to the Louisville Zoo. Their excuse was they wanted to spend time together and get away from wedding planning. Stella Ann had never been to a zoo. It would be a relaxing day trip to get their minds off wedding plans and family bickering. Part of their excuse was true, but the focus was not to see animals. It was to see Dean. Grammie gave Bradford his telephone number and address. She remained in contact with him through the years. Dean was in medical school in Louisville.

They met at Dean's apartment, and he took them to lunch. Stella Ann noticed interesting similarities between Dean and Bradford. They held their eating utensils the same way, had similar facial expressions and mannerisms, and managed their cigarettes the same. How could that be? They had not been around each other. Dean wasn't even at the hospital the night Bradford was born. After lunch, they set off for the zoo. Stella Ann's childish excitement about the zoo was obvious.

Dean had been a photographer for a well-known magazine and was quite accomplished. He had his camera with him and took lots of pictures of them at the zoo. The meeting was much like one would have meeting a family friend or uncle who had been gone a long time.

Bradford invited Dean to the wedding, but no promises were made for him to attend. For one thing, Bradford knew Norma would become unglued if her secret was exposed in town. They had plenty to talk about when they drove back to Columbia, but as they drove, they didn't say much. They were tired and emotionally exhausted.

Stella Ann had a mischievous thought, "Maybe Dean would be willing to photograph their wedding. It would solve the photographer issue with Norma. But it could make things worse." She giggled to herself.

By October, it was time for Stella Ann to revisit the pill. She didn't ask Brenda to go with her and made an appointment to see Dr. Pierce, the nice physician she had seen a year before. This time she was going to his off-campus office. It was a replay of her last visit. The next day she got a call from his nurse who said Dr. Pierce wanted to see her that afternoon at the student clinic. It was like she had been smacked across the face with such force she was numb.

It didn't make sense to her. She made it clear to Bradford there would be no bed parties until there was a solid commitment, engagement, and negative test result. He confirmed he was negative last year. She believed him, and passionate romance bloomed again. The only answer had to be Bradford never went to the clinic when she confronted him. She was again humiliated, angry, and betrayed, but she felt played, disrespected, and dumb.

It took a long time to get Bradford to tell the truth, but he finally admitted he never went to the doctor. He confessed he had lied about his test results. The next day she escorted him to Dr. Pierce's office. Dr. Pierce advised them to see a counselor. He also said it would be unlikely they would ever be parents. It was the worst thing she heard during the whole ordeal. How did he know for sure they would never be parents? Most women would have canceled a wedding at this juncture, but Stella Ann loved Bradford. She was not so confident about his feelings for her. His actions spoke volumes.

Stella Ann realized Norma, Hank, and Bradford weren't the only ones who kept secrets. She was now in the same category, and she hated it. She had always told the truth even if it meant punishment. She had never been deceitful or secretive but was becoming skillful about the process.

Maybe her daddy was right about her choices.

PART TWO:

Rock Walls

CHAPTER 4

Marital Miss

Stella Ann and Bradford came home every weekend except for two during fall quarter. When they were home, they attended cocktail parties, showers, teas, and dinners. They met with their minister, caterer, and florist. The list of things to accomplish grew shorter but more time sensitive as their wedding date closed in on them.

They bought their wedding bands and had them engraved. They picked out a dish pattern, crystal, and silver, even though they thought it was not necessary. They needed practical items like a vacuum, pots and pans, towels, and sheets. They needed everyday things they could use as they set up housekeeping in their small one-bedroom apartment in the married student apartments on Laurel Avenue.

Stella Ann spent hours addressing their wedding invitations and set the mailing date for the first week in November. Norma insisted on addressing her own invitations. The guest list was capped at 200, with 225 invitations ordered, but Norma continued to want more and more invitations for her acquaintances and social connections. To keep the peace, Lou decided to order announcements for her out-of-town family and gave the extra invitations to Norma. It shut her up for a while.

Norma was sitting at the table in her kitchen when Stella Ann delivered the extra invitations.

"Mama said this is the last set of invitations she could spare and hopes it will be enough for you to complete your list."

"Stella Ann, before you leave, I have a question for you. Who is playing at the reception?" Norma asked.

"What do you mean?" Stella Ann asked. "The reception is at the church."

"What band will be playing for your first dance?"

"There won't be a band. A friend of mine will play background piano music as people greet us in the reception line and mingle."

Norma said, "There is always live music at wedding receptions. You may not know it, but the trend is not to have a receiving line."

"Mrs. Taber, there will be no band, no dancing at the church, and no alcohol served. The church does not allow alcohol in the Fellowship Hall, and none of my family dances. Conversation, hugs, best wishes, cake, punch, nuts, and mints will work fine. Bradford and I plan to acknowledge each guest at the wedding and reception."

Sit-down dinners and big band dancing were not part of southern weddings, or at least not in the small town of Columbia. It was a tradition the future would embrace.

She could see Norma was not happy about the band and slipped out the kitchen door, stopping to pet the two large dogs on the back porch. Stella Ann did not want a confrontation with Norma.

At dinner, Stella Ann told Bradford about the band conversation she had with his mom earlier in the day. He was supportive and said the simple reception was appropriate and to ignore his mother. "Ignore his mother" would be a directive she would hear from him a lot. She would also hear the excuse, "That is the way mom is," and the dismissive statement, "Let her have her way."

They only had exams left in the fall quarter after Thanksgiving which meant they would be home over ten days before the wedding. Most parties and bridal showers ended before Thanksgiving, allowing them time to address wedding details.

The bridesmaids had the material for their dresses for weeks. Lou and Burt paid for their material, patterns, and trim. All they had to pay for was to get their dresses made and get their shoes dyed to match. Lou made herself a stunning green dress with a ruffle and pearls around the neckline. Norma decided to wear a burgundy dress with ivory lace. Grammie chose a hot pink chiffon evening gown, and Stella Ann's grandmother selected a rose crepe dress.

Bradford made sure all the groomsmen ordered their tuxedos and canes. Stella Ann was not thrilled the men were going to walk down the aisle looking like they were about to burst into a Fred Astaire dance number, but she had to pick her battles. At least they would not be wearing top hats.

Lou made the final adjustments to her wedding dress when Stella Ann got home for Christmas. It looked even better than the designer gown she had her mama copy. The fabric was lush, and Lou had hand sewn many heavy lace appliques and over 2,000 pearls down the front and along the train. Her cathedral veil was edged with the same lace, and the headpiece, her something old, was a Juliet lace cap that anchored her veil. It had belonged to her granny. There were satin covered buttons down the back of the dress, and a simple satin bow sat where the train was attached. Stella Ann's dress was perfect.

They had exams on the first three days in December. It was a refreshing break from wedding chatter for a few days. Before her last exam, Stella Ann got a phone call from Lou.

"Stella Ann, what do you know about a champagne reception at the Taber's house after the wedding?"

"Mama, what are you talking about?" Stella Ann replied.

"We got a white invitation with red engraving today. It reads, "Come celebrate the new Mr. and Mrs. Bradford Clark Taber at a champagne reception at our home after the reception at the church given by Dr. and Mrs. Henry Raymond Taber."

"What is she trying to do, Stella Ann?" Lou asked with tension in her voice. "She is determined to have her way and ruin your wedding. Isn't it enough that she demanded more invitations, her own florist, and free flowing drinks at the rehearsal dinner and the wedding day brunch? The rumors I have heard about this woman being difficult are beginning to have some validity."

"Mama, please calm down," Stella Ann said in a quiet voice. "I will talk with Bradford and see what he knows. I have a feeling he doesn't know anything about it, or he would have said something. We will talk about it when I get home tomorrow."

She immediately called Bradford to find out what he knew. "Bradford, I need to know something. Do you know anything about a champagne reception at your parents' house after the reception at the church?"

"No," he said." I don't know anything about a champagne reception. Mom hasn't said a word about it. What's the problem?"

"Bradford, the problem is your mother sent out separate invitations and never discussed it with my mother, the mother of the bride. It undermines our plans and is very disrespectful to my family."

He replied, "Did you say it is after the reception at the church?"

"Yes, that is how the invitation is worded."

"I don't see it's a big deal. Let my mom do what she wants at her house."

Stella Ann caught another hint of his loyalty to his mother. "Let my mom do what she wants."

"Bradford, I don't want to go to a champagne reception. It is disrespectful to my family. I think we should have been included in those plans."

"Look, we don't have to go."

"So, have we decided that we will not go to your parents' house after the church reception?" Stella Ann asked.

"That's right. We don't have to go."

She called her mother to tell her what she had learned.

That was easy enough. But was it?

The next day when they got back to Columbia, Bradford called with another surprise.

"Stella Ann, our honeymoon planned at Paradise Island in the Bahamas was canceled. Mom thought you needed to know the change of plans to arrange your packing."

"What kind of change, Bradford? Did the travel agent make a mistake?" Stella Ann asked.

"We are not going to the Bahamas for our honeymoon. Mom called the travel agent and changed our honeymoon destination to New Orleans," Bradford replied.

"Your mom insisted we go to the Bahamas. I have already packed clothes for a warm climate. Why did your mother change our plans?"

Bradford replied, "Mom thought New Orleans was a romantic city when she and Dad went several years ago, so she changed our plans. We are staying at the Bourbon Orleans Hotel, and she made dinner reservations for us at a couple of restaurants. She said there was plenty for us to do there, and we would enjoy getting coffee and beignets at Café Du Monde. She and Dad are paying for it, so I guess we need to go where they want us to go and be gracious about it."

It was another revelation of Bradford's devotion to his mother. She won again. Whose wedding was this?

Discussions heated up, and conversations between Stella Ann and Bradford were volatile. It was a time they should have been enjoying, but Norma would not back off. She continued her overbearing, bossy antics. She appeared determined to have her way.

By nightfall and ten days before the wedding, Bradford called Stella Ann and said he was calling off the wedding. He said he was tired of the bickering and being in the middle of her and his mom. Obviously, Norma pushed and prodded him from the time he arrived home.

When the conversation was over, Stella Ann stayed in her room and cried buckets of tears. Burt and Lou never knew the heartbreak of the phone call. She told them about Bradford canceling the wedding the next morning at breakfast.

Burt was excited, and Lou was disgusted that Bradford would call off the wedding. Lou did not jump to make vendor and guest cancellations immediately. She was more patient and logical than Stella Ann and Burt. She told them they would wait for things to cool off before they acted. After some thought, Lou decided it was better for Bradford to cancel before the wedding than decide after the wedding he didn't want to be married or leave Stella Ann at the altar. The hassle of undoing the plans already set would be massive, but they would never complain to Stella Ann.

Burt was still seething about Bradford's never asking him for Stella Ann's hand in marriage and was relieved the wedding charade was called off. His opinion remained steady. He thought his daughter deserved better. The loss they would take for forfeited vendor charges would be money well spent. His daughter would miss the bullet of an unhappy future—or would she?

Stella Ann cried off and on all the next day. It was nine days before her wedding day, and again, she was humiliated. She wandered into the living room, where her wedding dress was on a dressmaker's mannequin. She sat on the sofa and stared at it. Her mama had done such a beautiful job making it, and now she wouldn't even get to wear it.

What about her bridesmaids? Most of them lived out of town. When should she call them and let them know? Her mind was in overdrive. The tall tale tellers of Columbia would have something to talk about for a while. People were already making wagers the marriage wouldn't last six months. After crying through her disappointment over her canceled wedding, Stella Ann dried her eyes. She decided if Bradford's loyalty was to his mother rather than his future wife, they shouldn't get married.

The family was having lunch, and the phone rang. It was Bradford. Stella Ann ran to take the call from her bedroom phone. Bradford wanted to know if she would go to dinner with him that night. She agreed they had a lot of things to discuss. "I suppose we need to make a list of things to cancel and people to contact," Stella Ann said.

He replied, "I'll pick you up at six. We will go somewhere special. It will be a surprise."

Stella Ann was exhausted but managed to pull herself up and spend extra time getting ready. If he didn't want to get married, at least he would see what he was giving up.

The drive to Nashville was awkward and seemed longer than usual. Neither of them said much, and dinner was tense. When they got back in the car, Bradford asked her if she would like to drive to Centennial Park to see the lights at the Parthenon. The traditional white nativity scene was sold years before and shipped to Chicago, but the city still had a Christmas music light show nightly through New Year's Day. There was something comforting and familiar about being around the Parthenon at Christmas.

Bradford was the first one to start the conversation. "Stella Ann, you look beautiful tonight. Under the circumstances, how are you doing?"

"Thank you, Bradford, for the compliment, and to be quite honest, I am not doing very well at all. Is any woman who gets dumped before her wedding ever in a great place?" He tapped the wrath of a woman scorned, and Stella Ann had a temper to be reckoned with. It didn't show up much, but when it did rear its ugly head, people best get out of her way.

"Look, Stella Ann, I don't know what got into me. My mom has been hard to reason with lately, and she dumped a lot of information in my lap when I got home. I don't know what to believe, but I still want to marry you." He shrugged his shoulders and said, "Anyway, you might as well marry me. No one else would want you."

"What did you say?" Stella Ann screamed. "And what makes you think anyone else would want you either? Please take me home."

Dark silence was the mood in the car as they drove back to Columbia. Nothing was resolved.

Time was running out, and decisions had to be made. After an emergency meeting with Dr. Craft, their minister, and a long soul-searching lunch, Stella Ann and Bradford decided they cared deeply for each other and wanted to get married. Bradford told Dr. Craft he loved Stella Ann. Thank goodness there was a resolution before anything was announced publicly. Her mother was right to wait for any alternative action and was happy for her daughter. Burt was not as enthusiastic about the decision and had a man-to-man talk with Bradford a few days later. Stella Ann never knew the content of the conversation, but her daddy could be intimidating when it came to a face-to-face discussion and protecting his family.

Tensions settled down the week leading up to the wedding, and it gave Stella Ann an opportunity to stay up to date writing her thank-you notes. She knew she would not have time after they got back to school because she was doing her student teaching. She contacted her bridesmaids to make sure their dresses were ready, and they knew the plans for the weekend. There were a lot of things planned to keep the wedding party busy. Wedding festivities were scheduled to start at 11 a.m. the day before the wedding. Despite all the conflict, Stella Ann was excited.

Lou hosted a bridesmaid's luncheon at The Old South Tea Room in Columbia the day before the wedding. It was a beautiful setting in an antebellum house downtown. They were served a lovely meal of chicken turnovers, strawberry salad, green beans, petite yeast rolls, sweet tea, and chocolate brownie cake with salted caramel sauce and ice cream. All the girls attended. Stella Ann gave each of them a pearl necklace to wear with their dresses and a silver bud vase as a bridesmaid's gift. The mood was fun and festive.

After the luncheon, Stella Ann and her bridesmaids went to a relative's house to cut curly English ivy to take to the florist for their bouquets of burgundy, pink, and white carnations. Mr. Farrell used roses instead of carnations as a wedding gift to Stella Ann. The magic Mr. Farrell worked in the sanctuary and Fellowship Hall on Saturday was stunning and way over budget. He told Lou not to worry about it.

At Bradford's request, Stella Ann sent a picture to Norma of how she wanted her bridal bouquet to look. It was going to come from Norma's florist. Stella Ann wanted her bouquet to be a cascade of white Tibet roses, ranunculus flowers, small hydrangeas, and curly English ivy. She got one white orchid on a white Bible like Norma carried.

The wedding party was instructed to be at the church at 5:00 p.m. for the rehearsal, with a dinner to follow at The Dove Creek Inn. Everyone showed up on time, but there seemed to be different music from what Stella Ann had selected. The organist was Bradford's friend from Knoxville, and he left all his sheet music at his house. How that happened was a mystery since he had known for months he was playing at their wedding. He and Bradford spent much of the day in Nashville at a music center trying to replace the selected music. Stella Ann had to pick her battles. The replacement music they selected was fine, even though Stella Ann had a musical background and spent hours deciding on the perfect pieces for their wedding.

They finished the rehearsal and hurried to The Dove Creek Inn for a lovely steak dinner. Norma had the banquet hall decorated with red and white poinsettias and holly, ivy, and red bows. She had favors at each place setting. Candles were everywhere, and the dining area looked beautiful. When Norma entered, she had changed into a white pantsuit trimmed in white ostrich feathers. Stella Ann wore a simple, long, cranberry-red column dress with a matching jacket. Norma was the hostess, and if she wanted to upstage the bride at the rehearsal dinner, no one cared. Surely, she would have the decency to let the bride shine on her wedding day.

The food was delicious, and the champagne flowed. Groomsmen took many bottles of champagne and wine with them as they left. Stella Ann was concerned about the groomsmen being on time at Graystone Country Club the next day and asked Bradford to monitor their drinking. Instead, he joined them in a shot challenge. The innkeeper reported two guest rooms demolished at the hands of drunk, rowdy groomsmen, obligating Hank and Norma to assume all the damage and have the rooms redecorated after the wedding. It was no cheap bill.

The Dove Creek Inn was a historic Civil War-era home with additional guest rooms along the back. The restaurant was open daily, and they had an antique shop rivaling those in Charleston. Guest rooms were decorated with antiques. It was off Pulaski Highway and about a fifteen-minute drive from the church. Burt and Lou arranged for the out-of-town bridesmaids to stay in a charming bed and breakfast downtown. The only thing they had to attend the next day before the wedding was a brunch at Graystone Country Club hosted by Taber's friends.

The brunch was a beautiful buffet laden with breakfast and lunch items and mimosa drinks, coffee, sweet tea, juice, and water. Stella Ann was relieved there was no open bar. Norma could not leave feathers alone. The night before she wore white feathers. For the brunch, she sported a similar outfit with green feathers. Burt couldn't help himself and leaned over to Stella Ann and said, "That woman is dressed like the bird she is." Stella Ann had trouble containing her laughter.

By 3 p.m., the bridesmaids dressed and gathered in the bridal room for pictures. The girls looked beautiful, and the bridesmaid's dresses and Juliet headpieces looked amazing. Their flowers were delivered, and Stella Ann almost cried when she saw how lovely they were. Mr. Farrell outdid himself. She never mentioned her disappointment in her own bouquet.

When the photographer was finished with the bridesmaids and flower girl, he called Lou and Stella Ann for mother/daughter pictures. Stella Ann always thought her mother was pretty, but she was stunning in her mint green dress. It accented her dark hair and green eyes. Lou adjusted Stella Ann's veil, told her she was proud of her, and said she was a beautiful bride. Stella Ann thanked Lou for making her dress and for the wedding.

During the bridal session pictures, Norma walked in. She was wearing what looked like a floral bathrobe, but the fabric was fancy. It was a multicolored design of metallic gold, orange, turquoise, yellow, and green silk organza with ruffles flowing around the sleeves and down the back. There was dead silence in the room. One would have thought she was going to change her dress, but she already had a corsage of yellow orange roses on her shoulder. It was without a doubt the most hideous dress Stella Ann had ever seen.

Norma announced it was a designer original she had made in New York to wear to the gubernatorial inauguration ball in January. They were big donors and attended many high-profile political events. Years before, they attended the Kennedy presidential inauguration and one of the balls. There was no doubt the wedding guests would remember her dress. It was clear the bride was upstaged by the mother of the groom, and the pictures proved it.

They could see the walkway and entrance to the church from the bridal room. It was fun to see people walking into the church, and Stella Ann's excitement grew. Norma removed herself from the group and stood at a small window at the entrance of the room. Stella Ann walked over to speak with her. Norma had a tissue, and tears sprinkled her face.

"Mrs. Taber, is something wrong??" Stella Ann gently asked.

"Honey, I am fine. I get emotional at weddings, and this is my first child getting married. He is special to me," she replied. She added, "Do you think Dean will come?"

Stella Ann immediately thought Dean was the reason she was crying, not the wedding or Bradford. Norma didn't want her secret revealed to the town.

"No, Mrs. Taber, we have not heard from him. I don't think he will be here," Stella Ann said.

"Stella Ann, you look beautiful," Norma said.

"Thank you, Mrs. Taber."

Stella Ann thought, "It was the nicest thing Mrs. Taber said to her in all the years she and Bradford dated."

It was time for them to move toward the sanctuary. Stella Ann was met outside the door by her daddy. He looked handsome in his tuxedo, which he complained profusely about wearing, calling it a monkey suit. He put his arm out for her to grab and led her up the steps to the church entry hall. They waited for their signal to start down the aisle, and Mrs. Farrell adjusted her train and veil.

Burt kissed her on the cheek and said, "Stella Ann, you look beautiful. We can turn around and go the other way. You won't have to worry about a thing. You don't have to do this. I will take care of the fallout." She knew giving her away and walking her down the aisle was a difficult task for her daddy.

Stella Ann said, "Daddy, let's go forward."

During their vows, Bradford never once looked at Stella Ann and was prompted by the minister that he was marrying Stella Ann and not him. Dr. Craft omitted ten minutes of the ceremony. He later apologized, indicating he was nervous. However, Stella Ann knew he was distracted by the tension in the sanctuary. Dr. Taber, Bradford's best man, managed to get Stella Ann's small wedding ring stuck on his little finger. It lightened the atmosphere for a few seconds. Ron stepped up and managed to free the ring.

Stella Ann could tell Bradford had been drinking. They quickly kissed and headed up the aisle of the church as ushers held the tall antique doors for them. As they exited the doorway, it was snowing. Small snowflakes could be seen dancing in the light from the lanterns on Main Street. Stella Ann got her snow speckled wedding and interpreted it as a blessing from God. After more pictures, they walked to Fellowship Hall for cake, punch, hugs, and best wishes.

Norma and Hank did not attend the church reception. They left right after the formal pictures were taken to get ready for their champagne party.

People filtered out of the church reception quickly, and many got confused about where the reception was being held. Shortly after the reception, Stella Ann and Bradford changed into their travel clothes. Stella Ann wore a green pantsuit, and Bradford wore a brown leisure suit, which Stella Ann hated but knew his mother had bought. Stella Ann thought the person responsible for the men's fashion statement of leisure suits should be banned from the fashion design world.

Stella Ann's brother, Ron, and his wife, Jenny, took them to the hotel at the airport. On the way to Nashville, Stella Ann and Bradford could not remember signing their marriage license. Stella Ann was starving, and they stopped and got a fish sandwich and hamburger. Bradford called Dr. Craft from the restaurant, and he assured Bradford they had signed the license. Apparently, stress blocked their memory.

They were not scheduled to leave for New Orleans until the next morning. The bridal suite ended up being a regular room, and there was a snack basket with a bottle of champagne on the table. They learned wedding night sex was not what it was hyped up to be, and they fell asleep.

When they arrived in New Orleans and drove to the French Quarter, it seemed like a ghost town. There were few people on the streets, and the atmosphere was subdued. The taxi driver told them the tourist season was over, and it was a slow time in the French Quarter. He explained most places shut down in early December and didn't open again until the Sugar Bowl crowd arrived. She and Bradford looked at each other and could sense what each other was thinking. Stella Ann begged Bradford for them to spend a couple of days in New Orleans and go back home, but he refused. Seven days in New Orleans was going to be a challenge. Three days had been plenty when she visited with her roommate two years earlier.

They checked into the Bourbon Orleans Hotel, and it proved to be an elegant and lovely hotel. They ate breakfast at Brennan's twice, dinner at Commander's Palace, and went to Pat O'Brien's, where they enjoyed hurricane drinks. On the third day of their honeymoon, all establishments

75

in the French Quarter closed. Even the two restaurants in the hotel closed.

They bought a loaf of bread and a jar of peanut butter at a Quick Stop market in the French Quarter, and the rest of their meals were takeout meals from shrimp and oyster street vendors. Bradford got food poisoning from some bad oysters. The wedding vow phrase, "in sickness and in health," became very real on their honeymoon. Stella Ann felt sorry for Bradford. He was crawling on the floor and hanging his head over the toilet he was so sick. Stella Ann encouraged him to drink water and suck on ice chips, which was not an easy task.

The main sightseeing activity of the week was a tour up and down the harbor on a commercial banana boat. Stella Ann wanted to go home, pack the car, and return to Knoxville to set up their apartment.

It was a wedding and honeymoon to forget. It was time to move forward, and for Norma Taber to butt out.

Lou and Grammie sent them to Knoxville with enough casseroles to last for a couple of weeks and staples needed for a kitchen. Stella Ann had no idea how to cook and had little time to learn before she started her student teaching. Bradford was tolerant and kind about her lack of cooking skills. He didn't have any cooking skills either.

The apartment was small and furnished with what looked like 1955 motel furniture. They had four fish tanks, two large ones and two small ones. A fraternity brother influenced Bradford to start selling angel fish to a local pet store. Houseplants filled the tiny apartment. They were wedding gifts from their UT friends, and they received a couple of plant stands and many macrame plant hangers.

Money quickly became an issue. A neighbor influenced them to get involved in a pyramid program selling soap and household products. They ended up with boxes and boxes of laundry detergent and never climbed up the pyramid. They couldn't sell fish or soap and calculated their losses. They had used all their wedding gift money on their disastrous soap business.

There were things they learned early on about each other that had never surfaced when they were dating. Stella Ann did not know Bradford was a neat freak, had odd eating habits, and was a night owl. He had no idea she needed a lot of sleep and was not well organized. She also had a bad habit of procrastinating. They had been in their apartment for two weeks and were adjusting well until one day Stella Ann forgot to vacuum. Bradford expected her to vacuum every day.

"Stop, Bradford. Please stop throwing the vacuum cleaner. You are going to turn over the plant stand," Stella Ann pleaded.

"Look, your lazy brat, if you aren't going to vacuum, I am. We can't live in this nasty apartment," Bradford yelled.

"Please stop, Bradford. The apartment is not dirty," she said. "You are going to break something. I will do the vacuuming after dinner."

Before she could finish saying anything else, he told her to shut the hell up. Then he turned over a plant stand holding a cute yellow planter housing a philodendron plant. Pottery pieces, dirt, and plant parts flew all over the living room area. The tile plant stand broke, and Stella Ann started crying as she swept up the mess. Bradford threw the vacuum across the room and left. It took Stella Ann a long time to clean all the pottery and glass pieces up as well as the potting soil. She had to get in the mindset to start her student teaching the next day and was bordering on a panic attack. She had never seen this explosive side of Bradford.

Early the next morning, Stella Ann reported to the inner-city school where she was assigned to do her student teaching. She was greeted by the principal who took her to meet her supervising teacher, an older lady named Miss Barnwell, who had no idea she was getting a student teacher.

"I was not expecting a student teacher. I prefer not to have one as they have never seemed to work out. My class is overcrowded, and I don't know where I am going to put you," she said.

It wasn't a very welcoming introduction, but Stella Ann said, "I could sit over there in the corner in a folding chair. I don't take up much room and will stay out of the way until you want me to help."

"Are you aware I have a split second and third-grade class? When it is time for you to teach, you will need to make double lesson plans."

"That is fine, Miss Barnwell. I know I will learn a lot from you."

Stella Ann sat down in the corner and made a promise to herself that Miss Barnwell would like her before she finished her student teaching.

She didn't care what she had to do to win her over.

Stella Ann learned a lot on the first day of student teaching. The most important part about her day was she started making connections and developing relationships with the children. She was exhausted by the time she got back to the apartment. However, telling Bradford about her day gave her renewed energy, and he seemed genuinely interested. They never mentioned the vacuum cleaner episode, and Bradford didn't apologize for his behavior.

Miss Barnwell taught Stella Ann a lot and let her start teaching a week before she was scheduled to take over the class. She asked Stella Ann to go with her to make home visits. It was not a requirement, but she said it gave a lot of insight about a student. Miss Barnwell made two to three home visits a week, taking groceries and necessities to families. She also added a couple of storybooks to the bag. It was an eye-opener and heartbreaking. Many of the children lived in the projects with only one parent. They did not have enough food, nor did they have appropriate clothes to wear. In one family, all the children slept on bare mattresses in the living room. There was little heat in the apartment and few blankets. One thing was clear; they loved and respected Miss Barnwell and appreciated her help.

She learned a lot from the inner-city home visits. Miss Barnwell's outward appearance, demeanor, and never-married status did not lead one to think she had such a compassionate and caring side. She and Bradford were having a tough time being newlyweds, but they had no idea how rough life was for some little kids. By the time she finished the second/third-grade student teaching rotation, Miss Barnwell had handwritten some of her favorite recipes on cute recipe cards and presented them to her with a recipe box from the class.

"I thought I told you not to mash my clothes, Stella Ann," Bradford yelled.

"I am sorry," Stella Ann replied. "I will be more careful."

When she hung up his shirts, she had to smush them in to fit them in the closet. Each of them had a lot of clothes, and closet space was extremely limited in the tiny apartment.

"You idiot!" Bradford yelled. "Can't you do anything without messing it up?" He slammed his closet doors so hard they fell to the floor, causing a loud crashing noise. Then he threw his clothes on the floor. Stella Ann started crying and locked herself in the bathroom. She stood in the bathtub and closed the shower curtain.

She could hear Bradford pull the metal doors off her closet and throw them in the hall with a startling boom that would wake people on the floors below. Then she could hear him throwing all her clothes on the floor and cursing with each toss.

She cried louder and was screaming for him to stop. He told her to shut up, or he would knock the bathroom door down. A neighbor heard the commotion and knocked on the door to check on them. It was a long time before Stella Ann came out of the bathroom, even though she knew Bradford was gone. When she came out, Bradford had put his clothes in both closets. Stella Ann folded her things and stacked them in a corner of the bedroom. She had never experienced anything like that before in her life and tried to determine if something other than wrinkled clothes set him off. How could a few wrinkled shirts cause him to get so angry? She was exhausted and went to sleep.

Later, she recalled a conversation she had with Grammie in her gift shop several months before they married.

"Stella Ann, Grandpa and I are so happy you and Bradford are getting married. He will make you a good husband if you can learn to live with his temper and if he will grow up."

"Grammie, what are you talking about? Bradford has been nothing but a polite gentleman to me. We have had disagreements, but I have never seen temper tantrum behavior from Bradford."

"I suppose he has gotten beyond behaving hot-tempered as he has gotten older. But not too long ago, he got mad at his mother and threw her car keys on the roof of their house. They had to call the maid's husband to climb on the roof to get them down."

"Oh, I don't think he will get that mad at me," Stella Ann said. Grammie tried to warn her. Stella Ann missed that warning by a long shot.

They graduated in March. Both families attended the graduation service and came to their apartment after the ceremony for sandwiches before they returned to Columbia. It was a good day filled with laughter and hugs.

Bradford and Stella Ann announced they had decided to stay in Knoxville until June. Bradford was going to take some post-graduate classes to improve his grade point average for medical school. The decision put Stella Ann in bad standing with the Chattanooga school system. She had taken a job to finish out the year for a teacher on maternity leave and had to call and decline at the last minute.

Bradford had younger siblings who planned to stay with Stella Ann and Bradford through the weekend after graduation. The kids had never been to the Smoky Mountains, so Stella Ann and Bradford were going to take his little brother, Scott, and his sister, Liza, on Saturday. The plan was for them to drive the kids home on Monday and visit for a few days during spring break.

After the family left, Bradford took Scott and Liza to the park for a nature walk, and Stella Ann cleaned up the apartment. It was nice to have Scott and Liza with them again. They babysat for them when they were little, and Scott and Liza joined them many times on dates. They took them to Opryland, the circus, to movies, ball games, and out to eat. Hank and Norma would always give them extra money for the kids and were glad they did not have to hire a sitter.

They left Knoxville early on a Saturday morning to drive to the mountains. When they got to Pigeon Forge at the bottom of the park entrance, they stopped for breakfast at a place called The Pancake Cabin. The kids were fascinated by all the attractions and fun things they could do in Pigeon Forge. Bradford promised they would stop on the way back and let them ride the go-carts, but he wanted them to see the beautiful mountains and walk to Clingmans Dome. The weather was crisp and sunny, and they walked through the crowds on the streets of Gatlinburg late in the afternoon. It had become a tourist attraction loaded with restaurants, gift shops, hotels, cabins, and entertainment attractions.

They knew at some point, Scott would wander off, and he did. They spent half an hour looking for him. Liza spotted him buying fireworks in a souvenir shop. Scott told Bradford he didn't buy any fireworks, but Liza knew he did. Bradford decided Scott's disappearance signaled it was time to return to Knoxville after riding the go-carts in Pigeon Forge. They stopped for hamburgers and fries before they got back to the apartment.

Liza and Stella Ann were in the basement washing a couple loads of laundry the next morning when the emergency siren in the building signaled evacuation. Smoke filled the upper floors.

"Uh, oh, Scott," Liza said.

Stella Ann said, "Liza, what are you talking about? We need to leave the building."

"Stella Ann, Scott bought cherry bombs in the mountains. He said he was going to go to the thirteenth floor and drop them down the garbage chute when we got back to the apartment. I told him he'd better not because it was dangerous."

Stella Ann grabbed Liza's hand and looked for Bradford and Scott outside the building. They were standing by the fire trucks. Scott was fascinated by the big trucks and all the firemen who checked the building. People were everywhere, and they could not go back in until every apartment was checked and cleared.

"Bradford, I need to talk with you," Stella Ann said as she guided him to walk beyond the fire trucks still having the kids in sight. "Liza told me Scott bought cherry bombs in Gatlinburg and was going to drop them down the garbage chute when we got back. Do you think he did it?"

"Stella Ann, they have already determined that someone left beans cooking on the stove. They burned, causing all the smoke. I will take the cherry bombs away from Scott when we go back inside."

Stella Ann knew it was going to be difficult to find out if Scott had caused the smoke in the building. The kids were notorious for covering up for each other.

It had been a busy day, and after they watched a TV show, Bradford asked Scott to join him in the bedroom. The interrogation about the cherry bombs lasted for a long time. Before it was over, Scott admitted he threw cherry bombs down the garbage shoot and promised he did not have anymore. Bradford and Stella Ann decided it was time to take the kids back to Columbia, and they left the next morning.

Bradford and Stella Ann stayed with her parents while they were in Columbia. They had dinner at Bradford's parents' house before they left to go back to Knoxville. Stella Ann had never seen so many pork chops on a platter. Willa Mae, their cook, said she fried two dozen large pork chops that afternoon. They disappeared in seconds. No one came up for air or made eye contact during dinner except Norma. She had to stir something, and it wasn't in a cooking pot.

"Stella Ann, what are you going to do while Bradford is taking his extra postgraduate classes? Won't you get bored?"

"Mrs. Taber, it will only be a couple of months before we move to Chattanooga. There will not be enough time for me to look for a job and get trained. It will give me an opportunity to work on my cooking skills and get ready to move. I have been sending in my resume and applications for teaching jobs in Chattanooga."

"Stella Ann, you must work. You need to help with expenses while Bradford is going to class and studying. You are going to need money for the move."

Norma was right about needing money, but Stella Ann thought she was crossing a big red line. "Mrs. Taber, we will be fine."

When they got back to Knoxville, Bradford started hounding Stella Ann about getting a job. They never discussed it once when making the decision to stay in Knoxville. Norma had something to do with Bradford pushing her to get a job. Her parents were against Stella Ann getting a job for the short time they remained in Knoxville. She listened to Norma and Bradford about pulling her weight to the point where all she did was cry. She decided to look for a job to keep the peace.

She asked at shops around campus and at the campus bookstore, but they did not need any help. She checked the paper every day for job openings, and one caught her attention. It was a job in downtown Knoxville at a dress shop, but the path to get to the job was through a placement agency. Stella Ann paid the fee, completed an application, and got the job. The type of garments they sold looked like something a showgirl or stripper would wear.

The owner was a man named Erland, who was only a few steps away from being a nutcase. If someone put a garment on hold, he would take it to the holding area and increase the price. Stella couldn't believe his dishonesty and greed. She questioned a price for one of her customers when she came to pay for her outfit one Friday afternoon. Stella Ann was fired. Erland threw a wooden coat hanger at her, screamed obscenities, and would not let her get her things. He kept her purse, a new pair of shoes she bought with money Lou sent her for Easter, and her leftover lunch. He was livid as he pushed her out the door. She went to the shoe store next door and called Bradford.

An hour later, Bradford showed up with four of his fraternity brothers. They collected Stella Ann's purse, new shoes, lunch, and last paycheck. There was no more discussion about Stella Ann getting a job before they moved to Chattanooga.

They had three days left on their lease before they had to vacate their apartment. They had no money and no way to leave town. They wouldn't get their apartment deposit until a month after they checked out. Stella Ann felt they had no choice but to ask their parents for help.

"Stella Ann, I have an exam on The Hill this morning. Do not get in your car and go to Columbia," Bradford demanded.

"Bradford, how are we going to get out of Knoxville? We have no money. What is your plan?" Stella Ann asked.

"I don't know, but you stay out of your car. Don't you dare go to Columbia."

Stella Ann insisted the minister omit the word obey from their wedding vows, and she was relieved she remembered to make the request. As soon as Bradford cleared the bottom of the hill at the apartment complex, she loaded her car and set out for Columbia. She figured she could be there by lunchtime. She wore baggy jeans, a work shirt, and a bandana on her head. She had a dime in her wallet along with a gas credit card Burt gave her.

She arrived in Columbia before her daddy got home for lunch. Lou was in the kitchen making sandwiches and heard Stella Ann at the back door.

"Stella Ann, what on earth are you doing here?" Lou asked.

"Mama, Bradford and I need money to get out of Knoxville. He won't ask his parents. Can you and Daddy help us? Bradford registers for class in Chattanooga on Monday. It is important for him to take organic chemistry again and be there when class starts. Our lease is up in three days. We can pay you back when we get our apartment deposit."

"Stella Ann, we are still recovering from the wedding bills, but let's see what your daddy says when he comes home for lunch."

Her daddy always came home for lunch. It wasn't long before Burt drove down the driveway. As he entered the kitchen he said, "Stella Ann, what are you doing here? Where is Bradford?"

"Daddy, Bradford is taking his last exam and doesn't know I am here. He told me not to come to Columbia, but I had no choice. Daddy, we need money to get out of Knoxville. Can you help us?"

Lou, have you got sandwiches made?"

"Yes," she replied.

"Let's eat lunch, and I will take Stella Ann to the bank with me and see what we can do."

"How much money do you need, Stella Ann?" Burt asked.

"Daddy, a couple hundred dollars would help a lot."

"Stella Ann, how much money do you have in your wallet right now?"

"Not much, Daddy."

"Stella, I asked you how much money you had in your wallet. Give me a straight answer."

"I have a dime in my wallet."

"Stella, I have told you and told you not to travel without at least ten dollars in your pocket. Do you still have the gas card I gave you?"

"Yes, I have the gas card. I used it to fill up my car to get here."

After lunch, they went to the bank, and Burt got $300. She thanked him over and over and hugged him before she started back to Knoxville.

"Stella Ann, it should be enough money to get you and Bradford out of Knoxville and to pay for his class at UT Chattanooga. Be careful driving back, and I will see you in three days."

When Stella Ann got back, Bradford was at the dining table studying with a friend. He didn't look up and acted like she never left. Stella Ann started packing boxes and mentioned to Bradford they might need to get a trailer. He disagreed. But two days later, at 5:00 p.m., the night they were to leave Knoxville, he agreed they did need a trailer. They called all over the city and secured a small trailer in a Knoxville suburb. It was 8:00 p.m. by the time they started packing the trailer with help from Bradford's brother and some friends. Bradford had little sleep from studying but said he could drive. Stella Ann followed him in her car. They left Knoxville at 11 p.m.

A few miles outside of Nashville, Stella Ann noticed Bradford was driving extremely fast. He slipped off the shoulder of the road in the passing lane twice and swerved toward a bridge. She passed him, honked her horn, and blinked her lights for him to pull over. Stella Ann took the lead, keeping Bradford at 55-60 mph and alive. They arrived in Columbia at 3 a.m. and went straight to bed.

The next morning Bradford left for Chattanooga to register for organic chemistry. He was going to clean and paint the little guest house/garage apartment where they were going to live. Hank owned the family property in the historic district. There was a garage at the back that had been converted into a small guest house. Hank and Norma offered to let them live there while Bradford was in medical school. Both families were going to be in Chattanooga the next week to help finish the move.

What was waiting for them in Chattanooga was a nightmare.

CHAPTER 5

What do you want to be?

The next week was hectic preparing to move to a place Stella Ann had never seen in a city she knew nothing about. She sorted through wedding gifts they could use in Chattanooga and stored the rest in her parents' garage attic until a future move. They collected furniture Stella Ann inherited and loaded it onto Burt's truck. Both families joined the caravan to help them move. Her brother and his wife drove their truck. Bradford's parents, younger siblings, and grandmother and grandfather rounded out the entourage. Stella Ann's Uncle Bill planned to deliver her piano later in the afternoon on moving day.

Bradford called the night before the big move. His demeanor sounded subdued, defeated, and depressed. During the conversation Bradford explained he cleaned, made repairs, and tried to paint the living room in the guest house between the demands and requirements of organic chemistry. He said his efforts were futile.

"Stella Ann," he said, "I don't see how we are going to live in this house. Neglect weathered it, and the last tenants must have been drug dealers. I have swept up countless syringes, and mice infestation is rampant. I started painting the living room, and the paint soaked into the walls. It is apparent Dad has not checked on the place since he inherited it from Uncle Edward. The big house in front seems to have a couple of tenants and appears to be in good shape."

"Bradford, what are we going to do?"

"We don't have a choice, Stella Ann. We need to live here and clean it up the best we can. We don't have the money to move into an apartment. We can tolerate it for a little while and move as soon as we get jobs. I am exhausted. I am going to try to get some sleep. I am staying at the apartment of a classmate and his wife, Sawyer and Dawn Prescott. They have been generous and offered me their couch to sleep on this week. Sawyer is my lab partner. Tell everyone to be careful traveling tomorrow. I love you."

When they hung up, Stella Ann sat on the edge of her childhood bed. The first thing that occupied her thoughts was Bradford said he loved her. She had only heard those words a few times during their relationship. Then she cried herself to sleep.

As the caravan traveled east toward Chattanooga, they looked like hillbillies from a popular tv show Stella Ann enjoyed watching as a child. Three pick-up trucks and two cars made up the caravan. Before they got out of town, Bradford's grandpa had to stop on the side of the road to rearrange his load and tie the tarp tighter. They planned to arrive in Chattanooga before lunch. Lou and Grammie made a picnic lunch of ham and pimento cheese sandwiches, potato salad, and chips. Jenny, her sister-in-law, made her famous chocolate chip cookies, and her mother sent chess pie, homemade sourdough bread, and strawberry jam. Stella Ann and Lou followed Norma, Grammie, and the younger kids and were the caboose of the moving caravan.

About 100 miles outside of Chattanooga, Norma got a speeding ticket. Stella Ann and Lou instinctively knew it was going to happen and dropped back long before Norma met the highway patrol officer. Lou thought Norma was going too fast and insisted they not try to keep up. Stella Ann caught up with them within the speed limit and pulled behind

Norma to check on her, Grammie, and the kids.

"It looks like we have been left behind by the men. Do you know how to get to the house?"

Norma laughed, "Honey, I have driven my kids all over the country for sporting events. I have never been to the house, but Hank told me how to get there. I can always stop and ask someone. I just hope I don't get another speeding ticket. Now, keep up." She took off like a rocket.

Stella Ann and Lou got behind her again. Their view all the way to Chattanooga was Scott and Liza in the backseat, holding two large house plants as they swayed from one side to another. Norma could be witty and lighthearted. However, one never knew which Norma they were going to encounter: the funny, entertaining Norma or the difficult, manipulative Norma.

Cell phones did not exist, so keeping a caravan of cars and trucks together was impossible. Norma and Stella Ann arrived at the house in Chattanooga before the men and trucks. Dr. Taber forgot how to get to the house he inherited from his uncle. He led the truck group into Georgia and on the way to Atlanta when Dr. Taber realized they were going the wrong way. They arrived in Chattanooga an hour later.

Nothing was transferred into the house until they did more cleaning. Stella Ann and Jenny made a quick trip to purchase mops, brooms, bleach, sponges, disinfectant, bug spray, paper towels, and mouse traps. Burt located other cleaning supplies and the vacuum in his truckload. Everyone cleaned, even Scott and Liza, which helped to keep them out of trouble.

Stella Ann and Jenny went upstairs to check out the bathroom. It was in a horrible condition, and Stella Ann started crying.

"Jenny, we can't live here. Look at the bathtub. It is filthy. Hand me the scrub cleaner, please." Stella Ann started scrubbing, and the tears would not stop.

"Stella Ann, we can clean it up. It will be ok. It isn't that bad," Jenny said, trying to be optimistic.

"Jenny, it is worse than bad. Would you want to bathe in this germ-infested pig pen? I am disgusted no one bothered to check the condition of the place before we hauled three truckloads of furniture here, Jenny. I am sad and angry. They don't care. They want us to fail."

Jenny listened to Stella Ann vent and encouraged her to get back to her scrubbing.

Downstairs, an army scrubbed, cleaned, mopped, vacuumed, and installed window unit air conditioners. Grammie was in the backyard with several cans of white spray paint, trying to cover the rust on the lower metal cabinets she had Grandpa drag out of the kitchen. Scott and Liza, armed with brooms, swept and played sword fighting in the two rooms upstairs.

"Stella Ann, honey, I don't see how you and Bradford are going to live here," Grammie said. "Norma and Hank know better. You kids should not be treated this way."

"Thank you for painting the cabinets, Grammie. We appreciate all you and Grandpa have done for us."

Stella Ann decided one cry was enough. Only Jenny knew how disappointed and upset she was. With what little she could gather, she would make the house into a dollhouse, and she did. Three years later, a feature with pictures and an article ran in *The Chattanooga Review,* the local newspaper. It chronicled the history of the house and their medical school journey.

Burt and Lou decided to stay over and secured a room in a local hotel. Stella Ann and Bradford stayed at the house with sheets nailed up at the windows. She and Jenny managed to get the bathroom clean and disinfected to an acceptable level.

The stove didn't work, but Grandpa said he would get one delivered in two weeks from a friend who owned an appliance store. Grandpa and Grammie gave Stella Ann and Bradford a sofa, and Norma and Hank gave them two old club chairs, a kitchen table, and four chairs Norma no longer wanted. With the antiques Stella Ann inherited, they had enough furniture. The next day, Burt and Lou measured every window and went to a houseware store to get pull-down shades. Lou said she would make white ruffled curtains for all the windows when she got home.

Living in the guest house was nothing short of a nightmare. It was maid and butler quarters until 1959 when Dr. Taber's uncle renovated it as a rental. He also made two apartments on the second floor of the big house where he lived. Stella Ann was convinced the butler's ghost continued to visit an upstairs bedroom. There was evidence that a potbellied wood stove had once been in that bedroom.

They trapped and swatted mice playing without fear all over the place. In the winter, they argued over whose turn it was to stand next to the only wall heater. They hand-washed dishes before and after meals and washed clothes using a portable machine that hooked up to the sink and water heater. They built a fence, laid carpet, and plugged holes providing an entrance for varmints.

Stella Ann and Bradford became friends with the couple who lived downstairs in the large house at the front of the property. An older lady lived in an upstairs apartment on the left, and the second upstairs apartment had a constant string of tenants they never bothered to meet. Stella Ann and Bradford would laugh and say they lived in the ghetto, but it was far from a ghetto situation. It had been neglected for years, but it was on the National Historic Register. The five years they lived there humbled them.

By the time they settled into their new environment, each of them got a temporary job. Stella Ann worked at the county personnel office, and Bradford got a part-time job in the lab at a local hospital. His organic chemistry class consumed a lot of time, so a part-time job with a flexible schedule was perfect. They became friends with Sawyer and Dawn, the couple Bradford met through his class when he first arrived in Chattanooga. They enjoyed dinners, movies, and card games with them on the weekends, and Sawyer helped Bradford make outside improvements to the house.

Sawyer shared with Stella Ann a confrontation between Bradford and him. Stella Ann already knew Bradford's version. She wanted to know Sawyer's view of what happened.

"Stella Ann, we were in lab one day, and Bradford told me to get the hell out and threw a test tube at me," Sawyer said. "We had been working on an experiment for a long time, and I said something I thought was funny to break the tension. I can't even remember what I said, but it set Bradford off big time."

90

Stella Ann said, "The behavior you described happens a lot. I am still learning how to navigate his moods. And I am not doing a particularly good job of it. I never saw this behavior when we were dating."

"It embarrassed me in front of the class, so I grabbed my things and left."

"Sawyer, Bradford told me you smarted off when he was trying to concentrate. I urged him to call you. Did he apologize?"

"Yes, he did apologize. Stella Ann, I have never experienced anyone going from zero to a hundred on the anger spectrum over so little."

"I have learned Bradford is good at apologizing but not so great at changing his behavior. I have accepted this behavior as the norm in my life, and I hate I compromise myself to keep the peace."

Late in July, Lou called Stella Ann to give her a telephone number to call about a teaching job. The principal of a private school wanted to interview her, but he had no forwarding number for Stella Ann. They used her parents' number on her application because they knew they would be moving and would get a new number. She interviewed at another private school in Chattanooga and turned down the offer because it was too far to travel each day.

A position in a private school looked like her only hope. The city school system would not give her another interview after she declined their offer in the spring. The county school system enacted a hiring freeze. Her manager at the Hamilton County personnel office offered her a permanent job if she did not get a job teaching. She was a teacher, and she knew she was good. She had young blood enthusiasm and a treasure trove of new ideas. She made an appointment to interview at the private school.

She looked like a child interviewing to teach children. It was summer and scorching hot and humid in Chattanooga. She wore a white pique dress with red embroidered flowers and red sandals. It had been her initiation dress for her college sorority, but then it was all white. Lou had updated it to a different status with the red flowers. She was 105 pounds, soaking wet, and stood an average of five feet, four inches. She pulled her dark hair up in barrettes, and she wore little makeup. She felt confident and hopeful as she drove into the school parking lot in her unairconditioned 1966 bronze hatchback Mustang without a floorboard in the back.

In the interview, she learned about a new state law requiring kindergarten teachers to be certified. The principal was scrambling to hire all certified teachers. Stella Ann's certification was kindergarten through ninth grade. The conversation with the principal was pleasant. Stella Ann burst with excitement at the prospect of landing a job. She felt encouraged until the principal revealed the salary.

The salary offered was paltry, and in her bold innocence, she laughed and responded, "How funny! What is the real salary?"

The principal replied with a glare and said, "Mrs. Taber, that is the real salary."

"Would you mind if I discuss your offer with my husband and get back to you?" Stella Ann asked, knowing she didn't need to talk with Bradford. The salary offer was a joke.

"Of course, but I need an answer soon. School starts in two weeks. We would be happy to add you to our roster of outstanding teachers."

Stella Ann called the next day and declined the job offer. Two days later, she received a call from the principal. He offered her a better salary, but it was still insulting. The time for signing a teaching contract narrowed with each day. She took the job not realizing she signed a contract with one of the most prestigious private schools in the southeast.

Lou completed curtains for fourteen guest house windows and then got busy making Stella Ann a work wardrobe. Dress codes were strict for teachers. Requirements included skirts, dresses, pantyhose, and closed-toe shoes. Stella Ann spent her college years wearing blue jeans and work shirts. Her wedding wardrobe consisted of all winter clothes. She thought she was going to suffocate the first summer they lived in Chattanooga. She wondered how Chattanooga could be so humid and determined it was the proximity to the Tennessee River and the mountains.

By new teacher orientation, Stella Ann had a new professional wardrobe. Casual loafers, a pair of dress heels, and, gosh, awful pantyhose were all she needed to complete her teaching wardrobe. She thought pants would be much more practical to wear since teaching kindergarten required sitting on the floor a lot. The boss had rules, and she was not the boss. Two years into her teaching, pantsuits made the list of acceptable attire for teachers. However, when the teachers stepped out of the classroom, the pantsuit rule included a matching jacket to be worn to cover their behind.

Bradford finished his organic chemistry class and started the process of applying for medical school. It was a long arduous process. He had been diligent about staying current with the letters of recommendation he needed from professors, doctors, political figures, and friends. Writing was not easy for him, so Stella Ann helped him with his essay about why he wanted to be a doctor. Bradford's style of writing was fluffy, dreamy, forced, and apologetic. Stella Ann suggested they scrap his essay and let her write a draft to include some of his ideas. By the end of October, he sent his application in and learned he should know something about his acceptance by February.

Stella Ann spent hours and hours making lesson plans. Adjusting to the fast pace of all the tasks required of teachers was exhausting. She didn't have a planning period, so most of her work was done at home. She knew there were a lot of extra requirements teachers had to fulfill but had no clue her profession was constant. A teacher did not leave the job when he or she left school. The amount of planning, cutting, pasting, and time spent on the phone with anxious parents experiencing a child in school for the first time was overwhelming. Assignments outside the regular day and week kept her busy. Attendance at student ball games and birthday parties was encouraged. Teacher's meetings, tutoring children who were sick for an extended time, presentations, Saturday admission testing, dinners, plays, and any event connected with the school came before free time at home. She poured her soul and life into her job. She refused to think about her poverty level salary.

She often wondered how teachers with their own children juggled all the expectations and responsibilities of the job. Teacher's assistants in kindergarten were a necessity that had not emerged into the education system when Stella Ann started teaching. There was little time left to build a home life.

Teachers supported each other, helped each other, and mentored each other without an individual agenda. They worked together, which was comforting and created a team spirit. Many of her dearest friendships bloomed at school. Stella Ann didn't mind working so hard. Her principal made himself visible and supportive. He had a gift for motivating others and could make a teacher feel like he or she could move mountains. Teachers wanted to work hard because of his kindness, encouragement, and belief in them. He provided opportunities for underpaid teachers to make extra money. By Christmas, he increased her pay by twice the amount she was making.

Bradford and Stella Ann celebrated their first anniversary with a taco dinner at a fast-food restaurant. It was all they could afford, but it didn't matter. They were on a mission together, and it was to get Bradford into medical school and through medical school. They had to save every penny they could. Stella Ann didn't realize at the time Bradford never meant for her to be a permanent partner in their medical school mission. She wanted to believe in their marriage and trust they were a team sacrificing together. But when tempers flared and accusations flew, she thought maybe she was a means to an end.

Christmas was approaching, and Stella Ann and Bradford decided to go home after their anniversary and split their time between families. Going to each family celebration was a challenge, but home for Christmas was where they wanted to be. Her mama's family Christmas Eve celebration was moved to her aunt's house in Spring Hill. Her grandmother died two years earlier, and her grandfather was in a nursing home, having suffered a stroke while working in the cornfield.

They spent the night at the Taber's on Christmas Eve, and Christmas morning was with Bradford's family. Grammie and Grandpa came to open presents. The younger kids still had gift excitement, and it was fun to watch them. Lunch was at Grammie and Grandpa's, and Christmas dinner was with her daddy's family.

"Good catch," Hank said as Stella Ann caught his breakfast plate sliding across the kitchen table. Norma slung a plate of eggs, bacon, and biscuits from the stove toward Hank. Stella Ann had never experienced food being thrown. She realized after being in the Taber family for a while, she would see a lot of things thrown, slapped, cursed, broken, and knocked down.

As she held Hank's plate, she stopped in her tracks at the door between the formal dining room and the kitchen. She was unaware a marital war had transpired before she walked into the kitchen. She sensed Norma was about to explode. But this was Christmas morning. Joy and happiness should permeate the house, not grumpiness.

"Do not come through the dining room to get to the kitchen, Stella Ann. You will mash the carpet," Norma snapped.

Stella Ann said, "I didn't know we weren't supposed to walk in there. I am sorry, Mrs. Taber. I will be sure to come through the hallway and party room from now on." Stella Ann thought it was peculiar that one could not walk on the carpet.

"May I have some coffee?" Stella asked as Norma pointed her toward the coffee pot.

By the time Grammie and Grandpa arrived, the younger kids were jumping and begging to open presents, and Hank called the family into the huge formal living room. The heavily decorated flocked Christmas tree stood laden with mounds of presents. Each person had a designated seat and was expected to stay there to open their presents. Within seconds, the room exploded with white tissue paper, wrapping paper, and ribbon. Tension in the room increased with each package opened.

Norma received a beautiful tweed suitcase trimmed in leather from Dr. Taber.

"Are you trying to send me on a trip, Hank?" Norma asked.

"Well, I thought it would be nice for us to go somewhere together, Norma," Hank replied.

"That will never happen," Norma said under her breath but still audible.

More and more presents were delivered to recipients as the tree was emptied of its bounty. Bradford sat a large heavy box down in front of Stella Ann. He looked at her and whispered, "It is something we saw at Dove Creek Antiques."

Stella Ann started opening the box and let out a squeal of delight and surprise. She pulled out the red plates and teacups they had seen on a table at Dove Creek Antiques when they had lunch at the inn. She said nothing about wanting them, but Bradford noticed her looking at them several times. He could be very observant and thoughtful.

Bradford said, "I wanted you to have them. It may be the last nice thing I will be able to buy you for a while with medical school in our future."

Her excitement turned to confusion as chaos erupted. Norma had opened a beautiful blue and white antique bowl, and pitcher Hank had bought her. She immediately threw it up against the fireplace, and it broke into a million pieces. Everyone sat there like it was routine behavior. Stella Ann froze and wondered what would sail across the room next. She put the dishes back in the box, so they would not be next in the lineup.

Norma said, "You never listen to me, Hank. I told you I wanted the red dishes at Dove Creek Antiques. I wanted Stella Ann's dishes, not a stupid bowl and pitcher."

Hank said, "Norma, I went over there to get the dishes, and they were gone. I had no idea Bradford bought them for Stella Ann. The lady who worked there said you had looked at this bowl and pitcher and liked it."

The day after Christmas, Lou hosted a quiet, fun, informal dinner for the immediate family, and they exchanged presents. Bradford and Stella Ann spent the night at Lou and Burt's. The next morning, they packed their car and started the journey back to Chattanooga. They listened to James Taylor and John Denver cassette tapes as they drove and talked about the holiday.

Stella Ann told Bradford about two incidents at his parents' house that made her uncomfortable. On Christmas Eve, as she was getting dressed for bed, she saw Dr. Taber peeking through the crack in their bedroom door. She jumped into the closet to finish getting dressed. When Stella Ann went into the bedroom after coffee the next morning to get dressed for Christmas Day, Norma was going through her bag on the bed. Stella Ann requested they stay at her parents' house when they were in Columbia. Even though he thought Stella Ann may have overreacted, Bradford agreed.

It was a cold January, and Stella Ann and Bradford insulated the windows of the guest house with heavy plastic. They would wrap a blanket around themselves and stand next to the only wall heater in the house. They purchased two small electric floor heaters, one for their bedroom and one for the bathroom. They learned to take cold showers by necessity because the hot water heater was very temperamental.

January folded into February, and by southern standards, the winter was brutal. Stella Ann had the opportunity to help with the school admissions testing on Saturday, Valentine's Day. She and Bradford would be able to celebrate by going out to dinner because Stella Ann would be paid in cash. Bradford was working an early shift at the hospital and would be home by two o'clock in the afternoon. She finished the admissions testing and was home by one o'clock. She hadn't even changed out of her red dress when the phone rang.

"Hello," Stella Ann said.

"Where is Bradford? I have been trying to reach him for a couple of hours," said Dr. Taber, agitated.

"Hello, Dr. Taber. Happy Valentine's Day. Bradford is at the hospital. Would you like me to have him call you when he gets in? He should be home in an hour or so."

"Yes, tell him to call me immediately. It is important."

"Ok, Dr. Taber, I will."

Bradford got home right on schedule, and before Stella Ann could even tell him to call his dad, the phone rang. It was Dr. Taber.

Bradford answered. "Hey, Dad, how are things going in Columbia? Happy Valentine's Day!"

Dr. Taber said, "Don't you kids ever think of anything but an excuse to celebrate or have a party?"

"No, Dad, I don't guess we do. What's going on?" Bradford asked.

"Well, son, I got the biggest disappointment of my life today."

"Dad, what is it?" Bradford motioned for Stella Ann to get on the extension in the bedroom.

"First," Dr. Taber started. "Your mother and I don't think you and Stella Ann are managing your money well."

"What do you mean? How do you know?" Bradford responded.

"Your mail comes here, Bradford. "Your bank statements come here, and we look at them to see how you are managing your money."

Bradford's face got beet red. His response indicated his disgust. "Why do you think you have the right to open our mail, Dad?"

"Look, son, we can discuss your banking later. I have a letter here from the medical school for you. I have read it. You didn't get in the next class. How could you let me down like this? I have counted on you coming back to help me in the office so I can retire in a few years. You have always been a disappointment to me. I have the letter in my hand. Do you want me to read it to you?"

"Yes, you might as well," Bradford said dejectedly.

Stella Ann was sitting on the bed with tears in her eyes as Dr. Taber read the rejection letter. The letter was as dry as his voice. There was no mention or suggestion in the letter Bradford should continue to try to get in the next class.

Dr. Taber finished the letter and then said, "Well, son. I guess you will need to look for an alternative profession or look forward to drawing blood in the hospital lab the rest of your life. Your mother and I are washing our hands of your future. If you aren't going to go to medical school, you need to look for another place to live."

Dr. Taber's lack of empathy and compassion was over the line for Stella Ann. Her loyal protective side kicked in, and her temper took over. How he could say all the mean things he said to Bradford at the most disappointing time of his son's life was more than she could stomach. From that point forward, Stella Ann and Dr. Taber were at war with each other.

"Dr. Taber, you don't have to worry. Bradford will get into medical school without your encouragement or moral support. Together, Bradford and I will figure this out."

Then Bradford said, "I am sorry for the disappointment, Dad. I love you and Mom." He hung up the phone.

Stella Ann went downstairs, and Bradford grabbed her holding her tightly. They stood in the kitchen, and the only sound was their sobs over a broken dream. They were too exhausted to go out to dinner and shared a can of chili.

A week later, Bradford made an appointment with the dean of the medical school to see if he could get clarity about why he was not accepted. Bradford wanted advice about what he could do to improve his chances for the next class. It was not a promising meeting, but Bradford decided to talk to others and to visit the school often so his face and name would be familiar.

One administrator had little patience or admiration for Bradford's persistence and finally said, "You will never make the next medical class. We can offer you a position in either our dental school or pharmacy school." The response crushed Bradford, but he got applications for all three schools.

Stella Ann was sitting at the kitchen table making lesson plans when Bradford got home. He sat down and gave her a synopsis of the meeting and showed her the applications. He told Stella Ann he had a better chance of getting into dental or pharmacy school than getting in the next medical school class. He went on and on trying to convince Stella Ann either of the other professional schools would be fine. He asked if she would type his application for dental school. She got out her little blue typewriter and loaded the application as he was still trying to convince her this was best for him. Stella Ann's temper took over.

"Bradford, Bradford, Bradford," she said emphatically. "Do you want to be a doctor or a dentist?"

He replied, "We would probably have a better family life if I was a dentist."

"Dammit, that is not what I asked you," said Stella Ann. "Do you want to be a doctor or a dentist? Bradford, what do you want to be? Be honest!"

He looked her in the eye and said, "I want to be a doctor, Stella Ann. I have wanted to become a doctor all my life."

She took the dental school application out of the typewriter and tore it in half. She looked at Bradford and said, "Then you will be a doctor, Bradford. We are going to come up with a strong plan. We can make this happen. You will be an amazing doctor."

They came up with a plan and worked on it consistently. In the months following the heartbreak of receiving his rejection letter, Bradford studied vocabulary cards, and Stella Ann drilled him every chance she could, even when they were in the car or when Bradford was showering. She tutored him in the classics, art, and music. She coached him every night with interview questions and polished answers as they fell asleep. She practiced his delivery with him. She rewrote his essay. This time without his input. They worked on his self-confidence and body language. Stella Ann maintained a strong hold on her youthful self-confidence and determination, and it helped Bradford boost his motivation.

After receiving the medical school rejection letter, it seemed as if Bradford softened his attitude and feelings toward Stella Ann. He told her he loved her more often and called her from work to check on her. Her reaction was twofold. It thrilled her and made her happy he was letting her into his thoughts and heart, but she also wondered if some of the attention was manipulative to keep her working and loyal for his professional gain. Was he sincere?

Burt helped them finance a prep course for Bradford to take to improve his MEDCAT scores. Burt changed careers several years earlier, and one of his colleagues left the company to take a job in the medical school admissions office in Chattanooga. Burt's friend said he couldn't do a lot, but he could keep Bradford's application on top of the application pool. Stella Ann and Bradford were grateful for any help they could get. They would learn Bradford's application status by the spring or early summer.

The time between working on their plan and learning about Bradford's acceptance was stressful and volatile. Bradford's anger was tapped more quickly with each passing day.

After a nice Friday night beer and nacho dinner at a Mexican restaurant, Bradford erupted.

"You didn't feed the dog," he shouted. "What have you done all day? All you do is go to your stupid job keeping us at the poverty level and play with toddlers. You are not a professional. You are a babysitter."

"Bradford, the dog is fine. I will feed her now. There is no reason to get this angry with me. I was running late this morning and forgot to feed her." Stella Ann replied.

She did not take her coat off. She fed their dog and headed upstairs. Bradford was not letting Stella Ann's mistake go unpunished, and he followed her to the stairway. She refused to engage in an argument and continued upstairs. Bradford grabbed the chain dog leash hanging at the back door and threw it at Stella Ann, hitting her in the temple and knocking her down. She fell into a crumpled heap halfway up the steps.

Bradford apologized profusely and claimed he would never do anything like that again. Stella Ann could not understand why Bradford treated her that way. She just forgot to feed the dog.

The next episode came a couple of weeks later. They were with friends. Sawyer and his wife and another couple named Bob and Cheryl joined them for dinner at a barbeque restaurant in downtown Chattanooga. They were beginning to carve out a social circle and were feeling like they fit in. They were having a good time until there was mention of going bowling by Sawyer's wife, Dawn.

"What a great idea! I haven't been bowling in a long time," Stella Ann commented.

She barely got the words out of her mouth when Bradford pushed her into Dawn, causing her to spill some of her drink on Dawn. "Shut the hell up, Stella Ann," Bradford said.

No one said a word and did not budge. No one wanted to set him off further. Then Bradford said, "Come on y'all. Let's pay this check and go bowling." He acted like nothing happened.

When they got home, Bradford apologized to Stella Ann. "I can't believe I snapped at the restaurant. I am so sorry, Stella Ann. It won't happen again. Will you forgive me?"

"Bradford, I am exhausted from the work week, and tonight topped it off. I was embarrassed," Stella Ann said with a tear crawling down her cheek as she headed to bed.

Days later, they were getting ready for work, and Bradford put on Stella Ann's pants. She had accidentally placed them in his closet. They came up to his knees, and he couldn't button them. Stella Ann started laughing as she sat on the bed putting on her work-required pantyhose. Bradford did not think it was funny, called her some expletives, picked up one of his running shoes, and threw it at Stella Ann hitting her full force on the inside of her thigh. For days, she had the imprint of the shoe sole on her inner thigh. When Stella Ann thought things were getting better between them and let down her guard, she would do something to set off his anger. It was very confusing.

By mid-January, Stella Ann asked her principal for a leave of absence for two weeks. He granted it, and Stella Ann left. She went to Columbia. She thought some time away from each other would help cool the situation. She no longer wanted to wear the aftermath of Bradford's outbursts on her body. More than one time, she had to wear sunglasses all day because of a black place on her eye or face. He knocked her glasses off many times in his anger. She was tired of being a punching bag. Stella Ann had been calm during the explosions, but she knew the control of her own temper was wearing thin. Her instinct was to hit back if she was hit, and it got her in more trouble than ever. She needed some help, advice, support, time to think, and a shoulder to cry on. She turned to her family and knew she was putting them in a difficult position. She was desperate.

"Stella, I told you we could go the other way before we walked down the aisle," Burt said. "He is your husband now, and you two need to work this out. You know we don't believe in divorce."

"Burt, she doesn't need to hear a lecture right now," Lou said. "Stella Ann, why don't you go into the back bedroom and get some rest? You look tired. We will talk about this tomorrow."

She slept through dinner and all the way until morning. By the next afternoon, she was ready to talk with Burt and Lou and share what she and Bradford had been experiencing. They listened and suggested she call Bradford to see if he would be willing to see a marriage counselor. Burt and Lou offered to pay for several sessions to help out.

She called Bradford. He had plenty of time to stew and form his opinion of the situation while she was gone. He dominated the conversation.

"You should have never gone to your parents. You are alienating us from our families. You have exaggerated the situation. You always do. You ignored me in all this; my feelings were never considered."

He continued and his voice escalated, "Going home was not the answer. You should have stayed, and we could have gone to a counselor. I was never given the benefit of the doubt. We don't need our families in this. You have added more to my problems. I am tired of owning up. I am tired of the image projected of me. I've got faults. You do, too."

When he finished his rant, Stella Ann spoke, "Bradford, I tried to talk with you, but you blew me off. You said my concerns were no big deal, and I was too emotional. I don't want to get divorced. I love you, but I am not someone you can push around or hit and make go away. I am your wife, Bradford. I think marriage counseling will help us."

"I am sick of hearing about the dog chain, the shoe imprint, wearing sunglasses all day, and mean words. You know the chain was an accident, and I never meant to hurt you with my words. You can throw out some harsh, hurtful words as well. Maybe counseling would help us. I will go with you."

"Bradford, I know I have said some hurtful things, and I am deeply sorry. We should not be treating each other this way. We can figure our situation out with some help from an outside source. I need to learn your triggers and how to respond. It is obvious I don't have a clue about reading your moods or sensitivities. You say I provoke you, but I don't know what I do to cause it."

Bradford said, "I didn't know anything was wrong. You never talk to me. Stella Ann, I need a wife instead of a child. If you can't grow up, I don't need you. You have no regard for me. I will go to my own counselor. You and your counselor will make the rules, and I will have to live by them. It will be best for me to go alone."

His message was confusing to Stella Ann. He said he would go with her, and in the same breath said he would go to his own counselor.

"Are you going with me or not, Bradford?" Stella Ann asked.

He continued, "I never intended to be a poor husband. I don't know what I can do. It is hopeless for me. What can I do to regain your respect?

I didn't realize you were afraid of me, and you felt you couldn't talk with me. You have a distorted personality, Stella Ann, and you have a wild temper. I'm sick of being the villain. I am reasonable. You can talk with me, but do you think you can come back?"

Stella Ann realized Bradford was grabbing at anything to throw blame on her, and he repeated himself when he was upset. He was talking in circles. He was all over the place making judgments and accusations. She tried to diffuse his anger.

"Bradford, I am willing to come back and work on our marriage. I told you I don't want a divorce, but I don't want us to continue to tear each other down. If I find a marriage counselor, would you be willing to meet me for a session?"

"Yes, Stella Ann. I will meet you. Make sure the counselor is a man and faith-based," Bradford replied.

Two days later, Stella Ann drove to Chattanooga in a southern snowstorm. The storm blew up within minutes and dissipated just as quickly. They had an appointment to meet a counselor. The snow cleared as she drove further east. She didn't see Bradford's car in the parking lot but made her way to the counselor's office. He was a middle-aged man with a very calm and kind demeanor. Bradford never showed up. There was nothing she could do but go to the house, even though her anxiety ballooned beyond measure in anticipation of Bradford's reaction.

Bradford was not home when she arrived. She unloaded the car and started dinner. She had maintained contact with her school and notified the office she would be back in two days. When Bradford arrived, he was subdued, hugged her, and started crying. She never mentioned the missed counseling session. Stella Ann continued to go to counseling alone and invited Bradford each time. After her third session, he showed up. Stella Ann had renewed hope about their relationship and her marriage, but they had a lot of work to do.

Sawyer stopped by often, and sometimes his wife, Dawn, would come. They occasionally ate dinner with Bradford and Stella Ann, and it was nice having the company. Dawn told Stella Ann about the cracks in their marriage. By spring, Sawyer was coming over alone, and he and Bradford would have a beer or work on a project. Dawn was having as hard a time as Stella Ann during the wait to find out about medical school for their husbands.

Sawyer stopped by to see Bradford one spring afternoon. While Sawyer was there, Bradford called and said he had to work late because someone did not show up for their shift. Sawyer stayed a little longer to finish a conversation with Stella Ann about his and Dawn's marital issues. Stella Ann was not feeling well, but Sawyer needed someone to listen to him.

During Sawyer's visit, Stella Ann started feeling sick and was having abdominal cramps. She thought it was monthly cramping she experienced regularly, but it got progressively worse. She was bending double. She told Sawyer she was going to need to go to bed, and he should go home. Sawyer insisted she needed an emergency room and offered to take her. She declined, but she thought it might be appendicitis and agreed to go.

She had a miscarriage. She didn't even know she was pregnant. It happened so quickly she didn't have time to cry or grieve. Bradford didn't find out until it was over and didn't seem too concerned about it. He thanked Sawyer for taking care of Stella Ann, turned to her, and said, "This situation worked out like it should have, Stella Ann. We don't need a baby right now." Stella Ann kept her sadness within. The baby was never mentioned again.

The wait to find out if Bradford got into medical school was brutal. By the end of June, some of Bradford's friends were getting notifications of acceptance or rejection. Sawyer did not get in, and his wife filed for divorce. Dawn admitted she was not strong enough to endure the stress of Sawyer trying again. Bradford had heard nothing.

It was the first week of summer break, and a week before Stella Ann had to report to the bank as a summer relief teller. Stella Ann was deep cleaning the house and washing curtains. Mail, which was mostly junk, had piled up on the table during the previous weeks, and she swept it off with her hand into a waste basket. Cleaning was one way Stella Ann could divert energy and calm herself down. When Bradford came home, she was still cleaning.

"Stella Ann," Bradford said. "Have we received a large envelope with a blue and gold stripe in the corner?"

"I don't know," she replied. "I put a lot of junk mail in the trash. You might look in there."

Bradford went through the trash, and sure enough, there was a white envelope with a blue and gold stripe in the corner.

"Stella Ann, this means I got in. I got in."

"Don't you think you should open it first?" Stella Ann suggested. Stella Ann shuddered when she realized the letter could have been in a Chattanooga landfill if Bradford had not asked about it.

Bradford opened the letter, and he was right. He was accepted into medical school. Stella Ann dropped her spring cleaning, and they went to their favorite Mexican restaurant to celebrate with margarita drinks and nachos. He wanted to call his parents immediately. Stella Ann convinced him to wait; they didn't deserve to be first to know after the way Dr. Taber acted the last time. She and Bradford kept a comfortable distance from his family. They called Burt and Lou, who had always been supportive. Then they called Norma and Hank, and during the conversation, Hank offered to pay for Bradford's tuition. Things were finally working out for Bradford and Stella Ann.

Stella Ann and Bradford signed up at their church to chaperone seventh graders on a trip to Disney World. They hadn't been anywhere since their honeymoon and thought it would be a fun cheap trip. After medical school started, there would be no time or money for pleasure trips. They didn't realize they would ride on an unairconditioned church bus with teenagers for fourteen hours. The trip started by squelching a teenage emotional fire over seat assignments. More teen fires would erupt along the way. Stella Ann and Bradford made the best of it, enjoyed the kids, and had fun. When the bus stopped in Macon, Georgia, for lunch, they learned Elvis died.

There was an eerie silence as they got back on the bus. It seemed like everyone wanted to be back home in Tennessee.

CHAPTER 6

It ain't easy!

Despite their financial difficulties, the fall was an exciting time for Stella Ann and Bradford. They realized they had a future and something to work toward. The medical school had a barbeque for the new class, and they met Bradford's classmates, girlfriends, and spouses. It was an eclectic group of people, and they partied until late at night. Bradford commented on the way home only half of them would make it through the four years and become doctors.

The first semester was a tornadic flash and expensive. Dr. Taber helped with tuition, and Bradford and Stella Ann paid for books and lab materials. The supplies depleted all they had saved. They adapted to a new lifestyle of school only; her school and teaching and his school and studying.

There were massive amounts of lecture notes to compile and copy, study groups at their house, and pancake breaks. Stella Ann made stacks and stacks of pancakes, peanut butter cookies, scrambled eggs, and homemade bread to fuel the overworked brains of three to six medical students who studied at their house. It wasn't unusual for Stella Ann to be cooking into the early hours of the morning.

Before they knew it, Christmas arrived. Lou sent them an artificial tree, a box of ornaments, and red bows. They bought a wreath for the door at a discount store nearby. Stella Ann was handy with a sewing needle and machine, paint brush, and ceramic tools, so most of the family members' gifts were handmade. Their wrapping paper was old newspaper with twine or leftover calico material cut into strips.

It was the Jimmy Carter presidential era, and couples with two incomes struggled, so the financial pressure on Stella Ann and Bradford was tremendous, living only on her teaching salary. Interest rates were high, and gas was rationed. The dollar plunged, and even hamburger meat became a luxury. They ate a lot of beans, cheese, canned tuna, and macaroni. Lou and Grammie sent them care packages that included newspaper clippings from the hometown paper, pasta mixes, cookies, peanut butter, crackers, homemade banana bread, and what they called "spending money." The packages arrived when they needed them most and when their cupboards were bare. Stella Ann never wanted to forget what it was like to have nothing.

The second semester tuition deadline was approaching, and Stella Ann and Bradford did not have the money. Hank agreed to pay for Bradford's tuition, but never sent the check to them or the school.

"Dad, I got a letter from the school registrar. I have forty-eight hours to get my tuition check in, or I will be kicked out of school," Bradford said in a message he left with the call center. "Could you please send the tuition check?" Bradford was bordering on anger and despair.

Stella Ann stayed out of the way. Something told her Dr. Taber was not going to send the money, and she tried hard to give him the benefit of the doubt. Maybe he didn't receive the message.

Stella Ann was right. Dr. Taber did not send the tuition money and did not return calls. They had no one to turn to, but Bradford was able to stall for another two days. They sold wedding gifts and blood plasma and tried to get a short-term personal loan, which was denied. Stella Ann decided to ask their neighbor for a loan. His wife was a pharmacist, and he was in his last year of residency. Stella Ann babysat for them. They could not have been nicer about floating them a loan for a couple of months. Stella Ann had no clue how they would pay them back, but she would figure out something. She ran to the house with a check in hand, and Bradford left immediately for the bank and the school registrar's office.

Stella Ann knew a teacher whose husband worked at a bank. She immediately started inquiring about how they could secure a student loan. She decided they would never ask Dr. Taber for anything again. It took a lot of research and meetings for Stella Ann to learn the process of getting a student loan, but her determination was effective. She asked her neighbors if she could delay repayment for another two months until their student loan came through. Stella Ann was convinced the only way they were approved for a loan was because her friend's husband was kind enough to get involved to help them. Their loan was renewable for the next three years. Stella Ann didn't care if she was responsible for the repayment. She was only interested in the security of knowing Bradford would have tuition money, not how she was going to pay it back.

They went home for Mother's Day, and Norma invited Stella Ann to go to lunch with her, Scott, and Liza. They met at a fun area the kids liked called Five Corners. The area had several restaurants and many retail shops. During lunch, the kids asked Norma if they could go "roguing," a word Stella Ann had never heard before. She wasn't even sure it was a word.

"Scott, what does roguing mean?" Stella Ann asked.

"It's a word we use for a special kind of shopping," Scott replied.

Stella Ann almost choked on her food when she suspected what they were asking to do. She excused herself to visit her grandmother in the nursing home. She thought to herself, "Surely, they were teasing."

Before she and Bradford returned to Chattanooga, they delivered a small geranium each to Lou, Grammie, and Norma for Mother's Day. Norma and Hank were ready for them with angry words by the time they got to their house.

"Well, what are you two doing here?" Hank said, slurring his speech with a cigarette and drink in hand. "You never come around here unless you want money."

Bradford grabbed Stella Ann's arm, guided her into the kitchen, and gave Norma a card and potted flower.

"Why in the hell would I want a puny looking little geranium? If a flower and card is the best you can do, then leave."

"Mom, we can do better in a few years, but now this is all we can afford. We did the best we could and thought you would at least like the red color," Bradford said.

Stella Ann stood silent not wanting to add fuel to the raging fire. She wasn't going anywhere near either of the emotional bombs about to explode.

Hank said a few more choice words and ordered Bradford and Stella Ann out of his house. Bewildered and confused, Bradford led Stella Ann to the back door. They weren't prepared for a loud crash as Norma threw the flowerpot slamming it into the storm door as they left. It broke into a million pieces. Bradford told Stella Ann to keep walking. They had no idea why his parents were so mad at them, but tuition money was no longer an issue binding them in perpetual gratitude to them.

The first two years of medical school were a sentence of solitude for Stella Ann. She learned to make the best of it. She kept busy teaching and tutoring. She learned how to needlepoint, cross stitch, and smock, and took ceramics classes at church. She sold crafts and handmade baby clothes at a place where ladies could sell their wares to help with their expenses, and she worked at the bank during her summers off.

One thing Stella Ann failed to learn was to not compare her life with those of her pregnant and new mom friends. All she had ever wanted was children. It infuriated Bradford when she mentioned children even though he loved kids, too. He was good at blocking things out and compartmentalizing.

Cleaning was something that kept her busy on the weekends. One Saturday, she decided to clean the ledge between the kitchen and living room. She climbed onto the top of the piano and started dusting. The vases and pitchers she had on the ledge for decoration needed washing. When she put them on the kitchen counter next to the sink, Stella Ann noticed something in the blue one. It looked like garden seeds or tobacco. She dumped the contents on the counter. Underneath the bag she found rolling papers, and her suspicions were confirmed. She felt her face get hot, and her heart started racing. She realized the beads she saw while vacuuming under the sofa and chair cushions were marijuana seeds.

"What was he doing? They couldn't afford food, so where was the money coming from for him to afford this?" Stella Ann thought to herself. "How could he do this? How could he jeopardize his future, their future like this? How long had this been going on right under her nose?" Stella Ann knew a confrontation was necessary. She put the bag and the wrappers on the kitchen table.

A wave of raw emotion, anger, and fear engulfed her, and she started crying. She had never smoked pot, but the fact it was illegal and dangerous to one's health sent chills down her spine. She smelled its sour pungent scent at UT football games in college but never saw what it looked like.

Inflation was rampant, gas shortages were serious, and purchasing gas on a designated day according to a license plate number was the norm. The average salary was $17,000. Stella Ann made less than $10,000. She did all she could to keep them afloat and made her own personal sacrifices so Bradford could fulfill his dream. She had signed for his student loans, so Stella Ann thought the discovery of marijuana stored in a vase was a display of blatant disrespect toward her. She decided to take their dog with her upstairs to take a nap. For Stella Ann, when she was stressed, a nap always helped.

"What the hell are you doing? Trying to make trouble, Stella Ann?" Bradford said as he threw the bag of pot on the bed startling her.

"What do you mean?" Stella Ann asked.

"Are you looking for trouble by searching the house?" he replied.

"I was cleaning the ledge, Bradford. The only intention I had was to dust. I never expected to find pot. What was it doing there?"

"It must be Alex's. I guess he had it when he stayed with us last summer and put it up there so we wouldn't find it."

Alex was Bradford's brother. Dr. and Mrs. Taber sent him to Chattanooga to live with Bradford and Stella Ann for the summer while he completed a required internship for his conservation major. Alex didn't get an internship in the Smoky Mountains, but Chattanooga was the next best place to be assigned. It was a great area for all kinds of outdoor activities like camping, hiking, canoeing, kayaking, and fishing. Space was limited for the two of them, so Alex's presence made very tight quarters in the garage apartment. He slept on a cot in the kitchen and moved it behind the antique cupboard during the day. They had put in new carpet in the living room, so Bradford made the area off limits. Bradford did not want the new blue carpet to be ruined. Mashed or tracked carpet was something echoed from Norma.

Stella Ann always liked Alex and got along with him fine. She stayed busy keeping the laundry washed and food available. Their small garden next to the house helped provide tomatoes, squash, cucumbers, green beans, and peppers. The peach tree provided a sweet treat when they could collect them before the birds enjoyed them or neighbors picked them. Her summer job as vacation relief teller did not pay much, so Bradford did some vacation relief work at the hospital over his summer break to help. The Tabers never offered to help with the expense of having Alex live with them.

"Did you know Alex smoked pot? You made it clear to him he couldn't bring women into our house, and drinking was off limits. Did you tell him no pot?" Stella Ann questioned Bradford.

Stella Ann continued, "Your rules for him didn't do any good. He brought women in late at night all the time. He thought we didn't know about it. Remember the one who locked herself in the bathroom and would not come out? Beer cans filled the trash basket daily. Please get rid of the marijuana, Bradford, I don't want it in our house."

Bradford left the room with the bag of pot and rolling papers and promised to get rid of it. Stella Ann trusted he would toss it, but he hid it somewhere else in the house. Stella Ann discovered it months later with much less marijuana in the bag. It wasn't Alex's. She was beginning to learn to look the other way and say nothing to keep the peace. It contradicted her core values, but she learned to pick her battles.

Stella Ann's birthday was on the horizon, and Bradford asked her what she would like. He was always thoughtful about remembering events, and he enjoyed giving gifts.

"Bradford, all I want is for us to spend a little time together. We have been busy getting settled into school this fall. Dinner at our favorite

Mexican restaurant would be a real treat," Stella Ann said. "But if anyone else might happen to ask for gift suggestions, I need a raincoat. Carpool duty is brutal without a decent raincoat."

Stella Ann got a raincoat from Norma and Dr. Taber, a red one which was her favorite color. It was a size fourteen; Stella Ann wore a size six. She didn't think she would ever get used to Norma's subtle disapproval of her. She was notorious for leaving the tag on a gift so Stella Ann would know how much she spent. She gave her blouses or sweaters wrapped as a gift with her makeup stains and perfume scent on them. "White Echo" was Norma's signature fragrance and sent Stella Ann gasping for fresh air. To Stella Ann, the message was clear that she was not worthy of something new. Bradford told Stella Ann to ignore the subtle, negative messages. He always protected Norma. Stella Ann was gracious and thanked the Tabers in a carefully worded formal handwritten note. As much as she needed work clothes, she gave red raincoat, stained blouses, and sweaters to charity.

Stella Ann spent a lot of time alone while Bradford was in classes or at the hospital. They hoped to go home for Easter, but the gas situation was so bad they couldn't afford the trip. Going to the grocery caused Stella Ann anxiety, and they were always having car trouble. They attended church on Easter Sunday and had peanut butter sandwiches for lunch. Later in the day, a homeless man came by their house wanting food. Stella Ann packed him a peanut butter sandwich and a banana, and they took him to the Union Mission.

They used the last of their silver dollars to go to a movie after supper, but before they left, they called each set of parents to wish them a happy Easter. Stella Ann's parents were positive, rock solid, and glad to have a conversation. Bradford's parents were a different story, and the bickering during the conversation upset Bradford. He felt certain they were going to get a divorce. The verbal war between Norma and Hank increased every time Bradford called home. Stella Ann wondered if the arguing was physical and if they were having volatile confrontations in front of Scott and Liza.

It helped Stella Ann feel safer when she slept with their dog and a handgun while Bradford was at the hospital. Burt loaned her the handgun and gave her shooting lessons before she and Bradford moved to Chattanooga. She had been around hunting guns all her life, and Burt had drilled gun safety with her and Ron from the time they were little kids.

A drug gang pulled up to the house on motorcycles when Bradford was working late at the hospital one night. A gang member banged on the back door, the front door, and the landing door at the top of the outside steps leading to the bedrooms. They yelled for someone named Vicki and claimed she owed them money. Stella Ann sat up in the bed with the dog at her side, grabbed the gun from under her pillow, and pointed it at the landing door.

"What do you want? No one named Vicki lives here," she said. "I have a gun in my hand pointing at the door and a dog at my side. I will not hesitate to blow you off the landing. Get away from my house and don't ever come back here."

Their friend in the big white house in front came out in his boxer shorts with a gun as his wife called the police. Motorcycles revved up, and the drug punks flew around the side yard of the main house toward the road. By the time the police arrived, Bradford was home from his shift. They thought Bradford was the perpetrator. The police kept a keen watch over the area after that incident.

Bradford took the first half of the National Board Exam in June. There was a huge party for the class to celebrate the halfway mark of their medical school journey. It was nice to get out and have some fun with Bradford's classmates and their significant others.

If money problems were their only problem, they would have been grateful. Stella Ann was smack in the middle of a baby boom, and it made her happy for her friends but sad for herself. Friends from home and college called to tell her they were pregnant. Her mailbox overflowed with baby shower invitations. She was not the jealous, envious type, but all she had dreamed about as a child was getting married and having four children. She had baby fever in the worst way, and there was nothing she could do to console herself. She was not positive company and drifted into a period of depression. They were barely taking care of themselves, but her motherly instincts were extraordinarily strong. She grieved the reality the only children she would have in her life were her students, and she would only have them for a short time.

She made an appointment to get a check-up and talk with a doctor about her ability to have children in the future. The result of her doctor's visit was Stella Ann needed surgery when school was out for summer. She scheduled surgery after Bradford's board exams in mid-June. The surgery confirmed she had a condition which causes a lot of pain and makes it difficult for someone to get pregnant. It took longer than anticipated to recover, and she had registered for graduate school. Three days later, Bradford learned he needed surgery and scheduled it for early July. Lou and Burt came down to help for a few days.

Norma, Scott, and Liza came the day before Bradford's surgery. They arrived about 8:30 p.m. and checked in at a hotel. Stella Ann had been on her feet too much the day they arrived and didn't get enough rest. She was up all night with excessive cramping, pain, and crying. It was a lot for her and Bradford to have serious medical issues at the same time. She worried about Bradford.

The next day, Norma picked Stella Ann up at 10:30 a.m. to be with Bradford before his surgery. Scott and Liza were laughing and acting silly, making Bradford nervous and agitated. They had just crossed over into their teen years and were too old to act so rowdy in a hospital. Bradford's surgery was at 2 p.m., and he returned to the room by 4:30 p.m. Norma took the kids to dinner and swimming afterward at the hotel pool.

Sawyer sat with Bradford while Stella Ann went to eat dinner. When she returned to the room, he offered to stay with Bradford overnight. It was a blessing because Stella Ann was exhausted and had a doctor's appointment the next day. The following day, Norma and the kids stayed with Bradford until Stella Ann got back from the doctor. Bradford was supposed to come home later in the afternoon, but it was determined he needed to stay another night.

"Please, please let Scott stay to help me get Bradford home," Stella Ann begged Norma as she sat at the kitchen table with her head in her hand. "I will bring him home in a couple of days."

"Stella Ann, no, Scott has a summer job helping a neighbor paint houses in a new subdivision. He needs to go back and make money," Norma said with a cold tone in her voice.

"Please, Norma, we have been through so much. Let him stay. I am so tired and weak. I don't know what I will do if Bradford falls. I can't help him up."

Norma finally agreed to let Scott stay and took him to the hospital to sit with Bradford before she and Liza left. Grammie and Grandpa offered to come to Chattanooga to check on Bradford and pick Scott up two days later. Stella Ann was so relieved Norma agreed to let Scott stay she started crying again. It was not like her to cry, but her hormones were unstable from the surgery.

Stella Ann had no idea her brother and sister-in-law were bringing her mother back to Chattanooga. Lou knew Stella Ann and Bradford needed help. Burt had work obligations and could not leave Columbia right then. Lou also knew Stella Ann would not ask her to come back to Chattanooga again so soon after being there for Stella Ann's surgery, but Lou thrived on helping others. Lou had no clue what she was walking into.

When Ron, Jenny, and Lou walked inside the little house, Stella Ann was washing laundry. Black water hoses crisscrossed the middle of the floor connecting the washing machine to the sink and the hot water heater. It was necessary to jump over hoses when they were going through the kitchen to get to the stairs. There were mounds of clothes all over the floor. The place was in general disarray, which happened when Stella Ann got overwhelmed. Stella Ann tried to hold her emotions together, but tears of gratitude trickled down her cheek.

Her brother held up a pouch of tobacco on the table. "Stella Ann, I didn't know you chewed tobacco," he said trying to be funny. "This must be Bradford's."

"Nope," Stella Ann said. "It's Norma's."

Ron broke out in uncontrolled laughter as Jenny glared at him.

"You mean Norma chews tobacco, Stella Ann," Lou said astonished. "She tries to be so prim and proper and make people believe she is the pillar of Columbia society. She's just a country girl trying to be something

116

she is not."

Stella Ann replied, "I am trying hard to be friends with Norma. If her tobacco chewing and wild ways were all I had to deal with I would be happy. Grammie also chews tobacco. They always have red plastic cups for their chewing breaks."

"What can we do to help before Ron and I go back tonight?" Jenny interjected changing the subject.

"Y'all need to get on the road. You are going to be late getting back." Lou said. "We will be fine, and I'll finish up these clothes before I go to bed. I appreciate all you did to get me here, Ron. Be sure to check on Burt a couple of times this week. I left plenty of food in the refrigerator. Where is Bradford, Stella Ann?"

Lou gave several orders at a time and asked a million questions before anyone could answer the first question.

"Mama, the doctor decided to keep Bradford in the hospital an extra day. He was having a lot of pain. He may be discharged tomorrow. Scott is with him at the hospital tonight, and Norma and Liza went home this afternoon. Sawyer brought me home late this afternoon," Stella Ann replied.

"The doctor released me to drive today," Stella Ann continued. "I will be able to bring Bradford and Scott home tomorrow if Bradford is released. Grammie and Grandpa offered to come down Sunday to get Scott. They are anxious to see Bradford. I begged Norma to let him stay. I didn't know how I was going to manage helping Bradford up and down the stairs."

Lou stayed a week, and it was a blessing to have her there. Stella Ann's daddy and cousin came to take her home the following Sunday. Bradford and Stella Ann would have a full month to recover and regain their strength before school started.

By the end of July, their life goals were temporarily shattered.

"Why are you acting like a maniac? You cry all the time over nothing." Bradford said. "I should be the one crying. I am the one under pressure."

Stella Ann responded, "Oh, you are the one under pressure? I guess, I am floating through life without a care in the world."

The conversation went downhill from there. Bradford took the dog walking, and Stella Ann went upstairs to work on her sewing project. She knew she was not herself. Her doctor put her on an expensive experimental drug. He warned it had side effects like menopause and mood swings. Stella Ann was not tolerating it well.

Her graduate school class started, and it would be finished before in service at her school. She spent the next four weeks studying at the Hamilton County Library to keep peace at home. Stella Ann and Bradford's relationship got very tense toward the end of July. It was when medical students received the results of the National Boards.

Bradford was sitting in the living room in the dark when Stella Ann got home from studying.

"What are you doing in the dark, Bradford? Stella Ann asked. "I'll turn on some lamps."

"I am sitting here thinking about our future," he said.

She felt as if she was pulling conversation from him because he was so quiet and withdrawn. She noticed a marijuana cigarette in the ash tray but said nothing.

"Bradford, what is it?" Stella Ann prodded.

"Stella Ann, I have let you down. I have let myself down. I have let my parents down," he said." I failed the boards by five damn points. I will not get to start clinics with the rest of the class."

"Bradford, are you kicked out of medical school?"

"There is an appeal process. I must request a meeting in writing to appear before the appeals board which consists of administrators, professors, and doctors. Some appeal meetings are granted, and others denied. The board asks questions to confirm my commitment to the training process and the medical profession. I am allowed to state my case about why I think I failed the boards. It can be a humiliating process, Stella Ann."

"Bradford, if you must beg, plead, grovel, or swim across the Tennessee River, you will stay in medical school. Together we can make a great case for you and win, and you will not tell your parents about this."

Stella Ann coached him rigorously for his presentation. Bradford made a solid case which included the medical conditions discovered about him and Stella Ann before the boards. He showed the board his study schedule and timeline. He explained his worry about his wife because she was having surgery first. He revealed he was in a lot of pain with his medical condition before and during the testing dates.

Bradford was charismatic and convincing and showed the board medical records to substantiate his claim. His request to stay in medical school for another year was granted, and he joined his class as they navigated clinics. He was required to retake the first half of the boards the following summer. He was going to study constantly and take practice tests because standardized test taking was not easy for him. The appeals board would decide after his second test attempt if he would get to stay in medical school.

Stella Ann and Bradford knew the stakes were high. He could spend another year in medical school and still be kicked out, but the challenge was worth it. It was going to be a difficult year, but they could do it. Stella Ann finished her graduate school class and decided it was too much for both of them to be in school at the same time. She earned 15 graduate hours in a couple of years but stopped her pursuit of a graduate degree until later. She did not need any added stress, and graduate school could wait.

Bradford started clinics, and his first rotations were surgery and internal medicine. His time was consumed at the hospital and with study groups. Stella Ann was used to being alone, but never like this. She was still taking the medicine her doctor prescribed, and it was more than she could handle. She got depressed, anxious, angry, jealous, and hopeless. She resented her friends, family, and Bradford. It was like all her emotions were out of control. She had no one to talk with about her despair. Her mother couldn't understand why Stella Ann was so angry and distraught. Bradford had no time to talk with her about anything and told her to get over her pity party.

Stella Ann was having more than a pity party. She was having a breakdown, and no one was around to support her. Stella Ann prayed she would look back in a few years on all her anguish and realize how foolish she had been. Not all her behavior was in Stella Ann's control. Much of it stemmed from the side effects of the medication. She made an appointment with her doctor. She realized she could no longer take the medicine.

"I'm leaving your ass!" Bradford yelled. "I have enough pressure on me without coming home and looking at your sorry self in a heap on the couch crying and whining. You are selfish and self-centered. Can't you think of anyone but yourself?" He slammed the door, and Stella Ann heard him start the car and leave. Bradford knew the loyalty, commitment, and love she had for him. Why did he always leave or threaten to leave her?

For years, all she thought about was Bradford, family, friends, colleagues, and students. She felt nothing was for her or about her, and nothing belonged to her. She felt like she had never been first and had carried the burden of his dream for a long time. She was physically sick with a cold and situationally depressed. All she wanted to do was sleep, and she convinced herself she didn't care if he left. Maybe he was right. Maybe they should get a divorce. A lot of medical students were splitting up with their wives or husbands, or they were starting families.

Bradford returned late that night and never said a word, but the next day he was still angry. He ranted all day.

"Look if you don't like your situation, go home, get out, get a divorce. I don't care!" he said. "All you do is complain," he went on. "Can't you ever be happy?"

Bradford dealt the cruelest blow when he repeated, "I hate you!" over and over and left again slamming the door so hard it rattled the house. Stella Ann knew she wasn't pleasant to be around, but she couldn't for the life of her remember what she did to set him off. When he accused her of crying and whining the day before, she wasn't crying. She was trying to nap to get rid of her cold.

When Bradford got in one of his ranting moods, Stella Ann learned to retreat and say nothing because the situation would escalate to hitting or throwing things. She was scared and cowered like an animal. Stella Ann never had a chance to tell Bradford her doctor discontinued her medicine and told her to expect her emotions to level out in a few weeks.

They had a wonderful Christmas, and both families were very generous to them. Norma and Hank even got along during the holidays. No one threw anything or said hateful things.

When they got back to the guest house in Chattanooga, they were greeted by eight dead mice on the kitchen floor. Every pest company that came to give them a quote said they could try to control the mice, but there was no way they could get completely rid of them. Infestation was a mild word to describe the conditions in the house. They shook their shoes out to clear the mice droppings every morning. Any white or light-colored clothing was ruined in their closets. Stella Ann was constantly disinfecting.

It was enough for Bradford to throw up his hands and declare they had lived in ghetto conditions long enough, five years to be exact. He gave Stella Ann the task of finding them a rental. Most of the places they could afford were no better than where they were living, but Stella Ann was determined not to give up. As she drove around the neighborhoods they picked as desirable, Stella Ann saw a moving trailer in the front yard of an adorable house in the North Shore area. She pulled into the driveway and took a chance she would find someone inside. As she got to the kitchen, she saw a young man and his mother packing dishes and knocked on the door frame.

"Excuse me. Do you mind if I ask you all a few questions about your house?"

"Go ahead. I will keep working as we talk," the young man said. "I am leaving in a couple of days. I have a new job in another city."

"Are you selling your house?"

"This is not my house. I am renting from a nice Italian man and his wife. His mother and father built this house when they immigrated here from Italy after the war."

"Do you know if he is going to continue to rent it or sell it?" Stella Ann asked.

"I don't know, but I can give you his number."

"Thank you so much," Stella Ann said. "I hope your new job works out well for you."

Stella Ann could not wait to get home and call the owner. His wife answered and was kind and helpful. She gave Stella Ann his number at work. He was a butcher at a local grocery store, and his name was Mr. Cassini. He agreed to meet with Bradford and Stella Ann when he got off work. Sawyer happened to stop by after work and joined them when they went to look at the house.

The house was adorable and perfect for them until they learned the monthly rent. It was $425 and almost half of Stella Ann's take-home salary. Bradford started bartering with Mr. Cassini because he knew how much Stella Ann wanted the house. They finally agreed on a rental price of $350, and Bradford agreed to keep the yard up and do any maintenance necessary. He also got the deposit waived. With Sawyer's help, they moved two days later. It was a new year and a time of new hope for Stella Ann and Bradford.

Stella Ann loved nesting in the new house and making it cozy and comfortable for them. There was not a pest in sight. It boosted her spirits and gave her encouragement that there was a light at the end of the long dream-chasing tunnel.

They had been in their new rental for two months when they realized it was going to be more of a financial burden than they thought. Stella Ann's paycheck didn't seem to cover their expenses, and they were always juggling to see what bills could wait. She ramped up her sewing projects and crafts and sold more items at flea markets and crafts fairs. Lou sent them $50 a month and fabric for Stella Ann's projects. Grammie continued to send care packages every month. Stella Ann did more tutoring, and she and Bradford had periodic yard sales.

Stella Ann continued to be bombarded with baby news. She started sharing her hopes and dreams with Bradford as well as her sadness about not having children. She knew she was not very pleasant to be with, but she couldn't shake her feelings. Stella Ann knew she was running low on patience and happiness. She couldn't help it. She got no support from Bradford. He did not even want her to mention the future, and it made him angry every time she said something. He would snap, and Stella Ann would shut down. The pressure of having all the financial responsibility on her shoulders was getting to be more than she could handle. Stella Ann became more and more withdrawn.

Bradford cleaned the house one afternoon while Stella Ann was still at school tutoring. When she got home, he was about as angry as she had ever seen him.

"I cleaned the house, Stella Ann." Bradford said. "Someone has to keep this place clean, and it is obvious it is not you."

"Bradford, I cleaned on Saturday. The house was not dirty. It is only Wednesday," she said as she changed clothes.

"You are filthy, Stella Ann. You don't clean like I like it." Bradford said.

"Bradford, you are not being fair. I may not clean like your family's maids, but I am not filthy. I try hard to keep things nice and neat." By this time, Stella Ann was crying.

Bradford got up from his chair and called her to come to the hall. "You see behind this door?" He had left a dog hair fuzz ball behind the door. "I left this so you could see how filthy you are."

Stella replied, "Bradford, I usually vacuum behind the doors. I must have overlooked it because I was in a hurry. I am sorry."

She walked back toward the living room and to the kitchen to start dinner. Bradford came up behind her, picked her up, took her to the door, and threw her outside. He threw her purse and car keys, hitting her in the stomach.

"You keep your ass out of here, and if you go to your friend's house, I will kill you. Keep Sally out of this. You can sleep in the car as far as I am concerned." Then he slammed the door, and she heard the lock click.

Stella Ann was outside in the cold and didn't have a clue what she was going to do. She grabbed her purse and got in the car. She was glad she always kept a jacket and a couple of books in the car. She ended up in a parking lot at Renaissance Park. She fell asleep and awakened at 2 a.m.

She thought it might be safe for her to return home because Bradford would be asleep. It was a chance she had to take. She had to get ready to go to work. Before she got out of the parking lot, a police car pulled in behind her. The officers checked her license, asked why she was out at that time of morning, and offered to follow her home. She declined. She knew it would only make Bradford angrier. It would not be the last time she slept in the park or sought a safe place, but one thing was for certain, Stella Ann would always vacuum behind the doors first.

In the spring, Sawyer walked in as Bradford pushed Stella Ann into the tv and threw her across the room barely missing a picture window. Sawyer had an uncanny way of showing up when she needed help. Stella Ann, reduced to shame and tears, went to the bedroom, and Sawyer talked with Bradford to calm him down. Sawyer told Stella Ann Bradford was angry because she left her paint supplies on their small kitchen table. She planned to finish a painting when she got home from school. He did not like her to needlepoint, sew, paint, or do anything that caused disorder. She learned to have the house tidy, and all craft supplies put away. She felt Bradford's obsession with order squashed her creativity. The things which brought her happiness in her loneliness were fading away because she had no freedom and no place to do those things. Nothing seemed to belong to her.

Ronald Reagan was elected to be the new president, and the country was still having economic issues. Interest rates were high, and necessities like food, utilities, and gas cost more. Stella Ann and Bradford continued to have money troubles. They had to pay fifty dollars for Bradford to retake the boards and fifty-seven dollars in income tax. They had $114 in their checking account, so Bradford sold his Columbia Military Academy class ring for sixty dollars. The only thing they had left to sell was Stella Ann's engagement ring, and Bradford refused to let her sell it.

Norma invited Stella Ann to help chaperone Scott and Liza and three other teenagers on a spring break trip to Destin, Florida. Bradford encouraged her to go, but she was skeptical. Bradford said Norma's feelings would be hurt if Stella Ann did not go with them, and the salt air and beach would be good for her. He needed to prepare for his retake of the boards and being alone would allow him uninterrupted sessions to study. Stella Ann agreed to go only because the quiet in the house would benefit Bradford's study schedule.

She drove to Columbia to meet the travelers going to the beach. They were going to pick her up at Burt and Lou's house. They were traveling in Hank's Bronco. When they arrived, they found the weather beautiful, but by the second day, Stella Ann was ready to get on a plane for Chattanooga. To add to her misery, Norma decided they would stay an extra day. Fighting and bickering between Norma, Scott, and Liza was continuous and embarrassing.

Stella Ann walked in on Norma going through suitcases to see what the kids brought, and she mooned the boys one night while preparing dinner. Stella Ann was nothing short of disgusted a middle-aged woman would behave in such a way. Norma smacked Liza in the face at a restaurant because she left her purse in the car. She smacked Scott on the way home because she thought he was driving recklessly. A piece of lumber fell off a truck in front of them and knocked the muffler off Hank's Bronco. They were delayed three hours in Macon, Georgia, trying to get it repaired. Norma required her and the teenagers to pitch in any money they had left from the trip to fix Hank's Bronco.

It was late when they got back to Columbia, so Stella Ann decided to get a good night's sleep before heading back to Chattanooga the next day. She made a promise to herself she would never get in a car with Bradford's mom or siblings again. She never told Bradford about all the ridiculous behavior on the trip. He would think she was exaggerating and find an excuse for Norma's behavior.

Three days after Stella Ann returned to Chattanooga, Burt called to let her know Jenny and Ron had a baby boy, and mom and son were fine. She was genuinely excited about Ron and Jenny's baby. After all, he was her brother, and Jenny had been careful about Stella Ann's baby sensitivity. Stella Ann wanted to go right back to Columbia the next weekend to see the new baby, but she and Bradford only had $55 to last them two weeks.

Burt and Lou had given Stella Ann the money for the Florida trip. They were very generous to her even though they had to live conservatively. She worked hard and couldn't seem to make ends meet. She started second guessing their decision to move and was always on edge each month until they paid the rent. She had a fear of not being able to stay in their new rental, and it sent her into a spiral of "ain't it awful" and "when will we get to start living like others our age?" She was under so much pressure she realized she was not being very pleasant company or support, but she could not get a grip on it. The way she felt could not be blamed on the medication she was taking months before. Pure and simple, Stella Ann was acting ungrateful and bratty. She was mentally and physically exhausted.

Stella Ann finally got to Columbia to see the baby in June, and he was adorable but cried every time Stella Ann tried to hold him. The family went bonkers over the little boy. He was perfect, and Jenny and Ron adapted well to being a family of three. His nursery exploded with baby toys and cute baby necessities. Stella Ann brought their dog because Lou and Burt were going to dog sit while she and Bradford went to California with Grammie and Grandpa.

Their flight originated in Nashville, and they met Grammie and Grandpa in Los Angeles after Bradford completed his exam. Stella Ann had a couple of vacation weeks before she started teaching summer school. It was a perfect time to get away, and they loved being with Grammie and Grandpa. The purpose of the trip was to visit Bradford's great aunt and her family who proved to be warm, fun, and welcoming. They went to Hollywood, Beverly Hills, Disneyland, Mexico, and spent two days in Las Vegas.

Mexico had a direct way of waking Stella Ann up to how very blessed she was regardless of her present situation. The poverty there was astounding. Little boys followed them trying to sell paper flowers and begged them to let them wash their car. Las Vegas was not very appealing to Stella Ann, Bradford, or Grammie, but Grandpa loved the slot machines and playing Blackjack. To Stella Ann, the smoke-filled casinos and loud people drinking free alcoholic concoctions reflected a sad portrait of humanity. It made Stella Ann feel like she needed to go to confession when she got home. Grammie and Grandpa provided their airline tickets, Burt and Lou gave them spending money for the trip, and Norma bought Stella Ann a new red dress in her correct size and purchased Bradford a new shirt in his favorite color, blue.

By the end of June, Bradford received the results of his exam. He passed with flying colors, and the review board made a unanimous decision to let him continue with his class and graduate in the spring. His schedule was full but not as intense as the previous years. It was going to allow Bradford to work a few hours per week in the hospital lab to help Stella Ann out with expenses. It appeared the next year was going to be more positive for Bradford and Stella Ann.

PART THREE:

Milestones

CHAPTER 7

A Kiss and a Beer

"Stella Ann, I asked Dad if he would sell our last cow when he sends his next group to the sale barn."

"But Bradford, the cow is all we have left for emergencies."

"Stella Ann, we either need a new car or get both cars worked on and hold our breath they will last through the year. The repairs will take almost all the money we get for the cow."

Within a week of paying for the repairs for both cars, Bradford's car caught on fire, and it was totaled. They had no choice but to buy a car. They turned to Norma for help. Bradford made the call.

"Mom, I know you are going through a rough time with the divorce. Believe me, I hate to ask you for help, but my car caught on fire and burned beyond repair today. Is there a possibility we could borrow some money for a down payment on another car?"

"Bradford, I think I can help you. How much do you need?"

"Mom, we need at least $750 before they will even talk with us about a car loan, and the interest rates are steep."

"Bradford, I will send you a check tomorrow, and I want the red dishes," Norma replied.

"Mom, we really appreciate it and will get the red dishes to you the next time we are home."

Stella Ann was glad to relinquish the dishes that crashed Christmas years earlier. They bought a cute yellow Chevrolet Chevette. The car payments of $178 a month were a challenge, but somehow, they made their money situation work.

The January presidential inauguration of Ronald Reagan brought hope. Bradford was going to graduate, the country emerged from a financial slump, and the American hostages reclaimed their freedom with their release from Iran. It was a hopeful and optimistic time.

The closer they got to Bradford's graduation the more they got "the wants." They wanted new furniture, they wanted new clothes, they wanted a home, and they wanted a baby. People said, "Someday you'll laugh at what you went through," "someday your ship is going to come in," "think about how much money Bradford's going to earn," "someday you'll laugh at the hard times you went through," "someday it's all going to be worth it," "someday you'll be better off than your friends." Comments like those seemed patronizing and dismissive. None of those sentiments resonated with them because they had deprived themselves of any of life's little pleasures and expectations for years for Bradford's career aspirations. Over the years, Stella Ann learned there was no benefit in playing the comparison game or banking on the future.

They were young and weary from the medical school journey. As much as patience was not a virtue for Stella Ann, determination was on her virtue list. It was a huge part of her value system. She decided one thing she could do to stay out of "want whining" was to be productive. She started studying to take the LSAT. Bradford encouraged her and wanted her to go to law school, but they still had miles to go before it was her turn to go back to school.

By April, medical students finalized their residency placements. Bradford got a special delivery letter from a Chattanooga hospital offering him a spot in their residency program. He had several other options but decided to stay in Chattanooga. He would make $16,800 a year as a resident, and Stella Ann's salary was $11,150. They felt like they had arrived at the imaginary, "New Life Train Depot" on the "Rich Train," and they were optimistic and excited.

Norma and Hank's fights were more frequent and volatile as the year progressed. Scott and Liza called Bradford a lot because the fights upset them, and they needed to know what to do. The fights were physical and dangerous, and Scott had to intervene a lot to protect his mother. Norma wanted to file for divorce once the kids were in college but changed her mind to file earlier. Hank drank more than ever and had trouble getting along with office and hospital staff. His anger was out of control when he drank, and his strength overcame Norma when they fought.

Norma started working full-time in Brentwood, and she bought a new house not too far from the family farm. She and the younger kids moved into it in the spring. Scott and Liza graduated from high school in May. Before they left for college in August, the divorce was final.

As Bradford's June graduation approached, Stella Ann planned a reception at their house after the ceremony. They invited all those special to them and most came all the way to Chattanooga to celebrate. It was going to be a testy group and a tense situation. Stella Ann prayed guests would step up their behavior and realize this day was to celebrate Bradford's accomplishments.

Stella Ann had a lot of school events at the end of May, which added to her stress level and weighed heavily on her health. She had a lot of pain and sometimes needed help getting up from a chair. Her little kindergarten students helped her at school making a game out of it. Her doctor was insistent she have corrective surgery after Bradford's graduation. The surgery was set for the end of June. She would be able to enjoy Bradford's graduation and her high school reunion before the surgery, and she would have plenty of recovery time before school started again.

Words could not express the pride Stella Ann felt when Bradford walked across the stage at McKenzie Arena to receive his medical degree. He had worked so hard and was a step further in accomplishing his lifetime dream to be a practicing physician. She knew he would be a good doctor. The parade of characters who showed up to celebrate their joy and Bradford's accomplishment was interesting.

Norma, Liza, and Scott arrived the night before, and Norma said something strange when she got out of the car. She said it seemed like they were being followed all the way from Columbia. They thought the car following them was one of the invited guests because they followed them right to the house and turned around in the church parking lot across the street. The rest of their guests decided to drive up early the next morning.

Stella Ann's Uncle Bill fell asleep and almost tumbled out of his seat in the auditorium. Conner, Stella Ann's nephew, toddled around the area in front of the seats. Hank and Norma didn't speak. Liza was sweet and quiet, and Scott kept everyone laughing. Grammie went to the ceremony, but Grandpa decided to stay at the house to watch his two little dogs and Buff, their dog. Burt, Lou, Ron, and Jenny were supportive, watched the antics of the others, and made no comment.

Stella Ann barely made it through the ceremony she was in so much pain. She may have felt awful, but she looked good in the new navy-blue linen dress she bought for the occasion. Norma was like a fidgety schoolgirl when Dean, Bradford's biological father, showed up at the last minute. She ran to the back bedroom to refresh her hair and makeup and change clothes like she was meeting someone important for the first time. There was nothing anyone could do but hope Hank and Dean had no interaction.

Stella Ann rationalized graduation was a day for Bradford. She stepped into the shadows to let him enjoy the occasion. Even though she expected no recognition, she thought Bradford would at least mention her support and encouragement. All he said was, "Stella Ann, you don't mind working three more years do you, to get me through residency?"

She was speechless and heartbroken. She had already been a work horse who prodded and encouraged him for years. Her mind raced. "This was all she got? Not a thank you of any kind. Not I couldn't have done it without my wife beside me." His message was, "Keep on working Stella Ann. Help me, me, me." Another thought ran through her mind. "Stella Ann, keep on working until I find someone to replace you in my life. You have done your job helping me through school. You aren't worth keeping."

She collected herself and replied, "Of course, Bradford, you know I will help you get through residency. You didn't need to ask."

Shortly after graduation, Stella Ann and Bradford went to Columbia for Stella Ann's tenth high school reunion. She was thin, having lost so much weight from the stress and pain she suffered for months. To get haircuts and hair products free, she was a hair model for a local styling salon. She agreed to let one of the stylists cut her hair and perm it. It was a very stylish hairdo, but it was way out of Stella Ann's comfort zone of her typical shoulder length hair style. She looked as if she was plugged into an electrical socket like a cartoon character. She never got another perm. Comments to her at the reunion included, "You have lost a lot of weight, are you sick?" or "What happened to your long hair?" or "How many kids do you and Bradford have?" She had never weighed over 110 pounds, short hair was stylish then, and they had no kids. Some things or people never change, but she had fun at the reunion. It was great to see her friends, many of whom had become successful in the ten years they had been out of school.

Her surgery lasted longer than expected. There was a lot more damage than the doctor had originally assessed. Stella Ann stayed in the hospital for eight days. Burt and Lou went to Chattanooga when doctors released Stella Ann, and they took her back to Columbia with them to recover. Bradford had to start his residency and was not going to be home much to help her. His schedule required him to stay at the hospital three nights in a row, and then he would be off two nights.

While Stella Ann was in Columbia, she and Lou got up at 4 a.m. and watched the royal wedding of Lady Diana Spencer and Prince Charles. It was fascinating to watch, and it allowed people to escape daily life for a few hours. Lou and Burt took Stella Ann back to Chattanooga shortly afterward, and Lou decided to stay longer. Stella Ann's recovery was not immediate, so Lou stayed in Chattanooga for five weeks, which was a blessing. Stella Ann had not recovered completely when her school started in August. She went back to teaching too soon and rested every afternoon when she got home. She lived for the weekends to recover and prepare for the week ahead.

It was a relief Stella Ann didn't have to listen to the endless telephone calls between Bradford and his parents. Norma and Hank played the blame game. Hank refused to pay Norma alimony despite her marital rights. Bradford tried to mediate, but it was a lost cause. Hank said Norma spent buckets of money and got them in financial difficulty. Stella Ann had been with her on a few shopping trips. It was typical for her to spend $2000 in one store and never try on any clothes. Hank was one of the most successful physicians in the area and had inherited family money and property, so Stella Ann didn't believe he couldn't afford the bills.

She did not know the complete circumstances of Norma's and Hank's divorce but was aware of large amounts of alcohol consumed by Hank, and they argued a lot. They were also very sarcastic and demeaning to each other in front of other people. In response to Hank's opinion about not wanting a divorce and in front of the whole family Norma told Hank, "I don't care what you think or want, and you can go piss up a tree."

He accused her of causing problems in his office. Scott and Liza confirmed there was physical fighting, and Norma ended up bruised a lot on her legs and arms. Stella Ann had seen burn marks on Norma's legs from where Hank had thrown a space heater at Norma a year earlier. There were rumors in town that Hank had girlfriends but no proof. He claimed he wanted to keep his family together. Stella Ann believed him; he loved his family but wasn't willing to stop drinking. By the end of August, the divorce was final, and Hank and Norma could start to rebuild their separate lives.

Stella Ann and Bradford rarely saw each other. When they were at home they were sleeping or doing household chores to get ready for the next rotation. Only their family and close friends knew Bradford's call routine. Being on call during residency meant Bradford worked on the floor and slept at the hospital for three days and nights and was on the floor two days with those nights off. Many of the residents had their wives stay with them if it was a weekend. Stella Ann went a couple of times to stay with Bradford, but it was not very comfortable or desirable quarters, and the bathroom was a community bathroom down the hall. Bradford understood when Stella Ann declined to go with him for all night stays.

He rarely saw her anyway.

It seemed regaining her strength was taking forever. It was a Monday afternoon in early November, and Bradford was in the middle of a three-night rotation. Stella Ann was on the living room sofa trying to rest from a long day and fell asleep with the tv on. The phone rang, and it was an unfamiliar voice.

"Stella Ann, this is Margie Taylor, Dr. Taber's nurse. Is Bradford available?"

"Mrs. Taylor, I am sorry, Bradford is at the hospital. He will be there all night. May I take a message?" Stella Ann responded.

"Stella Ann, can you get in touch with Bradford right now?"

"Yes, ma'am, what do I need to tell him?"

"Stella Ann, have you been watching the news tonight?"

"No, ma'am, I was napping off and on watching tv but not the news."

"Stella Ann, I need you to listen. You need to get in touch with Bradford, and you two need to head to Athens to get Liza. Norma was kidnapped."

"She was what?"

"Kidnapped, abducted. Norma was abducted," Mrs. Taylor said anxiously.

"Police have helicopters and cars swarming all over the area to find her. Come straight to Columbia and go to your parents' house. They know about it. Alex is looking for Scott and will take him to your parents' house. We don't know where Norma is or if she is alive."

"Oh, my gosh, Mrs. Taylor, when did this happen?"

"They think it happened about 5:30 p.m. in the grocery store parking lot. Her car was found there. You need to hustle now and make plans to get Liza and get back to Columbia."

Sawyer dropped by their house several times during the week and would have dinner with them. He could not keep up with Bradford's call schedule, but Stella Ann was glad to see him when he showed up shortly after Mrs. Taylor's call. It was helpful to have someone with her when she called Bradford at the hospital. She had to call the floor, have him paged over the hospital speaker, and wait for him to call her back. He did not have a pager, and cell phones were unheard of then. It seemed like it took forever for Bradford to call her back. He gave her strict orders not to call him unless it was a dire emergency.

"Bradford, I have something to tell you. You need to get a leave of absence from your rotation for a few days," Stella Ann said.

"Stella Ann, is there something wrong with you? You know I can't leave."

"Bradford, please listen. Margie Taylor called a few minutes ago. Bradford, your mom was kidnapped. We need to go to Athens to get Liza and go to Columbia. Norma has not been found yet. We are supposed to go to my parents' house. Alex is looking for Scott now and will take him to Mama and Daddy's house. Please come home."

"Damn," Bradford said. "This is hard to believe. Who would do such a thing? I will be at the house within an hour. Pack our bags, and call Liza. Tell her we are on our way."

"Ok, Bradford, is there anything else you need for me to do before you get home?"

"No, Stella Ann, I love you. I'll be there soon." he said.

Stella Ann looked at Sawyer as she glared into space, and he said, "I am going with you all. I can help Bradford drive. It is going to be early morning by the time we go to Athens and loop back up to Columbia."

"Sawyer, there won't be room for us, Liza, you, and our dog, Buff, plus luggage."

"Yes, there will," he said. "I am going." She didn't argue. It wouldn't do any good. He had made up his mind.

Stella Ann's principal was kind and empathetic. A colleague assured her that her class would be in good hands and encouraged her not to worry about lesson plans. She grabbed a small piece of luggage and put enough clothes for her and Bradford for a few days along with some toiletries and makeup. Sawyer went to his house and packed a small bag and was back before Bradford got there.

It felt like they were going to be driving into a black hole. They didn't have much information and would not know until they got to Columbia if Norma was located.

138

When they got to Athens, at the University of Georgia to get Liza, it was after midnight. The dorm mother led Stella Ann to Liza's room. When Stella Ann walked inside the room, Liza was on her bed sitting in silence with tears streaming down her face and not knowing what to say. Stella Ann gave her a hug and told her they needed to get on the road.

"Liza, where is your bag?"

Liza pointed to her bag, grabbed a handful of things off her dresser, and shoved them into her purse.

"Stella Ann, do we know anything about Mom?" Liza asked. "I haven't talked with anyone but you and Bradford since this happened. No one is answering the phone at Mom's or Dad's house, and I did not want to upset Grammie and Grandpa."

"Liza, we don't know anything more than you at this point. It was best you didn't call Grammie and Grandpa. Alex went to their house to tell them in person. All we can do now is pray your mom is found and not harmed," Stella Ann said giving Liza a hug. "Come on, let's get you checked out downstairs. Bradford, Sawyer, and our dog, Buff, are in the parking lot waiting for us."

When they got to the car, Bradford got out and helped Liza with her bag and gave her a reassuring big brother hug. They settled into the car, and Bradford updated Liza. It was going to be a long drive from Athens, Georgia, to Columbia. It would take them at least four hours or longer to get there. The narrow winding back roads might slow them down. No one said a word as they drove, and no one could sleep.

They went straight to Lou and Burt's house. They were told Alex and Scott would be there, and Burt would know details with his connections in city hall. Everyone was awake when they arrived, and Alex had found Scott, who was also there.

Burt explained what he knew, "Norma was located early this morning. She is alive and was taken to the hospital. A seven-year-old boy was in the parking lot with his mother when the kidnapping occurred. He remembered three digits of the license plate of the two thugs who abducted Norma. She was picked up by police and an ambulance at a gas station not too far from the southbound interstate exit to Spring Hill. The men who abducted Norma have not been caught. The police are processing the case, collecting information, assessing the area close to the crime scene, and questioning Norma. No one is allowed at the hospital."

Lou suggested Bradford, Sawyer, Liza, Scott, and Stella Ann try to get some sleep. They were tired, had been up for a long time, and welcomed some rest. Lou thought they would know more information later in the day. They had to keep Scott at their house. He kept saying he was going to kill Hank, but there had been no mention of Hank's possible involvement. Scott had seen a lot during the divorce and immediately blamed his father.

By late afternoon, the family was allowed to visit Norma, and none of them were prepared for what they saw. Norma had been beaten badly and was almost unrecognizable. She had a concussion, one eye was shut, clumps of her hair had been ripped out of her head, her arms had human and brush scratches on them, and it looked like she might have a broken leg. A woman who prided herself on her appearance and was always coiffed, made up, and wearing designer clothes looked like someone from a war zone. No one should have to go through what Norma had been through or what she would face in the coming months.

While they were in the room, Hank knocked on the door and walked in meekly like he was in a daze. Alex immediately ushered Scott out of the room as he sensed the tension.

Stella Ann was usually quiet around Bradford's family, but she turned to Dr. Taber and whispered, "Do you have an idea who did this?"

"Shut up, Stella Ann," Hank said. She didn't know why she asked, but an inner instinct consumed her from the time she learned what happened. After all, Norma and Hank had been through a contentious divorce a few months earlier.

As difficult as Norma could be, she was personable, generous, compassionate, and could be a lot of fun. She would later tell her version of what happened. She wanted to go home but was denied. Doctors had a lot of tests to run, and a police photographer was taking pictures. Poor Norma had not been allowed to bathe. The family was ushered out of the room after a brief visit. A policewoman was assigned to stay with Norma around the clock.

Two days after the incident, Norma was discharged from Maury General Hospital, and the men who kidnapped her were apprehended in Florida just over the Georgia state line. They were brought to Tennessee, booked, charged, and carried off to jail to await trial. It was unnerving to the family when they learned one of them was released on bail. It was almost as unnerving to see much of it play out on television, radio, and in newspapers. They had no privacy, and the little town was abuzz with disbelief and shock. Reporters stalked them shouting questions and conspiracy theories. They were instructed to make no comment to anyone outside the family. Burt asked the police department to do drive by checks on Norma's house. Later, the family hired a private security officer.

People in the community who knew the family brought food and sent flowers to the house. No one asked a question. Norma did not want to be alone, so Alex agreed to stay with her for as long as she needed him.

Her attorney knocked on the back door, and Norma called everyone into the living room. She had to recount the details of the incident for her attorney and wanted her kids to listen.

"I need you to know what happened and document what I can remember. Stella Ann, will you please take notes?" Norma asked.

Stella Ann got a pencil and paper pad from a kitchen drawer and started writing.

"I took I-65 south to get home from work. If traffic is moving, it is quicker to use the interstate to get to Columbia rather than going down Highway 31. I got off the interstate in Spring Hill because I wanted to get some groceries. As I was putting groceries in the car, a long sedan type car pulled up. A passenger said something ugly to me, but I ignored them. It made them mad I would not talk to them. Before I knew what happened, the man on the passenger side jumped out, grabbed me, and threw me in the back seat of the car and pushed me to the floorboard. I screamed, but I don't think anyone heard me," she continued.

No one in the living room said a word. They let her talk.

"They said they knew who I was, and they said they were going to kill me. They said vile awful things to me. I told them I had money and could pay them. I begged them to let me go. I started wiggling my engagement ring off my right hand. I was going to offer it to them but decided it would be best to drop it in the car."

"My ring is somewhere in the car they were driving. Please tell the police about the ring. I forgot to tell them," she said.

Her attorney interjected, "Mrs. Taber, I will make sure the police know about your ring."

Norma kept talking, "The man in the backseat with me had a double name of some sort, but I can't remember it. It was something like Billy Joe or Jim Bob. He kept grabbing me by the hair and slamming my head to the floorboard. Then he started ripping my clothes off. I begged them not to do anything to hurt me. I told them I had sons their age, and I was an old lady. They told me to shut up. I could smell alcohol. Then one did the unimaginable. He raped me."

She continued, "They pulled off on a gravel side road and switched places. Then the other one started beating me and raping me. I thought I was going to die. I think they intended to kill me. They threw me out on a country road. I was naked. They threw my clothes out of the car and yelled something vulgar. They told me to lie in the middle of the road, and they wouldn't hurt me. They said they would drive off in the opposite direction. I heard them as they drove off, but I also heard them turn around in a gravel area. I knew they were going to come back, run over me, and kill me, so I rolled down a ravine and stayed there until I could tell they were gone."

"I could see a light ahead and walked toward it. I was naked and freezing. I got to a gas station where the attendants wrapped me in blankets and called the police."

By the time Norma finished, there was stone silence, and Liza and Stella Ann had tears streaming down their faces. The three boys were fighting angry. Norma was the strong stoic one. Her attorney told her she had been through enough recounting the story, and he would wait to ask her more detailed questions.

Then Scott angrily said, "Dad had something to do with this." Alex and Bradford told him to never say any reference to their dad having any involvement in their mom's abduction in public and to let the police do their job.

Before Norma's attorney left the house, he made it clear they were not to talk with anyone. He looked at Scott and urged him to keep his emotions and anger under control because it would compound the case. He urged them to let him, and the police do their jobs. He said the police and prosecutors were looking at asking for life sentences for the two men.

Liza was on the sofa hugging her mom, and Stella Ann finished writing Norma's statement. She had already given a statement to the police, but Norma wanted her children to hear about the nightmare as she talked with her attorney.

It was decided Scott and Liza would return to their respective colleges. Alex would move in with Norma for as long as she needed him. Hank was not to come to Norma's house for any reason, and they stopped short of putting a restraining order on him.

Bradford, Stella Ann, Liza, Sawyer, and their cocker spaniel, Buff, left to take Liza back to school and go home to Chattanooga on Sunday. All needed to get back into their regular routine and would be back in a couple of weeks for Thanksgiving. Bradford insisted they buy another car when they returned to Chattanooga. Stella Ann's car broke down a lot, and he was afraid she would get stuck in an undesirable situation when he was at the hospital. They bought a small blue Ford Escort. Stella Ann loved it even though they couldn't afford it.

Thanksgiving was good, and Norma was doing well. She was healing and was strong enough to go back to work. When she got to Grammie and Grandpa's for turkey dinner, she looked beautiful in winter white slacks and matching sweater. She was a pretty lady and very resilient. She was going to be ok through the trial the next year.

After Thanksgiving, something odd started happening every time Bradford was on a three-day rotation. Stella Ann didn't say much about it at first but had to say something to Bradford as it happened more and more as time wore on. Stella Ann would get phone calls every forty-five minutes all night starting at 10 p.m. on at least one of the three nights Bradford was away and on call at the hospital. There was static in the lines, and the man would say in a low voice, "I know where you live. You keep your mouth shut. You will be next, you little black-headed bitch." Then he would hang up. Forty-five minutes later, it would happen again. The man would say the same thing. The last call would happen about four in the morning.

Stella Ann could not sleep, and it was affecting her job. She told Bradford, and he immediately said he thought his dad might be doing it. Hank was known for staying up late and drinking. When he overindulged, he made angry phone calls. Bradford confronted Hank, and he vehemently denied making the calls. Bradford sensed Hank was lying but also thought he might not remember after a night of drinking.

Stella Ann told her daddy about it, and Burt agreed with Bradford. Burt called his police friend, who contacted the Chattanooga police, but the phone calls did not stop. Burt asked his police friend to go with him to Dr. Taber's house to confront him. Burt was very diplomatic, but this time Hank's behavior had pushed his diplomatic negotiating skills to the trash.

"Hank, may we come in a minute?" Burt asked when Hank answered the door. "We need your help with something."

"Sure, come on in. I was getting ready to watch a ball game. Could I get you two anything?" Hank said, ever cordial and refined.

"No, thank you," Burt said and got to the point. "We have a concern about something happening to Stella Ann when Bradford is on call. She gets phone calls one night out of the three Bradford is at the hospital. The calls happen every forty-five minutes until about 4 a.m. Each time the person says something like this, "You little black-headed bitch, you better keep your mouth shut; you will be next." She said the same static comes through the phone connection they hear from your house when they talk with you."

His friend stepped in, "Dr. Taber, do you know anything about who is making those calls?"

Nervously Hank said, "No, no, I have no idea about the phone calls Stella Ann is getting. Stella Ann and Bradford haven't said a word to me about any phone calls."

Burt knew Hank was not telling the truth because Bradford had already confronted him about the calls.

144

Burt interjected, "Let me make something very clear. If those phone calls are coming from here, we will find out. So, if you talk with anyone who might be making the calls, tell them to stop. It is interfering with Stella Ann's well-being and her job."

Stella Ann never got another call.

The kidnapping and rape trial was set for a year later before Christmas. The town of Columbia had not seen a trial of this magnitude in years. People offered conspiracy theories of every kind. Some thought Dr. Taber was involved. The families of the men who kidnapped Norma said it would be revealed in the trial Dr. Taber paid the men $5000 to kidnap and kill Norma. Some said they saw Dr. Taber talking to the two men at a bar outside the city limits. Others said his truck was seen at their trailer park. None of the theories were confirmed or proved. The two men were found guilty, and each got two consecutive life sentences. The family was relieved they could finally have some peace and live their lives, and those men would never see beyond barbed wire or bars again. Could the family ever live their life in peace?

The stress of residency and teaching weighed heavily on Bradford and Stella Ann. Residency wasn't much better than medical school, except Bradford got a paycheck. Stella Ann's body could no longer handle stress well, and she ended up with a virus that sent her to the hospital before school ended in the spring. The silver lining to a difficult year fraught with family problems, financial problems, car problems, health problems, school problems, and marital problems was Stella Ann was not going to work during the summer. Bradford borrowed $750 from his credit union at the hospital, and they went on a wonderful, much needed vacation. They had not been away alone together in seven years.

They left their dog in Columbia with Lou and Burt and went on a road trip through the mountains and down to the beach. A friend of Bradford's suggested they visit Sullivan's Island, a resort area near Charleston, South Carolina. They were able to get a three-day package to stay in the inn and immediately fell in love with the island and the area. The natural beauty, serenity, and wonder of the island was mesmerizing. They were treated like royalty with morning coffee delivered to their room, their bed turned down at night, and a chocolate mint left on their pillows. Charleston became their favorite city to visit. The Sullivan's Island Inn was torn down years later. Sullivan's Island always held grand memories for them, and they went back many times over the years.

"How quickly can you get to Dr. Patterson's office? He wants to talk with us together." Stella Ann said anxiously.

Within minutes, Bradford ran through the tunnel under the street, which connected the hospital and the professional building, and joined her in Dr. Patterson's office.

Dr. Patterson offered pleasantries and sat down behind his desk.

"The results are not what we had hoped for. You see, you have a combined problem. If you were each married to different spouses, you would be more likely to conceive. Together it is not going to happen, and I am recommending you stop putting yourself through endless, painful, and costly tests. You might think about filing for adoption or research surrogacy."

Stella Ann and Bradford had already filed for adoption and had gone through the home study process. They were warned it would be unlikely a baby would become available within their age window. At twenty-eight, they were getting too old. Surrogacy was a new concept, and there was a lot to learn about how the process worked.

Within a matter of ten minutes, their lives changed forever. Bradford had to go back to work, and Stella Ann was glad. She did not want him to witness her devastation, and she didn't want to know if he did or didn't share it. Stella Ann held it together until she got to the car. Then she screamed, beat her hands against the steering wheel, and didn't attempt to control a stream of tears blanketing her face. She drove home in a fog and made her way to the bedroom. She couldn't even greet Buff, their dog.

When she was too tired to cry anymore, she fell asleep. Sleep didn't help much, and the grieving continued. She would never have a baby shower, decorate a nursery, or have a blue or pink bow tied on their mailbox. She would never experience the highs and lows of parenting. They would always be left out of conversations involving babies, kids, and family events.

She became bitter, angry, jealous, and isolated. She refused to go to baby showers or help host baby showers, and buying baby gifts was as difficult. What was so hard to accept was it was not their choice not to have children. It didn't help that Stella Ann was in a stage of life where most of her friends were having babies, and she taught kindergarten where pregnant mommies peppered the hall. Her students kept her going. She threw herself into her work.

Shortly after the doctor's visit, Bradford told her they needed to separate or get a divorce. Divorce was the last thing on Stella Ann's mind. She was devastated and thought they were doing well. Bradford said he was very unhappy, and their relationship was stagnant.

Stella Ann thought it might have something to do with the visit to Dr. Patterson when it was discovered Bradford had not followed through with the tests and recommendations Dr. Patterson made. For Stella Ann, the visit was almost a relief because for the first time someone had the guts to tell them to stop trying to have a child. The doctor bluntly told them they would never have their own natural children. For Bradford, the visit was one of total hopelessness, and he was right. They continued making plans for adoption and filled out applications with several agencies.

It wasn't long before Bradford was restless again. He was talking of divorce and separation, and he seemed very depressed. He asked Stella Ann if she ever wanted to have sex with someone exotic, someone different, from a different race, country, or ethnicity, or if she ever wanted to have a threesome. Stella Ann was flabbergasted. "Where did these ideas come from?" She had never once thought of anyone romantically or sexually except Bradford. "What was he thinking?" Then he said all Stella Ann wanted was his money. He had no money. "Was he having a breakdown?" Bradford's wildly random thoughts were alarming to Stella Ann. A sad thought crossed her mind. "Was he having an affair?"

He was adamant he didn't smoke pot anymore, but Stella Ann had evidence that proved his claim wasn't true. Bradford told Stella Ann he didn't need a wife to cook, clean, and do laundry. He told her he needed to be needed. Stella Ann wanted to be needed also, and the only way she filled the gap in his constant absence was cleaning and teaching. "Why were they tearing each other down?" She would later find out the reason for Bradford's thoughts and depression.

For several years, Stella Ann experienced continuous sarcasm and criticism. She tried hard to be a good wife and make him proud of her, but her self-image was at its lowest. She quit painting because he didn't like the clutter from her materials. He didn't want her sewing because she left it out when she worked on a project, and he wanted her to work out or play tennis. He claimed he could never love a fat or overweight woman. Stella Ann weighed 110 pounds. He didn't take her anywhere because he hated the way she dressed. He said she looked like a dowdy schoolteacher in jumpers, clunky shoes, novelty blouses, and sweaters laced with apples. A lot of the way she looked was because they had no money for her to buy stylish clothes. "Why did he say things that etched away at her self-confidence and self-esteem?"

They didn't go home for Christmas because Bradford worked Christmas Eve and December 26. Norma, Scott, and Liza came to Chattanooga to be with them on Christmas Day. Liza was going to stay with Bradford and Stella Ann for a couple of weeks before her school started again. It was a long cold winter, and by April, Stella Ann was having a lot of chest pain. She was treated for costochondritis, but nothing seemed to help. She became very good friends with her heating pad and Tylenol. It was a Saturday in early April when Bradford and Sawyer went fishing, and Stella Ann decided to rest. The phone rang, and she thought it was Bradford. It was the university calling about Liza.

"Hello, this is the student medical center calling for Dr. Bradford Taber. Is he there?"

Stella Ann answered, "No, Dr. Taber is not here right now. Could I take a message?"

"Who are you and what relation are you to Liza Taber?"

"I am her sister-in-law. What has happened to Liza?"

"We can only talk with a family member. We cannot locate her mother or father. The next person on the contact list is her brother, Dr. Taber."

Stella Ann was getting frustrated. "Listen to me. Dr. Taber is fishing on a lake somewhere between Chattanooga and Nashville. He is not available. I am all Liza has right now. What is the problem, and what does Liza need?"

"Liza is in the emergency room and needs treatment. It appears she is having some stomach or intestinal distress."

Stella Ann went into overdrive. "Let me be very clear. I am giving you permission to treat her. If you don't, anything that happens to Liza will be the university's fault. We will be there as soon as I can locate Dr. Taber. Do you understand? Please call with an updated status of her condition as soon as possible." She knew she did the right thing.

Stella sat motionless and wondered, "What else can happen in this family?"

Bradford and Sawyer came home within the hour, and they took off for Athens. When they arrived, Liza was on the mend but very weak. Bradford signed her release. They went to her dorm to get her clothes and return to Chattanooga. No one talked on the way back, so Liza could sleep. Bradford and Stella Ann accepted a huge responsibility for bringing Liza with them, but she could not stay at the university until she was stable and could take care of herself.

The next day they learned Hank was in Texas, and Norma was in the mountains. Hank came to Chattanooga the following Monday. Liza did not want to see her mother and stayed with Bradford and Stella Ann until the end of May. Stella Ann did not realize how sick she was herself, and taking care of Liza was stressful. Stella Ann was beginning to believe she was a walking example of what stress can do to a person's health. Bradford and Stella Ann went with Liza to the university to withdraw her and empty her room. The plan was for her to move to Nashville and attend school there. The events of the year were more than a college freshman could handle, and Liza needed time.

Bradford, Stella Ann, and Sawyer took a trip to Disney World, Sanibel Island, and to the World's Fair in Knoxville in July. They had a great time, but Sanibel Island was the best time of all. They enjoyed the pristine beaches, rode horses, ate great seafood, and swam a lot.

The only disappointment of the trip was Stella Ann was in a lot of pain.

Bradford and Sawyer kept her knocked out on the back seat of the car as they traveled. They had no idea how sick she was, but she could not do much without resting every few minutes. When they returned to Chattanooga, Bradford took Stella Ann to the hospital for tests. The results were awful and showed her left lung filling up with fluid. Typically, she would put up a fight about being admitted to the hospital, but she didn't care this time. She didn't even think that school was about to start. The pain was blinding.

She was able to get her classroom decorated, have her initial parent meeting, meet her students, and get the year started. By mid-September, Stella Ann was back in the hospital for a few days. In October, she and her supervisor had a ridiculous disagreement over a playground incident which had been blown way out of proportion. Afterward, she felt physically and mentally exhausted. She stayed in her room during lunch and cried the whole time. She didn't realize added stress could send her right back to the hospital. She was unaware her health was so fragile. Her principal, a kind and compassionate man, excused her from faculty meeting and let her leave school early. Bradford took her to the emergency room when he got home. She was scheduled for emergency lung surgery the next morning. She was only thirty years old.

Bradford understood the seriousness of Stella Ann's condition and talked with her about the possibilities. One was death. He cried uncontrollably as he told her. Stella Ann wondered if they were tears of guilt or love. They called her parents, who left Columbia immediately to get to Chattanooga before the surgery the next morning. Bradford contacted her principal who told him to assure Stella Ann her class would be fine and to concentrate on her health.

The surgeon screamed at the two surgery attendants, "Hold her chest open. We are losing her. We are losing her. If you must break another rib, do it, but do not let go. I must get to her lung."

Stella Ann was hovering over the operating table, watching the whole operation. She couldn't understand all the frantic activity over her body and why it was such a big deal with all the shouting and orders. She was fine and so peaceful. She was going toward a bright light, a beautiful light.

It wasn't a blinding light but one with a soft glow and a peaceful radiance to it. She saw some of her relatives as she moved in the tunnel, and one asked her what took her so long to get there. The light had the most fabulous aura, and she wanted to get closer. It was like she was floating.

"We are losing her, we are losing her again," Stella Ann heard the doctor scream again over and over.

Stella Ann felt a hand gently pushing her away from the light. She saw a shadow figure in the glow of the light. The more the hand pushed back, the more Stella Ann wanted to go toward the light, but she was leaving the tunnel. There was some peaceful music, but Stella Ann could not determine the source or describe the song.

Hours later, Stella Ann woke up in the intensive care unit of the hospital, and there was a wave of activity. Bradford came in to see her, and the nurse assigned to her case came in when Bradford was there. Stella Ann could not communicate, but they were talking about something unrelated to Stella Ann or medicine. She heard something about a beer, an apartment, and then she fell asleep again. Burt and Lou came to see her, but visits were limited in time and frequency. Sawyer came later in the night.

"Will you please get the big green frog off of the coffee table, Sawyer?" Stella Ann asked.

"Sure," he replied. "Then I would like some of what you are drinking."

Stella Ann was heavily sedated, but she was awake enough to know Sawyer was there. They had a conversation.

"Stella Ann, I am going to be staying with you at night until you are out of ICU," Sawyer said. "I am not leaving you alone. Many on staff know me since I worked here when I was trying to get into medical school. I don't like or trust your night nurse. Bradford is busy. He had to go back to his rotation schedule. Your parents will be here during the day."

"Thank you," Stella Ann said and fell back asleep.

The same nurse came in with Bradford each time he visited, and Stella Ann would be in and out of sleep. Her eyes were so heavy it was hard to keep them open, but she could still hear what they were saying. They mentioned in-laws, an apartment, beer, kissing, and added another word, divorce. Stella Ann could not figure out what they meant. She was too medicated.

She was in ICU for three days and discharged after ten days in the hospital. She faced a very long recovery. Her mother stayed with them for a couple of months. Bradford still had his demanding rotation schedule, and Stella Ann could not be alone. She had to have help getting in and out of bed and could not lift anything. Teachers, parents, friends, and church members kept a food train going, so they had plenty of good food. Plus, Lou was an excellent cook. At times, a student would come to visit when their mom delivered a meal. They were so sweet and would usually bring a picture or a card they made for Stella Ann. Visitors were limited, but Stella Ann loved seeing the kids. Two weeks before Christmas, Burt came to get Lou to return to Columbia.

Stella Ann started talking with her administrators about returning to school after Christmas. Her division head wanted her to resign, and her principal couldn't have been nicer, offering her a half-day schedule. Stella Ann never considered resigning and was insulted at the thought.

Bradford and Stella Ann did not travel home for Christmas and spent a quiet holiday in Chattanooga. In February, Norma, Scott, Grammie, and Bradford's great-aunt came to Chattanooga to visit. Stella Ann made a full meal for them. She didn't realize how exhausting it would be to cook a full meal for company. It was a nice visit, and everyone seemed to enjoy the meal and the company. Bradford was home for a few days before his next rotation and helped Stella Ann pick up around the house and wash dishes after his family left.

Bradford gave Stella Ann a pair of small diamond stud earrings for Valentine's Day. She was excited and appreciative about receiving such a lovely gift. She knew it was a financial stretch for them. They exchanged cards, had a glass of wine, and talked. To Stella Ann, it was a very strange conversation.

"Stella Ann, you were very sick. At times, I didn't even know if you were going to make it," Bradford said. "A lot of people were praying for you."

152

Stella Ann wasn't quite sure how to respond. She wondered where Bradford was going with this conversation because she knew how sick she had been.

"Bradford, I am so sorry I imposed on everyone by being sick. Believe me, I would have preferred not to be sick. It has been awful, but I am so grateful for all your concern, help, and support," Stella Ann replied.

"Stella Ann, you know men have needs, and you have not been able to meet my needs for a long time," Bradford responded.

"Bradford, I am sorry. I didn't realize how hard this had been on you. I was struggling and trying to get back to normal. I am so sorry you felt neglected."

"Stella Ann, it is not so much I was neglected. You couldn't help it, but I need to tell you I did accept comfort from a lot of people. It was as hard on me as you. Stella Ann, I went to a nurse's apartment several times, but all we had was a beer, and we kissed."

Stella Ann sat on the sofa and froze. It was like she had been stabbed in the heart and not by Cupid. She didn't know how to respond. It was not OK. It was not excusable. It was heartbreaking he would be with someone else while she was incapacitated and almost died. The words, 'comfort from a lot of people" kept ringing in her head.

"I don't know what to say," she said. "It has been a long day. I am going to bed."

She walked to the hallway, turned around and asked, "Bradford, is that the reason you gave me the diamond earrings?" She didn't wait for a reply.

CHAPTER 8

Family

By the middle of 1984, Stella Ann's recovery was progressing, but she needed to pace herself and rest. Bradford was on the precipice of starting his medical practice. Recruitment was robust and competitive. Several Middle Tennessee groups recruited Bradford. A doctor in Springfield, Tennessee, was very persistent in asking Bradford to join his practice. He got offers from as far away as Denver, Colorado, and Charleston, South Carolina. He could go anywhere he wanted.

Their original plan was to return to Columbia, but with serious legal charges leveled against Bradford's father, they ruled out Columbia. Bradford felt his father's personal and professional behavior would impede him in developing a practice in Columbia. He was concerned people would hold his father's behavior against him.

There were a lot of decisions to make, and they tackled each with much deliberation. Bradford received a lucrative offer to stay in Chattanooga and start a clinic with the backing of one of the hospitals. It was a very good opportunity with little personal financial obligation involved. It would give them time to pay off the student loans signed by Stella Ann. Her goal was to get the massive school loan debt paid as soon as possible.

They wanted to buy a house, but high interest rates and low inventory blocked their try on every corner. There was no one they could ask in the family to float them a loan for a down payment. They only had Bradford's promise of work and Stella Ann's retirement savings. It would take an undetermined amount of time to process the request to withdraw Stella Ann's retirement savings. Lenders wanted to see a check not the promise of a check.

On Sunday mornings, they searched the papers for a house they could afford. After lunch, they went to open houses and returned home for nachos and wine. Sawyer joined them in their house search and offered constructive advice as they enjoyed their nacho feast. It was good to have his opinion. Their emotions vacillated between defeat and excitement. They loved the rental house, and their landlord had been gracious and kind, but they wanted something they owned. Their attitude of entitlement surfaced on a regular basis and did not serve them well.

They decided Stella Ann would take some time off from teaching to regain her strength and focus on her health. Fatigue and exhaustion were constant. She lost more weight while pushing herself to get back to school and full-time teaching.

Independent school administrators issued contracts to teachers in March. They allowed two weeks for teachers to resign or accept the contract as written. There was never a question about Stella Ann's decision. If her offer was ten dollars and a dozen eggs to teach in any position determined necessary by the administration, she would have to take it. For years she was in no position to bargain, which was demeaning and left her feeling powerless, but her status changed with her health issues and Bradford's new practice.

Stella Ann requested a meeting with her principal. What she had to say required a face-to-face meeting. She admired her principal, and their relationship was one of honest banter. They often agreed to disagree, and his decision remained the last word on a subject, for a while anyway. He knew she would be back. Stella Ann did not give up on issues she was passionate about. They always respected each other. It was a professional relationship that provided Stella Ann with a voice.

Stella Ann exploded with internal nervous anticipation as she sat in the office waiting for her appointment. She wore a new navy suit and matching pumps purchased on sale at Belk's department store after Christmas. The expectation was for teachers to dress professionally. When teachers looked nice, it aided the respect factor expected from students, colleagues, and parents.

"Stella Ann, Dr. Stafford will see you now," the receptionist said, looking up from her headphones and typing. "You may go in."

"Stella Ann, what brings you in today?" Dr. Stafford said. "Are we going to have one of our literary or educational debates, or do you want a lecture about grizzly bears?"

"Dr. Stafford, while I would love a debate or lecture on any of those subjects, I have come to talk with you about next year. You have been very supportive of me for the last six years, and I am beyond grateful. This year has been brutal for me because of my health. My doctor has recommended I take a year off to regain my strength and completely recover. Bradford and I agree. Bradford has accepted a job here for three years. His contract makes it possible for me to take off a year."

"Stella Ann, I am not surprised by your decision," Dr. Stafford said. "We will miss you around here. We will welcome you back when you are stronger. You have contributed much to the success of our kindergarten program and have advanced a love for reading and literature in the upper school students. You have also been a great help to our music teacher with programs and chapel."

"Thank you, Dr. Stafford. It was a hard decision to make. This school and church is my home, and the people here are my Chattanooga family. You have been so kind to me, especially this year. Some worked relentlessly to get me to resign. Thank you for your support and for allowing me to return."

"Stella Ann, things have a way of working out, and I refused to approve forcing you to resign. It wasn't right. You have given a lot of yourself to this school," Dr. Stafford said. We received some push back from a few parents and a couple of your unnamed colleagues. They settled down once they understood your dedication and your determination to finish the year. When most realized you taught here three years before I took over and six years under my leadership, they embraced a new understanding of your situation. Loyalty and longevity mean a lot."

"Dr. Stafford, I often think God's plan for me is to shepherd other people's children rather than having children of my own. I will be knocking on your door someday to return. I love this school and the people here. Before I start crying, I need to pick up my kids from art. Again, thank you. You are not only my boss but a good friend whom I respect."

Stella Ann's career was by no means over. Teaching suited her well, even though she dreamed of being a lawyer. She had a way of igniting a love for learning in her students and led with her heart. Her energy and the way she moved around the classroom to pull every student into her fold were gifts.

Her class and their parents hosted a lovely and emotional end-of-year luncheon at the home of one of her students. They couldn't have been sweeter or more generous, and they showered her with gifts, hugs, and memories. To Stella Ann, it was like she had never been sick for half the year. It was proof that children could be insightful and compassionate.

It was Stella Ann's belief children were not given enough credit for being perceptive and kind. They possess an amazing capacity to step up when someone needs a kind word or hug. Even her older students stepped up the compassion ladder when a need arose, especially for a classmate or teacher. Stella Ann felt adults should be more vulnerable and real with kids. Her students saw her laugh, get flustered or angry, and cry. Stella Ann believed to be an effective teacher one needed to be authentic with a professional boundary understood. She convinced herself she would return to the classroom someday.

Stella Ann and Bradford purchased a house on Signal Mountain with the help of a wonderful real estate agent who floated them a down payment loan until Stella Ann's $10,000 retirement withdrawal came through. She took a chance on them, and they were grateful. She knew she would get her money back.

They needed a lot of money before closing and could not take a chance Stella Ann's retirement withdrawal would come before the closing date.

Hank needed Bradford to take over his practice for two weeks while he had hip replacement surgery. They packed up and went back to Columbia for two weeks to make enough money for the closing. Bradford saw patients, and Stella Ann worked in the front office answering the phone. The school business manager contacted Stella Ann while they were in Columbia and informed her that her retirement check had arrived. They had more than enough money to cover the closing costs for their house.

The house was a two-story brick on Signal Mountain. It had four bedrooms, two and a half baths, and a large screened in porch overlooking a lovely, fenced back yard.

Moving was set for July, and Bradford started his job in August. They emerged from a nine-year time warp. They were ready to begin a new life. Stella Ann worried too much was coming to them too soon. It felt like their lives were in overdrive trying to catch up.

They spent weekends papering, painting, and scrubbing. They made endless lists of things to be accomplished immediately and things they wanted to do to the house in the future. They realized that being a homeowner was expensive, and chores were unending. Stella Ann paced herself because fatigue and pain continued to be a factor in her life.

Bradford's brother, Scott, helped with the painting and papering. Later, Burt and Lou came with their stored wedding gifts. They brought barbeque, potato salad, baked beans, and corn light bread from The Barn Stop, a restaurant in Columbia. Grammie sent Rocky Road brownies. Burt helped Bradford with outside chores and fencing while Lou helped Stella Ann get her kitchen in order.

They ran out of money before they ran out of ideas, excitement, and energy. After two weeks in the new home, neighbors stopped by to introduce themselves and to bring sweet treats. They wanted to meet the new doctor who had moved to the neighborhood. Stella Ann perceived she was insignificant in the introductions. Only one couple seemed interested enough to get to know them as a couple, and they had a brand-new baby boy.

Most of the neighbors were Bradford and Stella Ann's age with children ranging from newborns to high schoolers. In the afternoons, the cove across the street filled with kids playing ball and riding bikes as moms monitored the play sessions and sipped their wine coolers. Stella Ann peaked at the activity from behind the curtains of an upstairs window and wondered if she would ever be part of the fun. She didn't feel comfortable out there. She felt awkward and drank her wine cooler as moms exchanged parenting stories. She made up excuses to leave within minutes. She had nothing to contribute to conversations that revolved around diaper coupons, school events, ball games, babysitters, or recipes.

Stella Ann could not cook and had never hosted a sit-down dinner in her life. For the duration of their marriage, cold cuts arranged on a silver platter and potato salad compiled her entertaining experience. She had no clue how to change a diaper. She had nothing in common with the ladies in the neighborhood, and they had nothing in common with her, either. Most of the women had never worked outside the home and had no understanding of the pressure of being the sole provider. They sported designer clothes, drove new cars, had home decorators, and belonged to country clubs and ladies' groups. If they knew her story, they wouldn't believe her or would shun her. She kept her mouth shut and stayed to herself.

She shared her misfit thoughts with Bradford on several occasions. He felt the same way but was too busy to give it much attention. They didn't have anything in common with their neighbors. One night, Bradford made a very compassionate suggestion.

"Stella Ann, let's stick this out until Christmas. We love our house and are trying to make it a home," Bradford said. "We have spent a boatload of money fixing it up. If by the first of the year, we don't feel like we belong here, we will talk about putting the house on the market in the spring. We can move downtown close to the river and get involved in the arts and music."

Stella Ann was grateful for Bradford's move proposal and appreciated his sensitivity. What she did not know at the time was he was making his own plans. He was going to leave.

Stella Ann got bored quickly. Her life had been one of constant stress and chaos for nine years, and life as she knew it came to a screeching halt.

She was no longer on a schedule, didn't have to get up early, get dressed up, and out the door by 7:15 a.m., and was the new doctor's wife. She began to feel more like an appendage than a partner. Bradford went to work early and got home late. He either wouldn't make it home for dinner or returned to the hospital before they finished dinner.

She didn't dare go to his office with lunch in hand because Bradford told her to stay away from his workplace. She would love to take the staff surprises, snacks, or lunch, but she didn't because Bradford said his mother destroyed his father's office environment by working there or showing up at odd times. She was nothing like Norma, but honored Bradford's wishes even if he hurt her feelings. The only time Bradford allowed Stella Ann at his clinic was if she got hurt or sick. She had lost her identity, connection with people, and purpose. She could feel depression seeping into her life once again.

She played tennis as a child and played on her high school team. She heard young moms at school talk about tennis leagues and thought it would be something she would enjoy. It would also help her make new friends. Chattanooga had a wonderful tennis program. She signed up for league tennis, but fall teams were set for the season. If a captain needed an extra player, she stood a chance of landing a team. Otherwise, placement on a substitute list was her only option. Stella Ann was hopeful and went shopping for a tennis skirt and ball panties in case she was called to substitute. She needed a new racquet but would wait until she learned if she would land a team. For the first time in a long while, Stella Ann felt excited. She couldn't wait to tell Bradford when he got home, but he didn't get home until long after she went to bed.

Stella Ann started substituting for the school by mid-September and enjoyed getting to learn about different grade levels. She realized being a substitute was much different than having a class. The respect level for substitutes was nonexistent, and she wasn't teaching as much as babysitting. She didn't find it very fulfilling, and she missed the perks of being a full-time employee. The drive down the mountain at a moment's notice was irritating as well. She came to realize substitute teaching was not her gift. After a month of substituting, she decided on the way to school that her last day of substituting would be that day. Stella Ann was substituting for Kelly, a former grade level colleague. The school receptionist called Stella Ann to Dr. Stafford's office when the students were in PE class.

The content of the conversation came as a surprise to Stella Ann.

"Stella Ann, Kelly is getting married in December and has decided not to return after Christmas," he said.

"I had no idea Kelly was not returning. I thought she was going to live in Chattanooga close to her mom and dad."

"Her husband wants them to live at their farm in Georgia, and Kelly, of course, wants to be with him."

He continued, "My first thought was to ask you if you would consider returning to finish out the year in her class. You know the curriculum, and it would be seamless for you as well as for the parents and students."

Stella Ann took a deep breath and responded, "Dr. Stafford, I am honored you considered me first. I will have to admit I am getting to be a bored suburban housewife after a few months at home. When would you want me to begin?"

"Stella Ann, we need you to start next week. I have offered Kelly an opportunity to take the rest of the semester off to prepare for her wedding."

"Oh, I wasn't expecting you to say so soon," Stella Ann replied. "Do you mind if I have the weekend to think about it and discuss it with Bradford?"

"Of course, Stella Ann. It would be great if you could let me know something by Monday afternoon."

"Of course, Dr. Stafford, I will let you know my decision Monday."

As she drove home, Stella Ann hoped Bradford would come home early, so she could tell him about her day. She looked forward to their conversation. Bradford was adamant that she needed to pull her weight to contribute to the household and reminded her daily her worth was diminishing because she did not bring home a paycheck. Stella Ann not being offered the job as a full-time employee would be difficult for Bradford to support. Stella Ann wasn't happy about a part-time job

161

description either but would negotiate. For the first time in her life, negotiating was possible.

By bedtime Friday, Stella Ann decided to accept the position if she had full-time employee status and benefits.

It was a sunny fall Saturday, and Stella Ann and Bradford decided to tackle the flower beds in the backyard. They neglected the yard since they had so much to do inside the house. They had a lot of flower beds. Bradford took the large one in the back next to the fence, and Stella Ann took a smaller one next to the screened porch. About noon, Stella Ann heard the phone ring and ran inside to answer it.

"Good morning, Stella Ann, is Bradford around? I need to discuss a patient with him," said Dr. Talbot, her gynecologist.

"Sure, Dr. Talbot, he is in the backyard. I will get him on the line for you."

Bradford came inside to take the call, Stella Ann got a glass of water and decided to go upstairs to shower and rest. They were taking Bradford's office staff out for an appreciation dinner. As she walked down the hall, Bradford motioned for her to come back to the kitchen and sit down until he finished the call.

"This morning? Private adoption? A boy? What is the process? Who do we call first?" Bradford asked Dr. Talbot. Stella Ann was not listening but sat at the table looking at the paper.

Dr. Talbot replied, "This is a huge decision for you and Stella Ann to make, and it will be a difficult adoption. I will call back in thirty minutes to get your answer, and if you decide this is something you want to do, you need to call your attorney immediately. Babies don't stay in the nursery after three days, so you must act quickly."

"Can you hold the phone a second?" Bradford asked. He put his hand over the speaker as he walked toward Stella Ann.

"Dr. Talbot delivered a healthy baby boy this morning, and the mother wants a private adoption. He thought of us. Do you want to do this?"

It did not take Stella Ann thirty seconds after Bradford told her about the adoption to reply with delight, "Yes, yes, yes! of course. Do you want this, Bradford?"

162

He didn't respond to her but returned to the conversation with Dr. Talbot confirming they wanted to adopt the child. He immediately called Clint, their friend and attorney.

They called Stella Ann's mom first. Lou had learned to be calm about anything she heard from Stella Ann and Bradford. Anyone who knew the smallest detail about the couple would admit their ten-year marriage was tumultuous at best.

"Mama, are you sitting down?" Stella Ann asked.

"Stella Ann, I have learned over the years when I hear your voice, I immediately sit down," Lou responded with a little laugh.

"Mama, we are getting a baby. Bradford and I are getting a baby boy on Tuesday," Stella Ann said.

"What do you mean you are getting a baby? How did this come about so soon? You all just finished your paperwork and home study process."

"My doctor delivered a baby boy this morning, and the mother wants a private adoption. He thought of us first."

"Now, wait a minute. Are you sure? Don't get your hopes up. It might not come through. I don't want you two to get hurt," Lou said. It was a change for Lou to be so cautious. She was the optimistic one in the family.

"Mama, be happy for us. I don't know anything about babies. Can you and Daddy come down here this week?" Stella Ann asked.

"Stella Ann, your daddy is running for office again, and election day is Tuesday. We can come on Wednesday. I will talk with Jenny and see if she can gather up some of Conner's baby clothes. The small family baby bed on wheels may be at their house. I will see if I can locate it."

Every baby born in Lou's family started out in the small heirloom bed Stella Ann's great-grandfather made. It was an adorable bed with wheels, and Stella Ann remembered how it was passed around every time a new baby was born. The baby bed was one thing that kept the huge family in touch with each other. At the last count, about forty babies had slept in the antique baby bed.

Lou continued, "You all stay calm. This could all fall through. We will be in touch. We love you."

As much as Lou wanted to be excited and happy about a new

grandchild, she also wanted to protect Stella Ann. Lou knew Bradford was talking with someone late at night when she was in Chattanooga helping Stella Ann recover from surgery the year before. The conversations were not about the hospital or a patient. She never told Stella Ann. Lou thought it was none of her business, and Stella Ann's health was more important.

They called Norma first and then Hank. Neither of them was very excited about the baby. All Hank wanted to talk about was how he thought he had been set up by doctors at the hospital for the recent legal charges he faced. Norma talked about what a cheap scoundrel Hank was and how hard she worked. They called Sawyer, Liza, and Scott, and all were very happy about the news. Sawyer was their best friend, and Liza and Scott were more like their children than siblings. Stella Ann decided their baby boy's sweet arrival warranted a big beautiful blue bow attached to the mailbox and ordered one from the florist.

Neither of them could recall the sermon at church the next day. Their thoughts drifted to the baby boy they would welcome in three days. It was pouring rain when church was over, but they stuck with their plan to go to a department store to get baby supplies. When they told the saleslady they were getting a baby the following Tuesday, she looked at them quizzically like they were lying. After all, Stella Ann was skinny as a rail. The sales associate went to the storage room, got a huge box, and started filling it with baby items, most of which neither Bradford nor Stella Ann knew anything about. Stella Ann didn't go beyond identifying a blanket and had no clue how to swaddle a baby. They left the parking lot with the big box filled with baby items, a car seat, and a baby bed and mattress strapped to the top of the car. The rain stopped long enough for them to get home.

The first reality check for Stella Ann and Bradford was when they put the baby bed together on the stairway landing. It would not go through the door to the nursery. When Sawyer came over for his regular Sunday afternoon visit, he heard them arguing. He helped Bradford take the bed apart and put it back together inside the nursery. Stella Ann started unpackaging the baby clothes and bed linens to wash. She also started a new list of things to get the next day. Sawyer reminded them they needed a lot of diapers. Stella Ann realized she needed her mama, a sister, or even a good friend to help her. She didn't know what she was doing, but one thing she knew she had to do the next day was call Dr. Stafford.

"Dr. Stafford, I promised I would let you know my decision about the teaching position you offered me on Friday. Bradford and I discussed it, and by Saturday our decision shifted. We learned on Saturday we are going to be parents. Tomorrow we are getting a little boy through a private adoption. I will have a new job as a mom," Stella Ann said. "I am sorry I will not be able to help you fill Kelly's position."

"Stella Ann, I couldn't be happier for you!" Dr. Stafford exclaimed. "I have no doubt you and Bradford will be wonderful parents, and the little boy you are adopting is very lucky."

"Thank you, Dr. Stafford. We are beyond excited and have a lot to learn about babies," Stella Ann said. "Tomorrow is going to be a very special day in our lives, and many prayers have been answered. I also learned one should never assume the plan God has for their life. I remember telling you when we met in the spring, I felt God's plan for me was to shepherd other people's children and not my own. I have been humbled by my illness and by God's grace."

"Stella Ann, we will look forward to meeting your little boy. Our son is adopted, and it was a very special time in our lives as well as a forever blessing to us."

"I am nervous about meeting him, but I am going to do the best I can to be a good mom to him," Stella Ann said. "Oh, and by the way, is it too early to put him on the waiting list for kindergarten?"

"Stella Ann, as soon as you and Bradford name your little boy you can call the office and have him put on the waiting list," Dr. Stafford replied.

As soon as Stella Ann hung up the phone, she realized they had not decided on a name for the baby. She put "name the baby" on the mounting list of things to be accomplished within the next 24 hours.

They didn't sleep much the night before their special delivery. The excitement consumed them. The plan was for their attorney to go to the hospital, make all the proper contacts, and get the papers signed. He and his wife, Sally, would bring the baby to them. Stella Ann and Bradford could not go to the hospital because they could face a kidnapping charge. The baby's arrival time was set between 9:00 a.m. and 9:30 a.m. They were excited and ready for their little bundle, and the blue bow was on their mailbox. Stella Ann didn't know why a blue bow was so important to her except it was a joyful symbol of a baby's arrival.

The time was closing in at 10:00 a.m. with no arrival. Bradford was pacing, and Stella Ann was almost crying. It was raining again. Hard. Rain was the reason for the delay. Maybe the birth mother changed her mind. Something else must have happened. Every kind of "maybe" ran through their heads. Bradford stood inside the garage with the door open and smoked a cigarette. He wanted to make sure he saw Clint to wave him into the drive. Fifteen minutes later, they made it. Bradford and Stella Ann were beside themselves. Sally, Clint's wife, had the baby in her arms. Clint carried a brown paper grocery bag as he helped her out of the car. Bradford held an umbrella. The walk was short, so no one got wet.

Stella Ann was standing in the kitchen when Sally put the baby boy in her arms. Stella Ann had a massive case of new mom anxiety, but as soon as he was in her arms, he nuzzled close and yawned. They pulled the white borrowed baby blanket back to see him. He was perfect. Sally had dressed him in one of the least feminine day gowns she could find among her girls' clothes. Stella Ann realized she had not given a thought to what the baby would wear home from the hospital. He could have had a brand-new baby blue outfit from an exclusive children's store to wear for his homecoming, but it didn't matter. He was perfect in the little yellow day gown with a puppy on the collar. Clint explained the paper bag held some diapers and formula to get them started. Within minutes they left the new family.

Bradford and Stella Ann took the baby into the family room. Bradford held him, and Stella Ann took pictures. Buff, their cocker spaniel, wagged her tail and sniffed the little bundle joining the family. She was sweet and curious, checking him out.

"Bradford, do you think the name we selected for him fits?" Stella Ann asked.

"Yes, I do. Landon Langston Taber. It is a perfect name for a perfect little boy," Bradford said. "I am going to leave you two now. I have patients scheduled."

"Bradford, please don't go," Stella Ann said. "I thought this day would be for us, our new family. Plus, I am not steady about handling him right now. You know I still can't raise my left arm very high. How do I change a diaper? When do I feed him? How do I prepare a bottle? Please stay longer, Bradford." Stella Ann begged.

He left. Stella Ann knew she and Landon would face many days alone.

Sawyer came to the house after lunch to see the new baby and to help Stella Ann. He knew Bradford would leave shortly after the baby arrived. By 3:30 p.m., two of Stella Ann's teaching colleagues came to show her how to change a diaper and to make bottles. She could not wait until her mama arrived. She would be more secure with her there. Landon was a sweet baby and tolerant of Stella Ann's awkwardness with him. It was almost like he knew not to cry to make the transition easier for Stella Ann and Bradford.

Stella Ann was able to get a little catnap while Sawyer was there. Her energy level was limited. She continued to have a lot of pain between her shoulders and in her left side. The burning in her back was unbearable at times. Her doctor told her she would experience chest wall pain for the rest of her life, and fatigue would always be an issue. Sawyer offered to go with her the next day to the pediatrician. The little boy didn't know it, but Landon had a lot of people who loved him.

One year before, almost to the day she was on an operating table with an unknown future, and now she had a new baby boy. She was convinced she and Bradford were destined by a higher power to be blessed with this beautiful child. Stella Ann was especially humbled and grateful for the opportunity to be a mom.

Bradford made it home by 7 p.m. He wanted to hold his new son and to know all about their day. Sawyer filled him in as Stella Ann made a simple dinner for them. Sawyer stayed over, knowing they would need some help with the baby until Lou and Burt arrived. By 10 p.m., they learned Burt won re-election. Her parents went to two election parties and left for Chattanooga after a couple hours sleep. As Lou described the election events and parties, she included they announced at election headquarters Stella Ann and Bradford adopted a new baby boy, Landon Langston Taber. Lou said there was more excitement about Landon's arrival than Burt winning the election.

Burt stayed through the weekend, and Lou came packed to stay a couple of weeks. Neighbors were intrigued by the blue baby bow on the mailbox and filtered in to welcome Landon. A little 6-pound, 8-ounce baby boy tapped the love and interest of many. It was the beginning of a special time for Bradford and Stella Ann.

Clint called on Wednesday night to remind them to be in court early Friday morning to sign the initial adoption papers and to appear before a judge. Bradford and Stella Ann fell in love with Landon before he entered their home. They would be devastated if the birth mother changed her mind.

They received hugs and words of assurance from Burt and Lou as they left for court. In any situation, Lou always said things would work out the way they were meant to work out. All the way to the courthouse in downtown Chattanooga, Bradford and Stella Ann were a bundle of nerves. Bradford's stomach churned with anxiety, and he pulled off the highway in heavy traffic to find a bathroom. Stella Ann thought at any moment she was going to need a brown paper bag.

Clint met them in the parking garage close to the courthouse and briefed them about what to expect and how to respond. He took them to the law library and explained they would be there for about thirty minutes. After two hours of perusing many law books and public records books looking for familiar names, Clint checked on them. He explained the birth mother and grandmother were in a huge conflict, and nothing less than a family war was taking place in the judge's chamber. Clint told them to try to stay occupied and calm until he returned. After a tense four-hour wait, they left the courthouse with the necessary papers in hand.

With the papers signed, they started to settle in like a real family and develop a routine. Lou stayed three weeks instead of two, which was a blessing. They needed the help, and Lou was a natural teaching Stella Ann how to care for a baby. They were sitting down to dinner when the phone rang, and Bradford took the call in the family room. It was Clint. Stella Ann froze because she thought he was calling because Landon's birth mother wanted him back. She had 90 days to change her mind.

"Bradford, are you and Stella Ann ready to move?" Clint asked.

"Move? What do you mean?" Bradford asked.

"It has come to my attention someone close to your new family situation lives two streets over from you and Stella Ann. I am advising you two to move."

"Clint, we can't move now. We love our new house. We are not going to run," Bradford said. "We thought about moving before we got Landon, but things have changed."

"Bradford, I understand, but as your legal counsel, I am obligated to tell you the situation and offer advice. Let me know if you need anything," Clint said before ending the call.

Ron, Jenny, and Conner came to see Landon and brought more baby items and gifts from home. By November, Norma and Grammie came for the weekend to meet the new baby. Liza was back at The University of Georgia and came to their house on the weekends. She was great company and wonderful with Landon.

Christmas had a new meaning for Stella Ann and Bradford, and they enjoyed every minute of the holidays. They purchased a real Christmas tree for the first time. Things, baby things, began to appear in their mailbox as Christmas got closer. A Christmas bib, a baby's first Christmas ornament, a teddy bear, and a blue sweater appeared at different times before the holidays. Stella Ann thanked her college roommate, her neighbor, and a teaching colleague. None of them left baby things in the mailbox. Bradford called Clint to let him know what happened. Clint called the birth mother's attorney, and the gift deliveries stopped. Whether there was a connection or not was questionable, but Stella Ann was relieved when the presents stopped appearing in their mailbox.

Many of their extended family members came to visit Landon at Lou and Burt's house over the holidays, and Stella Ann and Bradford went on a few date nights while they were home. There was no lack of babysitters in Columbia. Even Hank enjoyed a visit from them at the big white house on Pulaski Highway. It seemed he enjoyed this Christmas more than others. Maybe it was because he faced a huge trial in February and was unaware of his future.

Stella Ann and Landon spent a lot of time in his room rocking by the window and watching the snow fall. It was particularly snowy in January. Tennessee didn't get much snow, but Chattanooga got more than most areas. It was a novelty for kids to see snow fall. Making a snowman was rare, and snow cream was a delicacy.

Stella Ann read an endless number of board books to Landon and sang, "Hush, Little Baby," a thousand times. The end of January would mark the end of the birth mother's waiting period. Stella Ann didn't answer the phone and didn't go to the door or the mailbox on the last day of January. She counted down the last ten seconds of the day. Landon was going to stay. He was their little boy forever.

A telephone pattern began to emerge. Stella Ann was familiar with telephone harassment. Every day, around one o'clock, when Stella Ann would put Landon down for an afternoon nap, the phone would ring. A lady would ask for Bradford, not Dr. Taber.

Stella Ann always replied, "Do you want to speak with Dr. Taber?"

"No," the woman said. "I want to speak with Bradford."

Stella Ann replied, "I am sorry, Dr. Taber is not here right now. He is at the office. Would you like the number there?"

"No," she responded and hung up.

It happened every day at one o'clock. Stella Ann told Bradford about the pattern, and he said he would report it to Clint. Bradford knew the caller, and the calls did not stop.

"I want to speak with Bradford," the caller said.

"I have told you over and over Dr. Taber is not here. He is at the office. I offered you his office number. Please don't call here again. We have a new baby, and your call wakes him up every day," Stella Ann pleaded.

"Who are you?" the woman asked.

"I am Dr. Taber's wife. Who are you?"

"I am Celia," the woman replied and hung up.

The calls continued until Landon was fifteen months old.

In February, Stella Ann's teacher friends gave them a baby shower. Burt and Lou came for the festivities and to help, and Bradford took the afternoon off to attend. The teachers brought the shower to their house to give her colleagues an opportunity to see their new home and to meet Landon. There was much love and support in the house, and Stella Ann almost started crying with gratitude and joy. Many of the teachers had walked beside her during their medical school and adoption journey. They were like family. The teachers brought decorations, food, presents, and lots of laughter. They set up in the dining room. It was lovely. It was the first time her dining room table was used.

Stella Ann thought she would never have a baby or baby shower. In the middle of the baby shower, Bradford had to take a call. Stella Ann assumed it was a patient or the hospital. He encouraged Stella Ann to continue opening presents. They received many useful and adorable things for Landon. When Bradford returned, Stella Ann could tell something was wrong.

The party was over by six o'clock, and the clean-up was complete by six-thirty. The ladies cleared out quickly. Lou took Landon upstairs for a bottle and rocked him. Bradford asked Stella Ann into the living room when the last person left.

"Stella Ann, the phone call I got was from Columbia," Bradford said. "Dad's trial is over. Dad was convicted. Guilty. He was handcuffed and taken to jail." There was almost no emotion in Bradford's voice.

"Bradford, I am so sorry," Stella Ann said. "Will he get out on bail until sentencing?"

"No, bail was denied. He was taken straight to jail. His attorney is working on another request to have him released on bail. Dad is a diabetic, has heart trouble, and walks with a cane, which is sad because he is only 57 years old. His drinking has not helped his situation. He is not a threat to society; he is not going to leave the country, so hopefully, the judge will reconsider and release him. I must go to Columbia to help Scott and Alex close out Dad's practice and empty the office. He lost his medical license effective immediately. Stella Ann, I need to leave tonight."

Burt and Lou agreed to stay with Stella Ann and Landon until Bradford returned. Bradford's partner assured him the staff would reschedule patients as needed, and he would take continuous call duty. Sawyer offered to help in the office and to check in on Stella Ann and Landon while Bradford was gone. As bad as she felt about Dr. Taber's situation, Stella Ann prayed the news about Dr. Taber would not travel over the mountain. It would be awful for them, and it might jeopardize their little family. She knew she was being selfish, but her mother's instincts kicked her into a protective mode.

They went home for the sentencing. It was awful waiting in the courtroom and watching Hank brought before the judge. They were becoming so familiar with the courthouse that it almost seemed like home. When she was growing up, walking on the sidewalk was as close as she got to the Maury County Courthouse. With the Tabers, it was one serious situation after another.

They pleaded to the court for leniency in a letter campaign. Many prominent people wrote letters on Hank's behalf. The judge was convinced Hank would not be a threat to society. He was sentenced to three months in jail and two years of strict probation with no chance of the reinstatement of his medical license. His career was over, which was the worst punishment of all. He was a brilliant, compassionate doctor.

Stella Ann and Bradford sent him a package every week filled with magazines, novels, snacks, cigarettes, and spending money for coffee and cold drinks. Hank told Stella Ann to stop putting jail on the address of his packages and letters and to put the number of the building and the street in the address. He didn't want people at the post office to know he was in jail. Poor Hank didn't realize all Middle Tennessee knew he was in jail and the reason he was there. The newspapers and TV stations were relentless in their reporting. Stella Ann continued to believe Dr. Taber did not commit the crime of which he was convicted. She also continued to believe he got a lucky pass in Norma's case.

Shortly after sentencing, Liza dropped out of school and moved in with Stella Ann and Bradford. It was more than she could handle having her friends know about her dad. She helped with Landon's baptism party and babysat. Landon was baptized in April, and many family members came to celebrate with them. They had him baptized at their Signal Mountain church and had a reception at home afterward.

It was a joyful time, but many life-changing events had happened to them within a few months. Bradford and Stella Ann decided they needed a vacation. They planned a trip to their favorite place, Sullivan's Island, South Carolina, and included a few days to stop in Gatlinburg, a mountain resort town in the Smoky Mountains. They took Liza with them. She needed the time away and could help them with Landon. It was a wonderful trip and timed perfectly since the summer vacation season had not started. When they returned, Liza kept Landon while Stella Ann taught vacation bible school.

In the late spring, Stella Ann became better acquainted with the woman across the street who had a baby boy about Landon's age. Her name was Claire, and her little boy was Michael. She and her husband came over when Stella Ann and Bradford first moved in to bring a sweet treat and to welcome them to the neighborhood. Her baby was five months older than Landon. Stella Ann and Landon, and Claire and Michael became best friends and shared many adventures providing laughter and memories. They remained best friends despite life events, distance, and growing older. Claire was a friend with whom Stella Ann could pick right up regardless of the time between visits or chats. Cups of coffee had no limit when they gathered in the cove to watch the children play.

The first year with Landon was like a beautiful dream. Stella Ann and Bradford were happy, got along better than ever, enjoyed life, shared new experiences, and were thankful for their little family. In her own bliss, Stella Ann failed to realize she was the only happy one in the marriage.

There remained an undefined tension between them. Bradford seemed always angry and in a hurry. Stella Ann was accustomed to Bradford's outbursts and anger and had learned to navigate his personality better than in the earlier years of their marriage.

Stella Ann confronted Bradford about Celia, and he blew it off as a friend pranking them. The woman who called herself Celia made the mistake of calling the house when Burt and Lou were babysitting. Bradford and Stella Ann were attending a party at The Chattanooga Country Club. Celia called the house three times. On the third call, Lou decided to engage her in conversation.

"I need to speak to Bradford," the woman said.

"Bradford is not here right now. May I take a message?" Lou asked.

"Who are you?" the woman asked.

"I am Bradford's mother-in-law. We are taking care of the baby while Bradford and my daughter attend a party."

"Baby! He didn't tell me he had a baby. Is he married? He told me he got a divorce. He promised to pick me up at the airport."

"What is your name?" Lou asked.

"Tell Bradford Celia called."

When they returned from the party, Lou delivered the message. Stella Ann went upstairs to check on Landon, and Bradford went outside to smoke a cigarette.

Stella Ann knew she had to pick her battles and did not want to start something while her parents were in town. She knew Celia was the woman who made the phone calls to the house every day at 1:00 p.m. when she put Landon down for a nap. Celia knew Bradford's marital status because Stella Ann told her she was his wife, and they had a new baby. The messages were confusing, so Stella Ann let it go.

Stella Ann learned to manage herself well by withdrawing during Bradford's tantrums, but she wasn't consistent with the strategy. Stella Ann started fighting back, which was a big mistake. When he got physical, she got physical, and she always lost. She tried hard to be the wife he wanted and worked diligently to prevent setting him off, but she could never be perfect enough to suit him. When he hit her, she hit back, and when he cursed at her she cursed back.

She had her share of temper tantrums. Early in their marriage, she broke several of his antique mustache mugs and tore pages out of his medical books. She stopped defending herself when she got sick. She could not risk her life, and after they adopted Landon, she could not risk the child getting hurt. She would do anything to protect him.

Anything could set Bradford's anger in motion. If dinner was not the right temperature or if she made something Bradford didn't like, he would throw it at her. If something was out of place, he would get furious, and arrange things like he wanted them.

Sometimes he threatened to "leave her ass," often telling her she would never see Landon again. He labeled her "worthless" and "of no use to him."

Years later, Stella Ann would learn Bradford was planning to leave her when they got Landon.

She responded, "Why on earth did you let us bring a child into this marriage if you wanted to leave me?"

He said, "I couldn't do it because you had been so sick, and after we got Landon, I couldn't leave you with a little baby."

"Isn't that noble of you, Bradford? It is about the cruelest thing you have ever done to me. Tell me, how could you do that to us? To me? To our precious baby boy? Why don't you love us?" Stella Ann said as her voice cracked. "Tell your lover to stop calling here, do you understand?"

CHAPTER 9

Happy Days and Disasters

The days, months, and years following Landon's adoption offered Stella Ann a period of happiness she would always cherish. Even Bradford's outbursts dimmed in comparison to the days she spent raising her son. She was living her dream of being a mother and housewife. She wanted to be like her mother and a family was central to her dreams. No one could ever be as amazing as her mother, but the opportunity to try to be like Lou was something she was getting to experience.

When Landon was eighteen months old, Bradford came home early in a horrible mood. Stella Ann's friends, Claire and Michael, were over for a chat and play session. The late afternoon, between three and five, was the most challenging with toddlers. Stella Ann and Claire took turns providing the boys with play sessions a few times a week. It also offered Stella Ann and Claire an opportunity for some adult conversation. Toys scattered the family room and kitchen. Bradford started slinging toys and grabbed a broom pushing the plastic containers from the kitchen cabinet in a pile.

"What the hell have you been doing all day, Stella Ann? Sitting on your fat lazy ass watching kids play, drinking coffee, and gossiping with Claire?"

"Bradford, I will take care of the containers, pots, and toys in a minute. Why don't you go upstairs and change into something more comfortable? It was our turn to have playtime. The kids have had a great time, and we had lunch together." With Claire and Michael still there, she tried to diffuse his anger.

"If I wait for you to clean this mess up, it will never happen," he snapped. "I'll bet you haven't even given a thought to making dinner. You can't cook anyway. Stella Ann, you are worthless. You are the worst kind of worthless."

It was embarrassing for Stella Ann to be bashed so rudely in front of Claire. Claire scooped up Michael, thanked Stella Ann for the play session, and headed to the door. When she got to the door, her face spoke volumes about how she felt about Bradford's tantrum. It was an expression of pure disgust.

Bradford's anger didn't stop. He couldn't let the messy house go. After Landon was in bed, Bradford brought the house and the play session up again.

"Stella Ann, I work hard and am under a lot of pressure. The last thing I need is for you to have the house in a complete mess when I come home. You have this house picked up, laundry done, beds made, vacuuming done, dinner ready, and everyone out of this house by the time I get home. Do you understand?"

He talked to her with contempt and disgust, not like a man should talk to his wife or the mother of their child. She often said he treated his workers and strangers with more kindness than she received.

Stella Ann lashed back, "It is my house, too. I do a good job running this house and taking care of you and Landon. Good grief, Bradford, I even iron your underwear like your mom's maid did when you were growing up."

She was frustrated and was almost crying. She took a deep breath and said, "Don't you ever speak to me that way in front of Claire again. Better yet, don't ever speak to me like that again. Do you understand?"

Stella Ann was grateful Landon was already fast asleep and didn't hear the confrontation. Yelling and anger could upset him.

Bradford's face turned red, his eyes blazed, he was biting his tongue, and he clenched his fists. It was a look Stella Ann had seen many times before.

She started walking off; he grabbed her by the hair and threw her down onto the family room carpet. Stella Ann pushed and kicked but did not have the strength to hold him off. He was relentless in his punishment, leaving bruises only on her upper arms and legs.

She begged him to stop as tears streamed down her face. He got up, said a few other choice words, and left. Stella Ann pulled herself up the stairs to check on Landon and to go to bed. The pain was excruciating, emotionally and physically. Her chest hurt too much to even cry. She fell asleep on the floor in Landon's room next to his baby bed.

Stella Ann and Landon learned playtime had to end in time to make sure all the toys were picked up and the house was in order before Bradford got home from work. Landon rarely played with his cars and trucks and lined them against the wall in the dining room. He would get upset if anyone moved one. It was not healthy for him to see Bradford behave so irrationally about toys being out of place.

The next day, flowers arrived from one of her favorite florists. There was no apology only an empty, "I love you, Bradford." The behavior pattern started again. There would be a honeymoon period, then escalation of emotions turning into anger, an explosion, a cooling off period, and unspoken remorse. Gifts would appear to negate the poor behavior and buy Stella Ann's silence. It worked. She loved her husband and wanted to keep her beautiful little family together. She made a promise to herself to do better. She would fix it.

Claire and Stella Ann continued their daily chats on the phone and weekly play sessions for the boys. Claire never brought up the subject of Bradford's outbursts until years later, after she witnessed several of his irate episodes and expressed concern over Landon's and Stella Ann's safety. Stella Ann blew it off. She always protected Bradford.

Stella Ann knew the only way she was going to survive and protect Landon was to better navigate Bradford's mood swings. This required perception, reading body language, and walking on eggshells.

Their new neighborhood and friends were a party group who enjoyed their kids and having cocktails in the afternoon. Bradford fell right into the good old boy club with his favorite liquid mixer and coke and a cigarette when he got home. Their screened porch became a handy clubhouse for the "boys," and Stella Ann admitted she enjoyed a glass of wine with the wives.

Bradford's "good old boy" afternoon cocktail parties were concerning. He didn't drink much during medical school. There was no time or money for such an indulgence. She found smoking paraphernalia in the workroom of the new house, which was distressing to Stella Ann. She thought his marijuana smoking was over. He had promised he would stop. What was even more disappointing was his attitude that it was healthier than having a cocktail and should be legalized. Neither vice was healthy as far as Stella Ann was concerned.

When Landon's adoption was finalized, Bradford and Stella Ann thought it would be nice to add another child to the family and provide Landon with a sibling. They experienced three unsuccessful attempts to adopt. One was a little boy they named Matthew who died of a congenital heart problem before he could be placed. Another was a little girl they named Mary Caroline whose teenage birth mother decided to let her mother adopt the child. Then there was a baby boy they never named.

The last opportunity for adoption was presented at a time when Stella Ann realized her marriage was faltering, so they withdrew from any further attempts to adopt. Each failed adoption sent Stella Ann into an emotional spiral, much like what a woman experiences after a miscarriage. Bradford had no patience with her melancholia. He made fun of her and told her she was too emotional and silly.

The last child was adopted by one of Stella Ann's friends. Stella Ann was invited to the little boy's christening, and years later, she was his teacher. It was a lovely year for which Stella Ann was grateful. He was placed in the perfect home to thrive and was showered with love. He was a phenomenal student with a gift for writing.

Stella Ann continued to need to pace herself and rest. It was very difficult picking Landon up, and two small children would be too much for her. They made the decision their one special little boy completed their family. They surrounded him with many friends and extended family. Their house and yard were always abuzz with neighborhood children.

Stella Ann's world revolved around raising Landon and making their house a home. She met with carpenters, painters, and drapery makers. She wanted to transform the look of the house from avocado green and harvest gold into a lighter pallet of blue and white. At Bradford's insistence, she enlisted the help of a decorator at a national upscale furniture store to help her with the living room and dining room. Those rooms ended up looking like strawberry shortcake.

She decided her own choices were better and ignored further suggestions from Bradford about getting a decorator to help her finish the house. He told her often she did not have very elegant taste in decorating or fashion. A few years later, she met and enlisted the help of a decorator she trusted. She made it clear a pink, plastic doll dreamhouse was not a look she was interested in creating.

It was the sweetest period in her life. Playing with Landon and reading to him, even if he preferred chewing on the books rather than listening to the stories, was a joy. Stella Ann savored every moment of his development and was attentive to his needs but let him figure a lot out for himself. She was not a helicopter mom. She tried to be nurturing, alert, and involved. Candyland was their favorite board game, and building blocks were fun to crash. Cars and trucks were lined up, and anything resembling a ball was thrown. Trips to get hamburgers, have a picnic, and play in the park with Claire and Michael were regular and provided some great times and memories.

Bradford played with Landon at night and on his afternoons off. On the weekends, he would teach him how to hit a baseball and shoot hoops. Bradford offered to coach a T- ball team at their church when Landon was in kindergarten. It was a way he could do something he enjoyed, assure Landon and Michael a place on a team, and be actively involved with Landon's athletic development. Bradford failed to realize a competitive spirit and listening skills were not fine-tuned in five- and six-year-old little boys. All they wanted to do was hit or throw a ball and have fun. Some simply enjoyed picking clovers and chasing butterflies in the outfield. It was always an afternoon of parental laughter and fun but frustration for Bradford. He tried to do a job with an ever-wandering team. Stella Ann loved it.

By the time Landon started to kindergarten, Bradford pressured Stella Ann to go back to work, to pull her weight, contribute to the family, and get off her lazy ass as he articulated it. Stella Ann had anxiety attacks wondering how she was going to do it, but she made a call to Dr. Stafford, her former principal, in early spring to see if any positions were available for a "seasoned" teacher. He couldn't have been nicer. He didn't have any open positions but would keep her in mind.

Stella Ann made plans to update her teaching license which had expired. She needed to go back to school in person; distance learning was a thing of the future. Jenny, her sister-in-law, helped her locate a weeklong course she could take in June at Cumberland University in Lebanon, Tennessee, and Stella Ann applied to take a two-week course in July at Union University in Jackson, Tennessee. Together the two classes would enable her to earn the six credit hours she needed to reinstate her Tennessee teaching license. She would need to stay on campus for both classes and take Landon to stay with Burt and Lou to spend time with Conner. She would finish in time to apply for her license renewal and go back to work in August.

By the end of May, Stella Ann signed a one-year contract to teach kindergarten at her old school. She figured she could do anything for at least one year. It was exciting that she and Landon would be starting school together. Few parents got to see their child in such a light, but parenting was about to get more complicated for Stella Ann. She had to plan for childcare during in-service, faculty meetings, and conferences, as well as find transportation for Landon when there was an after-school birthday party or ball practice.

When she and Bradford decided Landon wasn't ready for all-day school, arrangements had to be made for someone to pick him up at noon and sit with him until Stella Ann or Bradford got home. The teaching part was easy. The parental responsibility was a challenge and, at times, heartbreaking. Stella Ann wanted to be the one to experience all the special events with Landon. She got no sympathy from Bradford. Bradford stepped in when he could, but children wanted their mom. Stella Ann did not realize before stepping back into the classroom exactly what she was going to miss as a mom, and it saddened her. Under pressure from Bradford, she signed a contract for another year. She didn't understand why he pressured her to continue to work. They didn't need the money. It gave her clarity he was making plans to leave, and she wondered when the next shoe was going to drop.

Landon was blessed with fabulous teachers throughout his elementary years. His first-grade teacher was loving, kind, and perceptive. She never hesitated to contact Stella Ann or Bradford when she was concerned about Landon. By the end of first grade, she talked with them about Landon falling asleep a lot during class. He ate well, went to bed at 8:00 p.m., and was healthy.

They checked with their pediatrician, who sent them to a neurologist. After many tests, Landon was diagnosed with childhood migraines. It would take him 24-48 hours to clear a headache. There was not much that could be done to help him beyond pediatric over-the-counter medicine and lots of tender loving care. Landon's headaches got progressively worse during second and third grade, and by sixth grade, Landon missed a lot of school. By the end of high school, he could anticipate a headache. He learned the triggers that set a headache in motion and managed them better.

Bradford's main form of exercise became jogging. Sometimes he ran twice a day, and weather patterns never deterred a run. Nothing stopped Bradford from running when and where he wanted. Stella Ann observed they were always late to functions because he had to run first. "Honestly," she said in a girlfriend conversation, "I think he will run before he attends my funeral." In the back of her mind, she thought, "Or would he even be there?"

Over the years, doctors told Bradford to stop running because he was damaging his legs and his back. He didn't listen and ended up having back surgery at thirty-six. It was a success, and recovery was swift. During Bradford's convalescence, Stella Ann took over all the lifting and heavy work around the house and continued to teach. Within weeks, Bradford was back at work.

On the last day of school, instead of attending her class picnic, Stella Ann was on the operating table with a herniated disk repair. The sciatic nerve pain was unbearable at times, and teaching elementary students required a lot of physical movement, stretching, standing, walking, bending, and kneeling. Stella Ann was no stranger to pain, but the added responsibilities compounded it. The stress was tremendous, and Lou and Burt came to help them get back on their feet and take care of Landon. Lou and Burt always came to their rescue. She and Bradford decided it was best for their family for Stella Ann to stop teaching until Landon was older.

Bradford's afternoon off was Wednesday, and baseball practices were scheduled then. He moved from coaching T-ball to coach pitch and then to regular baseball. Landon was a good player and had a lot of potential. He started out loving the game, and people from around the area came to see the little kid in red shoes defend first base and slam home runs. It was rare for a ball to get beyond him at first base. It was a joy to see Landon play but embarrassing to listen to Bradford's over-eager coaching directives he yelled at Landon and the team. They were kids and wanted to have fun.

It seemed each year Bradford became more and more intense coaching. He stayed up late talking to dads on the phone about plays and strategies and assessed what went right and wrong in a game. In Bradford's defense, when parents called to complain their child was not playing enough, he made sure they got more time. It was amazing to see adult jealousy surface during soccer, baseball, basketball, football, and other kids' sports. Stella Ann saw jealousy in parents as a mother, a teacher, and volunteer coach's wife. She was shunned at games.

She was not aware one of the reasons she was shunned was parental concern Bradford might not be in the right mindset before he worked with the kids. A friend and mom of a student Stella Ann had taught had an honest and difficult conversation with her over lunch one day. She revealed some parents suspected Bradford of having a drink either before or while coaching. Stella Ann confronted Bradford. He denied it and said the parents were jealous. As usual, Stella Ann supported his claim.

She decided to be more alert to Bradford's demeanor when he arrived at games or practice. She decided that Landon would always ride in the vehicle with her instead of with Bradford. She also took any players who needed a ride home after practice. She made sure no child rode in the vehicle with Bradford.

Life was good for the Tabers, and they became more involved in their neighborhood and church. They joined a country club to have a place for swimming, tennis, and social events. For the first time in a very long time, she belonged. She had a circle of friends and a family. She could go shopping and not worry about the price of an item, although she remained conservative about spending. It took years to carve out their dream life. They sacrificed a lot and worked very hard. She thought her life was exactly like it was supposed to be. She was not aware she would only have a few snippets of time to enjoy it.

Bradford was already home when she and Landon got home from school. They made one stop at the allergist's office for Landon to get his shot. Landon noticed a "for sale" sign in their front yard and pointed it out to Stella Ann.

Bradford was sitting at the kitchen table, smoking a cigarette and looking at some papers.

"Did you know there was a for sale sign in our front yard, Bradford?" Stella Ann asked. "The realtor must have made a mistake."

"No, he didn't make a mistake," Bradford said coolly. "I told him he could put it there."

"What? We only casually talked about moving when we had our back surgeries. We talked about the need for a bedroom on the first floor someday, but I had no idea you were ready to move now," Stella Ann said with dismay.

"Stella Ann, we will move when I say we will move. I found my dream house, and I plan to meet the realtor at the house in an hour."

"But Bradford, we haven't discussed this. How could you arrange to sell our home without talking with me? What prompted this?"

"I finished rounds early and rode to Lookout Mountain. I have always wanted to live there. I came across an older house for sale, called the realtor, and made an appointment to see the house this afternoon. The realtor said the price had been lowered, and the house needed a lot of updating and repairs. He also said the owners were anxious to sell. We could get a good deal. Do you know how hard it is to buy a house on Lookout Mountain, Stella Ann? People there don't sell, and the same families have been there for years. I didn't realize you and Landon would be home so soon, so you two can come with me to meet the realtor."

"Why did you let the realtor put a sign in our front yard without talking with me and before we looked at the house?"

"Look, Stella Ann, I make the money around here, and I will decide how we spend it," Bradford said on the brink of anger. "We owe it to ourselves to have a showplace. I signed a contract with the realtor to sell our house. He said he could get your signature on the agreement later. I told him it was OK to go ahead and put a sign up. It's no big deal."

"Bradford, you may have forgotten, but the reason you can make the money you make and have the career you have is because I helped you and stood by you. I am your wife. I have every right to question this decision."

The house was beautiful, gigantic, and needed updating. Stella Ann wondered how in the world she would clean it and manage another redecorating venture as well as a renovation. She loved the house they owned with all the changes they made, and she adored the neighborhood. It was only the three of them. Was a house this big necessary?

Landon would have a whole floor to himself to include a playroom at one end and a study at the other, an oversized bedroom with a video alcove, and his own bathroom. He was only eight years old. There were also two more bedrooms with en-suite bathrooms. Bradford made good money, but this seemed like a purchase beyond their means or needs. It was a time in their circle of peers of more is better and spend, spend, spend. To Stella Ann, it was a dangerous attitude.

Shortly after they looked at the house, Bradford decided to buy a new luxury sports car. He talked about it one day and drove up in it the next. He was dashing, with signs of gray peeking through his dark hair at the temples, and had a killer smile. He always looked nice in his clothes but changed his clothing style to a more casual look and stopped wearing ties. He was always picky about his clothes, and Stella Ann was required to iron his shirts perfectly. If they weren't perfect, he threw them on the closet floor. It was devastating to see how little concern he had for her efforts. Stella Ann sensed they were on the brink of the midlife crisis years. He took pride in how he looked, and she made the effort to make sure his closet was in order.

They moved into the new house in mid-December. Stella Ann wanted to get off the spend, spend, spend ride and rest, but there was too much to do. Stella Ann purchased, wrapped, and mailed the family Christmas presents. She made countless trips to the moving company warehouse to collect packing boxes. She planned a simple neighborhood Christmas gathering before they moved and invited the neighbors for pizza and cookie decorating.

It was a bittersweet time, but Stella Ann didn't have a minute to spare in the days leading up to the move. She didn't have time to be overwhelmed or depressed. She also couldn't believe they were moving into such a cavernous house. It was what Bradford wanted, and she always supported him. The house had to be presentable for a birthday party Stella Ann had planned for Bradford's fortieth birthday. She planned much of the party before they purchased the house. There was no turning back.

At a glance, the house was beautiful, but it was a hell zone and a money pit. Shortly after they moved in, the shower pan in the master bathroom overflowed and had to be replaced. They discovered water damage in the foyer, and the floor had to be repaired.

The fence was in ill repair and had to be fixed because they had two dogs to contain. Carbon monoxide was discovered leaking in the attic. The sky light in the master bathroom leaked, the dishwasher broke, the cooktop broke, and the furnace had a broken coil. Brown recluse spiders were all over the house, and they had to have the house tented twice.

Landon ended up with a bite on his head, which did not help his migraine headaches.

In the spring, Stella Ann walked through the dining room and saw white bugs flying and falling to the floor. They were everywhere. She had never seen anything like it. They had termites in the worst way. There was considerable damage to the front door frame, the bonnet at the top of the door, and the surrounding walls. The damage was in the thousands of dollars and not covered by insurance. The bills mounted. It felt like a veil of disaster shrouded the house.

The first weekend in December of the following year, they made their initial trip with another family to New York and loved it. They enjoyed the decorations, the Rockettes, the theater, and the restaurants. It helped to be with a family who knew New York well, and they had a son Landon's age.

Later in December, they had a huge Christmas party with live music, a bartender, and Santa Claus. Stella Ann knocked herself out making all the food, and again Lou and Burt came to help. Lou had a gift for decorating and helped her deck the halls. They lost count of the bows Lou made. The house was so big it sucked up ribbon.

The house looked festive, beautiful, and elegant, and Bradford and Stella Ann invited Bradford's family down for Christmas. Norma, Charles, her new husband, Grandpa, and Scott and his family came Christmas Eve. Grammie passed away of cancer in the spring. Liza and her family drove down Christmas Day. They brought Hank and Liza's mother-in-law. Alex and Charlotte and their two kids were at her parents' home in Columbia on Christmas Day. Bradford and Stella Ann wanted more than anything to host a lovely Christmas for his family, but all hell broke loose from the moment Scott and his family arrived on Christmas Eve. The more they fought and argued, the more Scott drank. The walls in the back hallway next to the kitchen and back stairwell were splattered with various drinks from the glasses they threw. Bradford and Scott ended up in a fist fight. Norma and her new husband tried to break up the fight while Stella Ann took Scott's baby upstairs to play with Landon.

The tax man came knocking on their door with some devastating news about their tax situation in the spring. Bradford and his partner hired an accounting firm that was, from all evidence, incompetent. Both faced some stiff tax bills. To add to the tax tensions, the company they hired to process their hospital collections did not code charges correctly. A lot of money was lost.

Both issues were out of Stella Ann's understanding or control. The old demons of depression were working on her big time. They experienced the high before the crash for a few years, and things began to crumble. Life was not supposed to be this way. Bradford always told Stella Ann not to worry because he would come out smelling like a rose; he always did.

Stella Ann thought medical school should include mandatory classes about how to set up and run a medical practice. Most doctors did not have a business mindset, and Bradford was the worst. All he wanted to do was practice medicine and spend money. The business aspect of the practice was not important to him. Stella Ann was also guilty of spending too much money to make their home beautiful, improve her wardrobe, indulge Landon, play tennis, and fit in.

All the house repairs were completed by the spring, the tax situation was turned over to an attorney, a medical lawsuit was settled, and Landon managed his headaches much better. They decided to rent a cabin in the mountains for spring break. They invited Burt and Lou to join them. Burt could make anyone laugh, and they all enjoyed the time away. Burt and Bradford developed a nice relationship over the years, and it lightened the atmosphere in most situations.

By the summer, Stella Ann landed flat on her back with no indication of how she hurt herself. She prayed rest and a little pampering could keep her out of the operating room. Landon stayed with Burt and Lou after they made a weekend visit to Columbia to attend a family reunion on the Fourth of July. It gave them some time with Landon, and he visited with his cousins. Stella Ann rested, took care of her back, and planned to return to Columbia to get him the following week. Getting in and out of bed was a struggle for her.

When it was time for Landon to return, driving or sitting for just a short time was difficult for Stella Ann, so Lou and Burt offered to bring him home. The plan was for them to come back to Chattanooga on Friday and stay the weekend. They planned to get to Chattanooga sometime after lunch to avoid Friday afternoon traffic. Before they arrived, Jenny called.

"I stopped at Burt and Lou's this morning to drop off some bread Mama made, and Burt was on the back porch. Stella Ann, I thought I should call you and let you know about a conversation we had before they left for Chattanooga."

"What did Burt tell you, Jenny?"

"As we were waiting for Lou and Landon, Burt said his arm didn't feel right, and he thought something was going on. He said it was hard for him to get a deep breath, and he was going to see if you could take him to Bradford's clinic when they got there. I suggested they postpone the trip and told him he should go to his doctor immediately. Of course, he refused," Jenny continued. "He also made me promise not to say anything to Lou. Honestly, I didn't know what to do."

"Does Ron know about this, Jenny?"

"No, he is out of town and scheduled to return later this afternoon."

"I will call Bradford and let him know. Thank you for letting me know about your conversation. We will be in touch."

Each minute that ticked by seemed like an hour. By 2 p.m., when they had not arrived, Stella Ann stood out in the middle of the street looking for them. She even thought about calling the highway patrol. Then Stella Ann let anger filter through. Her dad was driving under duress, and her child and mother were sitting ducks to possibly be injured in a car accident. Her heart started racing, and she called Bradford again.

"Stella Ann, as soon as they get to the house, put Burt in your car and bring him to the clinic. My staff and I will be waiting for you. Do not tell Lou or Landon anything. It is best to leave them at home for now," Bradford directed. "Call me, if they do not arrive within the hour."

She followed Bradford's directions when they finally arrived at 2:30 p.m.

"Stella Ann, we sure are glad to see you," Lou said. The place where we usually stop for lunch was busy and short staffed. We didn't think we would ever get our food."

Stella Ann reached to hug Landon, and then Lou and Burt.

"Mama, I need you and Landon to go on in the house and get settled. We can unload the car later. I need to take Daddy to the clinic. Bradford said he wanted to check his blood levels since Daddy told him he had been tired lately," Stella Ann said.

"We can go with you," Lou said.

"No, Mama, I need you to watch Landon, and Friday afternoon traffic is awful. I need to do the driving."

"But how is your back?" Lou asked.

"It is better, and I am fine to drive a short way. I will rest later." Truthfully, she was in agony, an agony set aside for more important things, her daddy's health.

Stella Ann turned to Burt who looked an ashen color, "Daddy, come on, let's get in the car."

For once, Burt did not do his "I am the boss" arguing with Stella Ann. They didn't talk, and she drove as quickly as she could to the clinic. She drove to the back entrance where Bradford and two nurses were there to help get Burt out of the car. They took him into a treatment room and immediately started an electrocardiogram on him. His blood pressure was at stroke level. Bradford gave him some pills and told him to sit in the room as he tried to get Burt's blood pressure down.

Bradford left the room to make some phone calls to cardiologists he knew and trusted to see Burt. What needed to be determined was whether Burt should be admitted to the hospital immediately. The decision was made for him to return to the house with Stella Ann and rest. More important decisions would be made when more information was gathered. Telling Lou the results when they got back home was going to be a challenge. She would have ten thousand questions to ask with no immediate answers available.

The following Monday, Stella Ann took Burt to the cardiologist for tests. One test led to another; they went for tests for three days. Lou stayed at the house and kept Landon. Tests revealed Burt had four blockages and would need surgery. Doctors were amazed he drove from Columbia to Chattanooga without a heart attack. It was also determined it was dangerous to try to transport him to Nashville. Chattanooga had some of the premier heart surgeons in the country. A lot of decisions had to be made. Bradford was direct and knowledgeable as he explained the results of the tests and what Burt needed. He made it clear he had to remove himself as much as possible from the case. There was a huge conflict of interest, and Burt meant the world to him and the family.

Burt's surgery was scheduled for July 15. Heart surgery was serious but had become a routine surgery over the years. Doctors explained the patient usually returned home within a few days to recover. They also explained everyone should be back in Columbia within ten days. The professional opinion of the attending doctors was that the surgery should be done in Chattanooga. Ron, Jenny, and Conner came and brought enough clothes to stay until Burt was released to go home. Jenny's mother sent a mountain of fresh vegetables from her garden, homemade sour dough bread, strawberry jam, and a couple of pies.

Stella Ann flew through life on blind trust. It was a flaw or gift depending on one's perspective born from lack of experience and a sheltered life. In her narrow little world and with huge faith, she felt everything would work out. Burt was the family rock. They stayed in the hospital waiting room during the surgery, and the doctors and nurses in the operating room updated them continuously about their progress and Burt's condition. When the surgery was over, doctors advised the family to go home, get some rest, and return the next day ready to see Burt. They went home to have grilled hamburgers, chips, and pie.

Bradford called the ICU every hour to check on Burt. Each time, the report was Burt had not awakened from anesthesia. Stella Ann could tell by his facial expressions, Bradford was concerned. What could have happened? The family made sure the doctors and hospital knew Burt did not respond well to anesthesia and only a little was necessary.

Friends from the old neighborhood helped by taking Landon and Conner swimming, to a movie, or to play with their kids on a rotating basis. They were invited for a sleepover, but the boys wanted to be with the family at night.

It was three days before Burt woke up from the anesthesia. He coded and was put on a respirator. His recovery was a roller coaster ride. One day he would be better and then take a nosedive. The family was told many times he would be moved to a regular room, and it would quickly change for him to stay longer in ICU.

Family and friends from home realized the gravity of the situation and started making trips to Chattanooga to be supportive of the family. For the first time, Stella Ann was grateful they had a house big enough to accommodate all the visitors. Stella Ann felt all she did was go to the grocery and the hospital even though she tried very hard to maintain a normal life and schedule for Landon. Many days, breakfast was a selection of ten or twelve egg sandwiches from a fast-food chain and fruit. Stella Ann never knew how many people would be in the house and need breakfast.

Ron, Jenny, and Conner stayed with them for weeks, and they alternated visitation at the hospital. Lou never left during the day. She could only see Burt three times a day, and she sat in the waiting room day after day until they would let her in for a visit. Burt never knew she was there. She would hold his hand and talk and talk and talk. The whole family became fixtures in the hospital chapel. One of them could be found there at most any time of the day except Lou. She would not budge from Burt's side.

Stella Ann was in a very difficult position. The number of people coming each day was overwhelming, and she was trying to keep things normal. Bradford would get snippy and agitated because he felt his home had been invaded, and he had no control or privacy. The privacy issue included his secret in the garage. Special phone calls late at night were also interrupted. Bradford turned on her with verbal attacks which became meaner each time. He would unleash on her in front of family or friends, which was humiliating but excused because of the pressure the family was under. Fortunately, he controlled his physical attacks. Stella Ann felt like she was a whipping girl.

"Stella Ann, drop your mother off at the hospital entrance. You don't need to come in with her. I don't want people to know you are my wife. You dress in baggy clothes, and you have gotten fat. I told you years ago to never gain weight because I could never love a fat person."

"Bradford, I am sorry you are embarrassed for people to know who I am, but fashion and dieting is the last thing on my mind right now. Our family is in a crisis, and I am doing the best I can," Stella Ann said apologetically.

"Stella Ann, you make excuses all the time for letting yourself go. The lack of pride you have in yourself is disgusting," Bradford said.

Stella Ann locked herself in the bathroom, turned on the shower and vent fan, and cried so hard she started heaving. She weighed 135 pounds and wore a size ten. He thought she was fat. Sure, she had gained weight over the years, but obese was not a word to describe Stella Ann. It was as if he was always looking for and verbalizing anything he didn't like about her to make her feel inferior. And he did it in front of friends and family.

He might as well have slapped her, and gut punched her at the same time. Her stress levels were off the charts and looking like a fashion queen was the last thing on her mind. No one thought for a second the outcome of Burt's surgery would be so disastrous. Her father was fighting for his life. He coded twice, and they planned his funeral twice during the ordeal. What really happened in the operating room?

Ron, Jenny, and Conner went back to Columbia as summer was winding down. School was starting. Jenny taught second grade, and Conner was in middle school. They promised to return Labor Day weekend and insisted Bradford, Landon, and Stella Ann take the weekend off to go to the lake.

Two vacations had already been scrapped because Burt took a turn for the worse each time. They were scheduled to go to Sullivan's Island with Ron, Jenny, and Conner in late July, but it didn't happen. A friend offered them use of his condominium in Orange Beach, Alabama, in August, which was also cancelled.

Before Open House, students were given the assignment to draw a picture showing what they did over the summer. Amid drawings of camp, vacations, parties, and ball games, Bradford and Stella Ann saw Landon's drawing. It was his interpretation of the hospital waiting room that included green chairs, vending machines, and family members lining the wall. Bradford and Stella Ann felt awful for Landon.

Ron, Jenny, and Conner were a tremendous help to Stella Ann as she tried to keep a somewhat normal routine. They were a positive support, especially to Lou. When Lou wasn't washing or ironing, Jenny took over the laundry duties. They made the best of the living conditions, and schedules were horrific. All pitched in to keep the house in order, laundry updated, and meals prepared. Bradford kept the yard looking nice and well-manicured.

Ron and Stella Ann took turns sitting overnight at the hospital with Burt. It seemed every time it was Stella Ann's turn to sit with Burt, he took a turn for the worse. Ron and Jenny were supportive without judgment, and Stella Ann knew the bulk of the responsibility would be on her shoulders when they left. Ron would come back to Chattanooga when he could, but his job took him out of town a lot. It was sad when they pulled out of the driveway loaded with luggage, boxes, hanging clothes, and a new puppy. Bradford felt sorry for the boys and bought each a new puppy. The gesture was genuine, but it was like having two new babies added to the list of responsibilities already at capacity.

Landon was scheduled to go back to school, and Lou had to be driven twice a day to the hospital to see Burt. It was decided Lou would ride to the hospital with Bradford each day with a sack lunch in hand. Stella Ann would take Landon to school and then go to the hospital to sit with Lou. She would stay until time to pick Landon up from school and take him to ball practice. Then, she would return to the hospital to pick Lou up and drive back to the ball field to pick Landon up and go home. Thank goodness friends, neighbors, church members, colleagues, and visiting family members kept hot meals available. There was little time for cooking.

Burt's recovery was progressing rapidly by mid-September, and he was able to return to Stella Ann and Bradford's house to recover and build enough strength to return to Columbia. The time in the hospital was stressful, but no one was prepared for home recovery. The first obstacle was getting Burt up a huge flight of stairs to the bedroom and bath he and Lou shared. It was an open stairwell, and they held their breath the medics did not drop him over the banister to the ground floor. Once he was settled and took a nap, the phone calls from home healthcare workers, physical therapists, speech therapists, dietitians, visiting nurses, family, and friends were endless and exhausting. They stopped locking the front door and put a sign on the door for helpers to come in, go up the front stairs, and turn to the right to get to Burt's room.

Bradford described the situation very bluntly when he said we brought a dead man home to revive. Stella Ann thought Bradford harsh, but as the days unfolded into weeks, she understood Bradford's description. She remembered the arduous process of her own recovery experience years earlier.

The bulk of the nursing landed on Lou. Stella Ann had never seen such a strong determined will in her mother. She also saw anger and hurt. Stella Ann wanted to make things better for Lou, but she didn't know how. Lou was inconsolable, out of her comfort zone, and scared. Lou focused totally on Burt and even shut down any conversation with others. Lou wanted to get home to Columbia as quickly as possible. She was willing to work hard and do whatever it took to push the process along. She wanted life like it was prior to the operation. She was in denial but deep down knew their life would never be like it was before the operation.

From Stella Ann's perspective, nothing was going to be all right. Stella Ann believed her daddy's situation was all her fault. If she had made the trip to Columbia to get Landon, she believed nothing like this would have happened to their family. Stella Ann was riddled with guilt and was wedged between saving her marriage and honoring and supporting her parents. She needed her brother. Ron and Jenny were consistently supportive and nonjudgmental during the whole ordeal.

By early November, doctors gave Burt permission to make the trip home to Columbia. He was better, not well. Home healthcare was lined up as well as doctors' appointments and physical therapy. Ron and several of Burt's friends came to Chattanooga to help Burt and Lou make the journey home. Jenny and other family members made sure the house was clean and food was in the refrigerator. They moved a new bed to the middle bedroom for Burt and freshened the sheets in the main bedroom for Lou.

Ron drove his truck, a friend drove Burt's car, and Lou and Burt rode in the car with Stella Ann as they caravanned to Middle Tennessee. They stopped for lunch at a familiar restaurant and again for a bathroom break. It was the first time Burt had been in a restaurant in months. He was as excited as a child to get coffee and a hamburger.

When they arrived home, they had a welcome crew holding signs and cheering for them as they pulled into the driveway, but Burt was exhausted. They got him into bed and quickly unloaded the car and truck. Stella Ann was going to stay through the weekend while Bradford and Landon stayed in Chattanooga. Bradford did not decline to make the trip; he refused to come with them.

Like Stella Ann, he harbored guilt and didn't want to answer any questions from hometown relatives. Bradford knew a lot more about Burt's case than he told anyone. Stella Ann knew it but did not pressure him for information. She didn't want to know.

CHAPTER 10

Revelations

When Stella Ann got back from Columbia after an emotional trip to take her parents home, she entered a quiet house. She didn't recognize the house as her home at all and could not bring herself to stay. Bradford was making rounds at the hospital, and Landon was with Claire's family. She needed to see her son and went to Claire's to pick him up. It was difficult to hold back the tears when she saw Landon and hugged him, not wanting to let go.

Claire assured Stella Ann he had a good time, and they enjoyed having him at their home for the weekend. Landon always loved staying at Claire's house, and her kids were like his siblings rather than friends. It was a lot to ask her to keep Landon since Claire and her family had moved across the street from her parents to take care of her mother. Claire had more than enough responsibilities on her plate.

Stella Ann was cleaning out the refrigerator, and Landon was upstairs doing homework when Bradford got home from making rounds. He got a drink, lit a cigarette, and sat at the kitchen table. He didn't ask about her trip home but informed Stella Ann he would be off for the Thanksgiving weekend.

"Stella Ann, I have been thinking about the stress we have been under the last few months and the two vacations we had to cancel over the summer. Would you like to go somewhere for Thanksgiving?" Bradford asked. "It would give us a chance to get away, and you wouldn't have to cook a huge Thanksgiving dinner."

Stella Ann was appreciative as well as excited. Bradford could be perceptive, thoughtful, and kind. "Bradford, I love that idea, but where would we go? We have our family trip to New York City the weekend after Thanksgiving. Would we still be able to go?"

"We could still go to New York with our friends. We need to decide what we want to do and where we want to go for Thanksgiving and make plans."

"Bradford, I have always wanted to go to Williamsburg and Richmond. Could we go there?" Stella Ann asked.

"I was thinking more like Charleston or somewhere in Florida, Stella Ann, but Williamsburg would be OK. It might be a good learning experience for Landon," Bradford said.

"So, Williamsburg would work for you, Bradford?" Stella Ann asked.

"Sure, start making calls and plans tomorrow. Let's leave on Tuesday before Thanksgiving," Bradford directed. "I have time off I haven't used yet."

"Thank you so much, Bradford," Stella Ann said with tears in her eyes. "It will be good for our family to get away and spend a special holiday together."

The next day, Stella Ann called a colleague who had visited Williamsburg often to get ideas and suggestions about hotels and restaurants.

Stella Ann worked diligently to make sure they had hotel and restaurant reservations for the duration of their trip as well as car rentals. They were going to start in Richmond and stay at the Jefferson Hotel then drive to Williamsburg where they would stay in the historic district. The Williamsburg Inn was full, which was disappointing, but they planned the trip at the last minute.

She tried to put her grief over the family nightmare the previous summer aside to focus on the trip and make sure their time together was perfect. She carefully packed a suitcase for each of them. She didn't want anything to upset Bradford on the trip. She prayed their trip would be good family time they so desperately needed.

The excitement of the trip was stifled when they got horrible news about one of their best friends. Will was an attorney who had written Lou and Burt's will while they were in Chattanooga. He was Bradford and Stella Ann's next-door neighbor in their old neighborhood. He had three sons and a sweet pretty wife. Will was without a car because one of his sons totaled his. Bradford trusted Will and let him borrow their silver Cutlass until he could afford a car.

Will often came to their house on the way home from his office. He and Bradford hung out on the deck and smoked cigars, laughed, and told jokes. Will didn't drink. He shared limited information with Bradford and Stella Ann about a client, a friend from his hometown in Arkansas who was remotely connected to a high-profile national case. Will thought he was being followed and returned their car. He got a car from a client who had a dealership in Little Rock. Stella Ann and Bradford thought it was odd Will had clients in Arkansas but didn't question him about it.

Within a week, Will was dead. He was driving his wife's green Camaro on the backroads around Monterey, Tennessee after a visit to see his brother. It was determined he fell asleep and ran off the road, but with the information Will told Bradford and Stella Ann before he died, it was more like someone ran him off the road. The truth would never be known. It was horrible. Could the year get any worse?

When they got home from the funeral, Bradford received a phone call from an anonymous source who identified himself with the highway patrol. The person asked if the car and license number he described belonged to him, and Bradford confirmed it. The man told Bradford not to drive the car, to get the car out of his possession and out of town if possible. He indicated there was reason to believe it was targeted, and he could not disclose further information.

"Just get that car out of Chattanooga," he demanded.

The next day, Bradford enlisted the help of a friend who owned a car dealership in Chattanooga to take the car to the used car auction in Nashville. By noon, the car was gone. There was never an investigation into Will's death.

Will's wife gave Bradford his Bible and Stella Ann his Waterman pen. His wife said," Will always thought you would be a great attorney someday. Stella Ann, I hope you can use this on legal documents you draft." Many years later Stella Ann gave the pen to Landon when he graduated from law school.

It was a long time before Bradford and Stella Ann reconciled the death of their treasured friend. His death made no sense yet opened a lot of political and scandalous questions of which they would never learn answers.

As they got ready for the trip to Williamsburg, Stella Ann gave Landon some reminders.

"Landon, we are going to Richmond and Williamsburg. I want you to have a good time. You know the importance of the area in our country's history. You have seen pictures of many things you will see and things we will do while we are there. We will be staying in nice places and will be eating in nice restaurants. Your father was generous to offer us this time away from Chattanooga for a few days before we go to New York."

"Mom," Landon said, "Will we get to order dessert?"

"Landon, we might get to order dessert for a few meals, but you know how your father is about us ordering dessert," Stella Ann answered.

"Mom, why doesn't Dad like for us to order dessert?" Landon asked.

"Landon, your father is very conscientious about health and body image. He does not want us to get fat or eat too much sugar. Unfortunately, getting fat has already happened to me. I gained a lot of weight eating the good food friends brought for us when your Granddaddy Burt was sick. If your dad is in a good mood, he will let us get dessert, but it is best not to make a big deal about it."

"Well, at least he might let us have dessert on Thanksgiving Day," Landon responded.

Their flight left on Tuesday night. From the moment they loaded the car, Bradford seemed tense and angry about something. Maybe something happened at work he would share later. When he was in a bad mood, it was not worth going anywhere. It took a while for Bradford to work through what was bothering him. Stella Ann wished they were staying

200

home. Asking questions made things worse, so she warned Landon to stay very quiet on the way to the airport.

When Bradford was in a testy mood, it was usually directed toward Stella Ann. She wanted to make sure Landon was not a target for Bradford's anger. Stella Ann got the impression from Bradford's condescending remarks about her weight and fashion style, he loathed her and didn't want to be seen with her. She was certain she had done nothing since he got home to make him angry.

Their flight was somewhat turbulent, and they were happy when they landed in Richmond. The Jefferson Hotel was beautiful much like The Read House in Chattanooga. They were tired when they arrived and went to bed immediately. The next day, Bradford and Landon walked down the street to the YMCA to work out while Stella Ann got dressed for the day. It was sunny and brisk, so it would be a good day to see the city and visit historic sites. They ate lunch at The Jefferson Hotel and visited St. John's Church, where Patrick Henry gave his "give me liberty or give me death" speech. They drove to Williamsburg in silence. Bradford was quiet and snapped when addressed. Landon and Stella Ann tried to remain silent.

When they got to the hotel in Williamsburg, Bradford was so angry he threw their luggage across the parking lot. Stella Ann ran to get a luggage trolley in the lobby. She always tried to make things better and defuse Bradford's anger. She was in a constant state of fixing. Their room was on the first floor, so luggage management was easier. There was a pool in the hotel if Landon wanted to swim. She had packed his and Bradford's swimsuits. She left hers at home since she no longer had the confidence to wear one.

They went to lunch and walked the streets of historic Williamsburg, where Stella Ann bought a few Christmas tree ornaments to commemorate their trip. Stella Ann hoped the next day would be better. It was Thanksgiving, and they had many reasons to be grateful.

While Bradford ran the next morning, Stella Ann and Landon watched the Macy's Day Parade on tv and got ready for their Thanksgiving dinner at the Cascades Restaurant.

Before they left for dinner, there was an overblown fight about Landon's new dog.

Stella Ann asked, "Bradford, do you know if the new dog's papers are in your truck? I could not find them at the house when I took the dogs to the kennel. If you don't have the papers, I can take her to the vet when we return and get the appropriate paperwork for the stay next weekend. The kennel accepted her since we have been long time customers, but they need papers on the new dog before we go to New York."

Bradford was furious Stella Ann mentioned paperwork as they were leaving for dinner.

"Stella Ann, don't you know I have better things to think about than the papers for a stupid dog? Why did you mention this now?"

"I am sorry. It crossed my mind, and since we had a little time before dinner, I thought we could discuss it."

"If you can get papers from the vet, why bother me? You know how busy I am."

"Bradford, I thought you could look in your truck since you went to get her."

"A lot has happened since then, Stella Ann. Can't you even take care of the dogs?"

"Of course, I can, Bradford. Forget I said anything."

Thanksgiving dinner was silent, but they did get to order dessert because it came with the meal. Later, they caught the bus and went to the historic area to the Governor's Palace and Wythe House. They decided they were so full from their huge Thanksgiving dinner they were not hungry for supper. A few snacks held them until breakfast.

The next day was filled with more sightseeing, shopping, and a ghost tour. On Saturday, they spent the day in Jamestown learning about John Clark, John Rolfe, and Pocahontas. Then they went to Yorktown where Landon got to see a real cannon fired. They made a quick stop at the Williamsburg Pottery shop where Stella Ann bought a sugar spout. Stella Ann loved pottery and was getting quite a nice collection. Before they got to Jamestown, they stopped at an antique bookstore, and Bradford bought several books that were real treasures. Bradford loved old books and knew the value of the ones he purchased. Their shopping spree in the bookstore was a few moments during the trip he seemed happy.

Saturday night, they had dinner at The Williamsburg Inn Restaurant. The meal was fabulous as well as the service. Bradford was enjoying the experience until the bill arrived. He made a comment about canceling their New York trip scheduled for the following weekend. Stella Ann could not tell if he was kidding or if he was genuinely angry. On the walk back to the hotel, Stella Ann asked if she could go into a pewter shop. She saw some Jefferson cups she wanted to price. She bought eight cups. Bradford told her it was fine, but when they got back to the hotel, he came unglued. He bashed her for buying souvenirs, for gaining weight, for eating too much, and for random characteristics he didn't like about her. What hurt more than anything was he did it in front of Landon. His verbal loathing of her crushed Stella Ann.

Packing to leave the next morning was stressful. Bradford was known for packing and repacking a car many times before he was satisfied with the way luggage fit in the trunk. By his third time arranging the luggage, he was throwing bags across the parking lot and cursing Stella Ann. It was very embarrassing to Stella Ann and scary to Landon, but he had learned from his mother to let Bradford's anger fit play out.

They had breakfast at a wonderful quaint restaurant and made their way to Richmond to catch their flight back to Chattanooga. They had a three hour wait, and the weather was bad. Storms were coming into the Detroit area through North and South Dakota, and many flights were canceled. Their flight was routed through Detroit, so it was uncertain when they might get home.

Three days before their trip to New York, Sandy, a friend they were traveling with along with her husband and son, called to see if they wanted theater tickets to "Phantom of the Opera." Stella Ann knew Bradford wanted to see the production again and asked Sandy to get them three tickets next to them if they were available. She told Bradford about it when he got home from work, and he nodded approval.

Bradford stopped in the kitchen doorway and said his receptionist was having a difficult time financially and couldn't buy her little boy any Santa Claus presents for Christmas. Stella Ann told him to get a list, and she would go shopping for what the child wanted. He also asked if Stella Ann minded if he gave her an extra $500 for Christmas to which Stella Ann agreed. Stella Ann never thought anything other than they were helping someone going through a hard time.

They were scheduled to leave early Friday afternoon for New York City. Wednesday night, Bradford woke Stella Ann from a deep sleep screaming at her about a phone call. At first, she thought it was a call he had taken from a patient or the hospital until she was more awake.

"Stella Ann, Sandy called about the theater tickets she got for us, and they are $150 each. Are you out of your stupid mind to approve that price?"

"Bradford, you said you wanted theater tickets, so I asked her to get us three."

He was furious, and his face was beet red. He was biting his tongue and clinching his fists.

"Please calm down, Bradford. Don't wake Landon. We can call Sandy tomorrow and see if we can cancel our tickets. Bradford, we paid that amount and more for a performance in the past. I don't understand why you are so angry."

Bradford grabbed her arm, pulled her out of bed, and dragged her by her nightgown to the foyer. He physically threw Stella Ann out of the house through the front door with no shoes and no coat. Then he yelled some obscenity and threw her car keys and purse at her as she lay in the cold front yard crying.

It was not the first time he had done this to her. Stella Ann thought about going to the police station because of his rage and her fear he would hurt Landon. He had never hurt Landon when he was mad at her, but there was always the potential for a first time. She couldn't go to the neighbors. Bradford's anger was one reason she kept a distance and low profile in the neighborhood. She would wave and smile but resisted becoming friends with the ladies. She was too embarrassed about what they might discover about the life they led. She was always protecting Bradford.

Instead of seeking help, she got in her car to warm up and think things through. She would not leave, and she was not going to try to get into the house until Bradford fell asleep. She had beach towels in the garage and covered herself with a couple of them and fell asleep on the back seat.

She awakened early and was able to get into the house through the kitchen door that led to the garage. She went up the back steps to Landon's room to check on him and stayed upstairs until she heard Bradford's car leave. After she dropped Landon off at school, she went shopping for toys from the list Bradford's receptionist sent her. She thought it was something she could do to put Bradford in a better mood. When Bradford got home from work, he acted like nothing had happened. He probably didn't even remember throwing her out of the house into the cold night.

Their flight was set for 3 p.m., which would get them to New York City in time to check in, have dinner, and get to the theater. Stella Ann was going to pick Landon up from school early to save time getting to the airport. She didn't have the excitement for the trip like she did the year before. Their disastrous trip to Williamsburg, and the tantrum over theater tickets dampened her spirits. She made up her mind to make sure Landon had fun even if it meant she had to walk on broken glass.

When they arrived in New York, Jim, Sandy's husband, suggested the men get the luggage, and the women secure a limousine and watch the boys. Sandy couldn't do much because she was recovering from knee surgery and was using crutches. Stella Ann got the boys and Sandy into the limo and walked to the back of the limo to see if Jim needed any help. She didn't see Bradford anywhere.

"Where is Bradford?" she asked.

"I don't know. He walked off as I headed to the limo with the luggage. He went to smoke a cigarette," Jim said. "Will you help me count the luggage? How many pieces did you all have?"

"We had three small suitcases and a small black toiletry and cosmetics bag," Stella Ann replied.

"Hmm, I don't see the small bag, Stella Ann. We will contact the airlines. When they locate it, they will deliver it to the hotel. It will probably be here by the time we get back from the theater. We need to get moving, or we will get caught up in horrible traffic."

"I am sure we can get some toiletry replacements at the hotel desk until the bag is delivered," Stella Ann said. "Do you see Bradford anywhere?"

"Over there, by the side of the building" he said as he pointed beyond the line of limos. "I see him coming now."

When Bradford got into the limo, he said nothing. Jim explained the missing bag and told Bradford he had called the airline about it. Bradford didn't respond.

There was no conversation all the way to the St. Moritz Hotel where they were staying.

The lobby was bustling with people checking in and trying to get to the theater or to dinner reservations on time. Because of the crowd, it took a long time to process their reservations. As they stood in line, Bradford's body language became more and more tense. Stella Ann made the mistake of suggesting he tell the clerk they were expecting a bag from the airline. He blew up.

"If you hadn't been such a lazy assed bitch and had counted our bags correctly, this wouldn't have happened."

"Bradford, please not now, not here. It is just a bag, and the loss had nothing to do with my counting ability. We can get what we need from the desk clerk. I was watching the kids and helping Sandy into the limo. Did you have to go smoke a cigarette when we were trying to get to the hotel?"

"Get away from me, bitch. I will handle this, and he threw his wallet at her. All you want is money anyway. Here take it."

People in line started backing away from them. She collected the wallet from the floor and walked off. Landon was with Sandy and Jonathan in the sitting area of the lobby.

Jim finished checking in and told Stella Ann the airline had located the bag and would deliver it to the hotel within the hour.

They got to their rooms and were able to take a breather before getting ready for dinner. Landon was invited to stay with Jonathan to play card games. Stella Ann noticed the roll away bed for Landon had not been delivered, so she called housekeeping. It was promptly delivered, and Stella Ann asked Bradford if he had a few dollar bills to tip the bellhop.

He was still fuming, picked up his wallet, and threw it at her again. He called her a few choice names and said again all she wanted was money. The leather wallet hit her face hard leaving a red square on her cheek and tears in her eyes. She quickly gave the young man a few dollars and thanked him.

She asked if Bradford needed the bathroom before she freshened up for dinner. As she came out of the bathroom, he was still holding his wallet and was sitting in the chair in the corner of the room drinking a glass of wine. She changed into a winter white sweater and slacks and added pearl earrings she received for their tenth anniversary and a pearl and diamond cocktail ring Bradford gave her before a hospital fund raiser.

She sat down on the bed to read. Bradford came out of the bathroom angry and made an unnecessary mean remark about Stella Ann leaving her makeup bag on the bathroom counter. When she went into the bathroom to move the bag, Bradford picked her up and threw her against the roll away bed. Her pants hung on a spring and ripped. It all happened about the time Jim showed up to see if they were ready for dinner. Bradford picked Stella Ann up again and threw her on the bed. Thank goodness Jim showed up when he did. He pulled Bradford off Stella Ann and encouraged him to settle down. Stella Ann was grateful for Jim's presence and for the fact Landon was in their room playing with Jonathan. Stella Ann's leg was bleeding, so she cleaned the wound and changed into her black pants.

At dinner, she made the comment that all the selections on the menu looked so good it was hard to decide on an entrée.

Bradford announced at the table and in front of the waiter, "Hell, she doesn't need anything for dinner. She is fat enough as it is."

There was an embarrassing silence at the table. Even the kids got quiet. Stella Ann ordered a salad and fish, and a tear slid down her cheek. It wouldn't have been any different if she had been a hundred pounds overweight rather than ten. Obviously, everything about her disgusted him. Was his contempt for her recent or had he always felt that way about her and held it in? There was very little table talk after Bradford's cruel announcement. It was sad and awkward that he never realized how ridiculous he sounded and acted like nothing had happened.

They walked to the theater, and Bradford walked ahead to smoke a cigarette and get away from them. Sandy noticed it.

"Stella Ann, what is going on with Bradford? He seems so different and distant."

"Sandy, I don't know, but the unusual stress we experienced over these last few months with Daddy being ill and having so much company was difficult. He is having a delayed meltdown." Again, Stella Ann covered for Bradford's behavior.

"That is understandable, Stella Ann, but a grown man does not treat his wife and child the way he is treating you and Landon. Has he always said mean things in public to you?"

"Sandy, he can be generous, complimentary, patient, and kind, and when he snaps, it is best for me to keep my distance until he works through the issue. He doesn't talk much about his feelings, but he has been yelling a lot lately. I have been walking on eggshells."

"Stella Ann, if you ever need anything, call Jim or me. I can't do much alone, but we can get you some help."

"Thank you, Sandy. I appreciate it and hope this conversation will remain between us."

"Stella Ann, actions speak volumes."

The rest of the weekend included more excuses from Stella Ann about Bradford's behavior. Stella Ann made sure Landon enjoyed the Christmas decorations and all the fun things they could fit into their schedule. Jim made reservations for the boys to make Christmas tree ornaments at the American Museum of Natural History. They also had a great time looking at the exhibits. A trip to New York City was not complete without a trip to Times Square and to FAO Swartz toy store. They topped off a great afternoon at the candy store where the boys had fun picking out their $20 limit of candy. Dinner was at Carmine's where they had a family style Italian feast and a divine chocolate dessert.

After an elegant brunch at Tavern on the Green the next day, they left for the airport. Despite the tension between them all weekend, Stella Ann made the best of the situation. She simply could not figure out what was going on with Bradford. It had to be more than the family situation they had experienced during the summer. Why did he hate her so much?

On Monday, Stella Ann returned a pair of pants with a broken zipper. She was waiting on the saleslady to check on another pair and saw Bradford across the store at the perfume counter. Stella Ann froze in disbelief.

She said to the saleslady, "Oh, my goodness, my husband is at the perfume counter. He never shops. He should still be at the office."

The lady responded, "Maybe he is getting you a Christmas surprise."

"No, ma'am, he is the one who is getting a surprise. I will be back to get the pants."

Stella Ann walked up to the perfume counter, and Bradford was so deep in thought he didn't see her. She got closer to him and asked what perfume he was buying. He looked shocked like a child getting caught eating cookies before dinner.

"Kristy is having a very hard time, and she mentioned this designer perfume. I thought I would get her a bottle as a surprise and you a bottle for the way I behaved in New York. I don't know what got into me."

"No, thank you, Bradford. I don't care for that perfume. It smells cheap. I am going to finish my exchange and pick Landon up from school." Stella Ann knew nothing about the fragrance but was certain she did not want to smell like his receptionist.

Stella Ann got to the car, put her head on the steering wheel, and took a deep breath. She knew the problem now. She could define it in one word, Kristy.

Stella Ann sat the toys she purchased for Kristy's little boy at the back door. She and Landon ate early, and she left a plate on the counter for Bradford. Nothing was mentioned about their encounter at the department store, but Bradford purchased a bottle of the same perfume he bought Kristy for Stella Ann, even though she had declined it. He left it on the kitchen counter.

The next day when Bradford came home, he barely spoke and poured a drink. Stella Ann was plating the spaghetti she had made for dinner. Landon had already eaten and had gone upstairs to study. Bradford sat at the table and lit a cigarette. Stella Ann hated for him to smoke in the house.

"Stella Ann, "I am moving out after Christmas. I am not happy. I have no feelings for you. I don't hate you, but I don't love you. I am indifferent toward you, and I want out."

There was nothing she could say, but she had a strong urge to throw the pot of spaghetti at him and destroy the pristine blue oxford cloth shirt he wore. She left the room. The decision was made. What selfish arrogance she thought! He was indifferent. She went upstairs to the study to think. She was too distraught and hurt to cry.

There was one thing for certain; telling someone you were indifferent toward them was one of the cruelest things you could say to them. How could someone feel indifferent toward someone with whom they had shared so much and built a life? Bradford didn't care if Stella Ann lived or died. She reflected on a character in a book she loved. She understood the character, Mafatu, in Armstrong Sperry's book, *Call It Courage*, even more. His tribe was indifferent toward him because he was afraid of water after his mother died in a storm. Stella Ann was in a storm of her own. After over twenty years together, she received the gift of indifference from her husband. The next day Stella Ann moved to an upstairs bedroom.

The following weekend, Stella Ann and Landon went to Columbia to deliver the family Christmas presents. Bradford was on call for most of Christmas, and they would not be able to be with the family. It was going to be difficult to stay in Chattanooga for Christmas, but Stella Ann wanted things to be as calm and normal as possible for Landon.

While Stella Ann and Landon were in Columbia, Norma called. Stella Ann thought Norma had mellowed over the years, and her new husband offered her stability and happiness.

"Stella Ann, I need to talk with you about Bradford. When are you going back to Chattanooga? Bradford told me you and Landon were in Columbia delivering Christmas presents. Can you talk now?"

"Norma, we will be home Sunday. Landon still has a week of school left, as well as his Christmas program, but we are staying in Chattanooga for Christmas. How is everyone at the lake?"

Stella Ann and Norma had gotten to a level of cordial friendship each enjoyed, but it would be a long time before complete forgiveness would kick in.

"We are doing fine. Stella Ann, I want you to go buy the prettiest, sexiest cocktail dress you can find in Nashville and make plans to attend the hospital Christmas party on Friday night."

"Norma, things aren't very good between Bradford and me right now. Bradford said he wanted to go to the party alone."

"Stella Ann, I had to take Grandpa to Bradford's office yesterday, and I didn't like what I saw. Kristy had her hands all over Bradford. She was going through his desk drawers and looking at the Christmas gifts from patients and other doctors on his desk. I don't think she knew I was Bradford's mother."

"Norma, I think Kristy has had her hands in a lot of places for a long time. Bradford has not been himself and told me he was leaving Landon and me after Christmas."

"He said what?" Norma screamed. "Let me tell you something, Stella Ann, he is at the age where men have a midlife crisis, and he is going to make a huge mistake. All he wants is for someone to tell him he is handsome, brilliant, and wonderful, and he will promise them the moon. You have to doll yourself up and go to the hospital party. Promise me you will?"

"I promise I will make an effort to get a dress and show up at the party, but I don't think much will change, Norma."

Stella Ann made plans to go shopping the next day. She purchased a beautiful red sheath dress with a diagonal neckline and new heels. It was a classy, understated look and made her look slimmer. Going to the hospital party would give her the opportunity to wear the three pieces of ruby and diamond jewelry Norma gave her from her collection the year before.

She went to the party. She wished she hadn't. Bradford didn't sit with her or acknowledge her. She sat with the office staff and nurses from the clinic. She liked all the ladies but would have preferred being with her husband. Bradford blew her off, telling her he needed to sit with a group of doctors across the room to discuss his nomination for chief of staff.

After his campaign meeting with the doctors, he sat at another table with Kristy. When the music started, Bradford and Kristy made fools of themselves on the dance floor. She had on a dress with a hem leaving little to the imagination and a neckline down to her belly button. Bradford was an excellent dancer and was making hip gyrations Stella Ann had never seen before. It was embarrassing to watch, and Stella Ann could tell the ladies at her table were extremely uncomfortable watching their boss's inappropriate dance show.

The following Monday, Stella Ann received a phone call from Bradford's registered nurse. She said she was leaving his clinic to take a position with a large hospital offering her more career growth. She said she had loved working for Dr. Taber and getting to know Stella Ann, but she knew she could not work for him any longer. The tone of the conversation shifted from her career growth to extended reasons she was leaving. Rose said she could not leave until she had a conversation with her.

"Oh, Rose, I am so sorry to see you go. You have been with Bradford for almost fifteen years." Stella Ann commented.

"Mrs. Taber, the office and clinic girls felt so sorry for you at the hospital Christmas party. We could not believe Dr. Taber was treating you so badly and ignoring you," Rose said. "And we can't stand Kristy. She is up to no good and is taking Dr. Taber for a fool."

"Rose, stop for a minute," Stella Ann said. "Before you say anything else, let me ask you a question. Should I be concerned about Kristy?"

"Yes, Mrs. Taber, you should be concerned and alert regarding Kristy and Sally," Rose said.

"Sally? She is one of my best friends, Rose. Are you sure?"

"Yes, ma'am, I am positive," Rose said. "Mrs. Taber, I don't mean to stir up trouble. I have known Dr. Taber for fifteen years and respect him as a wonderful doctor. He is having a midlife crisis. He is playing dangerous games with your family, Mrs. Taber."

"Rose, thank you for your call. I appreciate it more than you will ever know. It took a lot of courage for you to call me."

"Mrs. Taber, will you please leave my name out of any conversation between you and Dr. Taber about what I told you?"

"Of course, Rose, and thank you again."

The next day, Stella Ann had a serious talk with Landon and told him of his father's plans. Bradford should have done it, but he was never around anymore. Landon asked if they were getting a divorce, and she answered honestly. She didn't know.

On New Year's Day, Bradford moved out. She gave herself one day to cry and feel sorry for herself. The next day, she called Claire to see if she wanted to have coffee. She needed to talk with a friend she could trust, and Claire had always been there for her. Claire knew Stella Ann would do whatever she had to do to protect Landon. They met at Redmond's coffee shop and were there for hours. Stella Ann told Claire everything.

Claire was not surprised and offered her some solid advice. Claire told Stella Ann women needed their own money even if only a small amount, and she needed to get an attorney as soon as possible. She told Stella Ann to get to a marriage counselor or therapist even if she was the only one to go. Claire warned Stella Ann she only needed to confide in a few people. The less she said, the better off she would be. If she couldn't talk to someone, she should write in a journal. Stella Ann did all Claire suggested. She retained an attorney, started seeing a new psychologist who dealt with women's issues, and opened a bank account in her name only. She also bought a new journal.

Shortly after Bradford moved out, Stella Ann talked with her mother to see if they needed anything and to check on them. Her mother's question about Bradford surprised her.

"Stella Ann, how is Bradford doing? I know he was under a lot of pressure when we were down there, and I hated it for him. I would give anything if we had never left our driveway that July morning, but what's done is done," Lou said.

Then Lou asked, "Stella Ann, you have said nothing about how you all are adjusting after our return home. Is Bradford at the house with you and

Landon?"

"Mama, why are you asking these questions? Landon and I are fine, and I suppose Bradford is, too."

"Stella Ann, stop it," Lou responded. Your daddy and I know he is gone."

Stella Ann felt electric shock waves run through her.

"Mama, how do you know?"

"Stella Ann, he called me before you all went to New York and told me you two were not getting along. He said he was going to move out for a little while after Christmas. He said he thought you needed a little space. I think, Stella Ann, he has just been under too much stress with your daddy's situation."

"Mama, since he cried poor little me on your shoulder, did he also tell you he was involved with his receptionist, Kristy?"

"No, Stella Ann, he didn't. I am so sorry. Do you know how long it has been going on?"

"No, Mama, I don't, and I prefer not to talk about this anymore. I need to pick Landon up at school. I love you and Daddy."

"We love you too, Stella Ann. Things will work out like they are supposed to. Stay strong."

She stood in the kitchen processing the conversation before she got her purse and keys. How could Bradford call her parents and put another burden on them? How could he tell them before talking with her? How could her mother keep the information from her?

She felt betrayed by everyone she loved. At least Norma, the person who made her life hell for years, called and warned her about Kristy. Stella Ann sensed depression invading her life yet again. It grabbed her with a vengeance. There was nothing she could do about it. She couldn't confide in her mother. Lou was overwhelmed taking care of Burt. Claire was busy taking care of her mother, and she didn't have the heart to pull her into her problems again. She had no one to talk with. As much as she fought it, the demons of depression consumed her. Some days she would find it an effort just to get off the sofa or to take a shower and wash her hair. The fight in her was gone. She was devastated.

Within three weeks, Bradford called and asked if he could return home. He admitted he made a huge mistake. Kristy was fired by the hospital for stealing controlled drugs from the office, and she used the extra money Bradford had given her to buy another boyfriend some cowboy boots. Admittedly, Bradford felt like a fool.

Stella Ann told Bradford she wanted to keep their family together, but he would need to agree to go with her to counseling and spend more time with Landon and her. Things were going to be vastly different. She made it clear she would continue to stay in the guest bedroom until they could make progress in counseling.

Depression continued to consume her, and she asked Bradford to help her after he returned. He said he had no sympathy for anyone with depression. He believed people used depression as an excuse to get controlled drugs. Stella Ann was on her own.

Stella Ann decided to do something for herself for a change. She signed up to take two computer classes at the local tech college and arranged to take some tennis lessons with the tennis pro at the public courts close to Landon's school. She needed to learn more about computers to make an informed purchase for the family. Technology was the direction life was going, and she needed to learn how to use it. Stella Ann thought tennis would offer her the motivation to lose weight and to exercise while doing something she always loved to do. Several weeks of tennis were the thing that pulled her out of her depression.

By spring, she moved back into the master bedroom, they had started going back to church, and they did more family-oriented activities. Bradford agreed to limit his drinking, and Stella Ann agreed to focus more on bedroom activity. Stella Ann became estranged from her family to save her marriage. Conversations were mostly about what went wrong during the surgery, who to blame, and what had been lost. Stella Ann felt worse than anyone, but she just couldn't take the unintentional browbeating any longer. She felt responsible for what happened to Burt and carried the burden every day of her life.

They began to spend more time at the lake with Bradford's family. It used to be a dreaded visit because there was so much chaos, but since

Norma married, she was fun and lighthearted. It was best never to get into a deep conversation or share too much information with her. After they married, she and her new husband moved to the lake close to Grammie and Grandpa. Leaving Columbia seemed to be a positive move for Norma.

By spring, Stella Ann felt their marriage was healing, her depression was lifting, and their future seemed positive. Bradford walked into the study where Stella Ann was helping Landon with a school project. The information he shared resulted in a strained conversation and disappointment for Stella Ann.

"Stella Ann, I got a call from our minister today. He said the board of deacons and elders want me to go through training to become an ordained elder of the church."

They had joined a church on Lookout Mountain when they moved. Both were active in the church. Bradford taught an adult Sunday school class. Stella Ann helped with a Wednesday night girls' class and helped to prepare meals for members going through a family crisis or who were ill and needed some help.

"What a nice honor, Bradford. What did you tell him?"

"Of course, I asked if I could think about it and talk it over with you. What do you think?"

Stella Ann was caught off guard by Bradford's announcement and chose her words carefully.

"How long is the training?" Stella Ann asked.

"The training is ten weeks, but the whole process will take a year. There is an ordination ceremony when the process is complete. They only asked four members to participate in this class and serve the church in the capacity of elders. The minister said several church members in the Sunday school class I taught early in the spring submitted my name for consideration. They were impressed by my testimony, my knowledge of the Bible, and my dedication to the church."

Bradford thrived on adoration, flattering accolades, and attention. Their minister said the perfect things to pull him into the process of becoming an elder.

"Bradford, you have a young family, a demanding career, and have been through a difficult year. Landon and I need you with us. Is there a possibility you could ask the committee to consider you for an elder position later when Landon is older?"

"Are you telling me to tell God no?" Bradford replied indignantly.

"No, I am not telling you to tell God no. I am suggesting you ask for a little grace. God's work needs to be done in your home with your family for now. We need all our focus to be on our family for a while."

"I am accepting the invitation, Stella Ann," Bradford said as he walked out of the room.

Landon looked at Stella Ann and said, "Well, I guess we will see Dad less than we ever saw him."

The ordination ceremony was the most difficult thing Stella Ann had to witness. She felt it was wrong on so many levels. Hypocrite was a perfect word to describe how she felt about Bradford. She also realized the term applied to her and their marriage. Neither of them was living the truth.

PART FOUR:

Demolition

CHAPTER 11

Research and Results

Marriage counseling sessions became further and further apart, and Stella Ann went alone most of the time. They were getting along better, so she eventually quit going.

Hope and excitement consumed her emotions when she thought about the possibility of a vow renewal. She had her eye on a charming, restored house that had opened as a wedding venue, and she dreamed of a romantic vow renewal with just the two of them and an officiant. She eventually got the courage to ask Bradford if they could renew their wedding vows to celebrate their anniversary. His response was disheartening, "Stella Ann, I married you once. What makes you think I would want to marry you again?" Stella Ann was heartbroken. The relationship and hope died more during that exchange.

She threw herself into her computer classes, tennis lessons, and clinics. She enjoyed the challenge of learning about word processing and other functions. She also learned about the Internet and how to use it in the most elementary, primitive way. At the time, most internet services were dial-up services through a landline. You bought a plan according to how many minutes you intended to use. It could be expensive to use the Internet in its early stages.

Stella Ann realized even minimal knowledge of the computer world would help her understand what Landon learned in the computer lab at school. She and Landon had interesting conversations about computers. They educated themselves about the best choice for a home computer. They collected their information and made an educated decision about the type of computer they needed for home and school use. Bradford was not interested in computer talk but had some knowledge and use of computers. The office and hospital made the conversion to an electronic database forcing Bradford to learn the basics of technology.

Her tennis skills refreshed quicker than she expected. She played as a child and in high school, so she knew the game and was a willing student to learn new strokes, techniques, and strategies. One phrase each pro-tennis coach would yell at her was, "Watch the ball, keep your eye on the ball, Taber!" The only thing that had changed with that coaching directive since her early years on the court was her name. She was reminded to focus and tried even harder. It became exhausting for her, but her determination prevailed. She loved the game.

After three months of lessons and play, Stella Ann noticed she had lost weight. She never looked in the mirror because she was reminded relentlessly by her husband that she was fat and unattractive. She had to hook her tennis skirt with a safety pin, and her top fell off her shoulders. On the way to pick Landon up at school, she stopped at a tennis shop and purchased two skirts, four tops, ball panties, and a new pair of court shoes. She had a renewed passion for something she loved, and she made new friends on the court. She was excited about something for the first time in a long time. She felt better and thought she was defeating the demons of depression.

Stella Ann and Landon made many trips to Columbia to check on her parents and to fill the lonely gaps left by Bradford's work schedule. They went home for Burt's birthday in late winter and planned to leave Columbia on Sunday afternoon to return to Chattanooga. Landon did his homework early Sunday morning in Lou's office. As the day developed, snow moved into the area, and Stella Ann decided they should get on the road after lunch. They ran in and out of snow flurries until they got to Monteagle, a small resort town, where the roads became treacherous, and Stella Ann was glad they left early. When they got home, Landon took his bag and books up the back stairs. He asked if he could watch football on the study TV, and Stella Ann gave him permission.

Stella Ann grabbed her luggage and started toward the master bedroom when she heard talking. At first, she thought Bradford was talking on the phone to someone at the hospital or to a patient. As she got closer to the bedroom, she recognized the voice as Sally's, her best friend at one time. The bedroom door was closed. She couldn't understand what they were saying and decided to walk into the room. They were in the master bathroom, which was more than odd to Stella Ann. Bradford was standing at the sink without his shirt. Sally's back was to her. It was awkward. Stella Ann felt like she was intruding in her own house.

"Hey, you all, what's up? Stella Ann asked.

"Oh, nothing," Bradford answered.

"I came over to get some sample medication for the kids. Both are sick." Sally said.

"Bradford is not a pediatrician, and we don't keep the sample medication in our bathroom, Sally," Stella Ann said. "We keep it locked in the laundry room cabinets."

Sally had been caught with nothing in her hands except Stella Ann's husband. She gave Stella Ann a cold look without saying a word. She ran past Stella Ann who was standing in the doorway, went down the long hall to the foyer, and out the door where her car was parked in front of their house. Stella Ann and Landon entered the driveway at the side of the house, so Stella Ann had no idea anyone was visiting. Stella Ann never saw or heard from Sally again. Ever. Maybe she was getting medicine, but the perception of the event gave way to suspicion.

"Well, that was strange, Bradford. Do you want to explain the situation to me?" Stella Ann asked.

"There is nothing to explain." Bradford replied as he put on a shirt.

"Bradford, Sally is or rather was my friend. When did you two become so close?"

He said nothing and didn't substantiate Sally's medication excuse. He pushed her out of the bathroom doorway and walked to the family room without a word.

Stella Ann made a point to cut through the road where Sally lived when she went to pick Landon up from school. Bradford's car was parked in the drive more times than Stella Ann bothered to count. Stella Ann thought to herself, "What was once her perception had become her reality."

The isolating demons of depression were edging their way back into her life. Her classes and tennis lessons gave her a new purpose, but she had to fight every second of the day to keep the demons at bay. She had to force herself to show up for herself. It was exhausting.

The classmates in her computer classes were much more knowledgeable about computers and the dangers of the internet than Stella Ann. She didn't understand many of the questions they asked about internet safety. She had no clue people could talk to each other on the computer and never entertained the idea danger loomed behind the computer screen. For personal information to be stolen was beyond her comprehension.

She was smart, but realized she was way behind the learning curve in the new computer age. She had been sheltered growing up, and as a teacher, mother, and housewife, isolation was a built-in shelter from the real world. Teaching provided a sense of protection. When you were always in a child's world, you maintained an adult innocence, unlike those in the business world who are exposed to adult behavior.

When a conversation about internet safety started, her computer teacher shut it down. He could sense the anxiety it caused in many of his students. It was information Stella Ann needed to know. Stella Ann knew enough to be dangerous to herself in the vast world of the internet.

They purchased a Hewlett-Packard computer after she completed her computer classes. There was a gift membership for three months for an online search engine included in the purchase of the computer. She and Bradford set up email accounts and screen names. Stella Ann monitored Landon's internet usage. When he was on the computer, she was right beside him even though he knew more than she did.

Shortly after they installed the computer, Stella Ann was practicing checking her email when an instant message came through on her screen. The message said something shocking and inappropriate. She learned in class to ignore messages from anyone unknown and to stay away from chatrooms.

She didn't know about chatrooms but was curious. She bumped into one and never participated but instead watched the conversation. She wanted to see what they were all about. One could do a search on a particular topic and a list of chats would come up. You could join in the chat or watch to see what others were saying. For example, Stella Ann tried a search on the topic of tennis, and at least twenty-five chats were taking place on the topic. If a chat was full, you either had to wait to get in, leave, or join another chat with an opening. It seemed like a huge waste of time to Stella Ann, but she was curious.

She was starved for interaction with Bradford, but his hours at work became longer and longer. He promised to spend more time with her and Landon, but it never happened. When he did come home earlier, he would go straight out and mow the yard or go running. The humiliating comments increased, and Stella Ann retreated upstairs and cried. He didn't even notice her weight loss.

It was a regular occurrence for Bradford to fall asleep on the couch watching tv with an ashtray full of cigarette butts, a jar of peanut butter, a 32-ounce Coke, and a bottle of devil elixir on the floor beside him. Landon often heard the telephone ring and ran downstairs to wake Stella Ann. Together they would go into the den and banter about who was going to wake Bradford up to take the call.

"You wake him up, Mom," Landon said.

"No, Landon, you wake him. He will hit me. He won't hit you."

"Mom, let's do it together and run."

"Landon, you say, "telephone, Dad." I will shake him on the shoulder.

Then we both need to run toward the fireplace. Got it? Ready, one, two, three."

Bradford usually came up cursing and swinging. He often said some naughty things in an angry tone to the nurses who called from the emergency room. He never remembered the conversations. Stella Ann would take the phone, apologize to the nurses, and redirect them to his partner. She and Landon would then go back to bed.

Stella Ann had no one with whom to talk. She could not involve her parents as they were under enough stress with her daddy's recovery. Her brother and sister-in-law had busy work schedules. Claire was even busier taking care of her sick mother and children. Colleagues were busy with families and school. Friends at church could not be involved, or Bradford's reputation would be tainted. He would lose his elder status in the church. She didn't feel safe confiding in Norma, and she had to protect Landon. Stella Ann knew something had to change, a decision had to be made, but she froze. She was scared to act. Too much was on the line, a fine line.

She felt like she had been abandoned by those she cared for the most. Stella Ann never felt so alone in her life and sank into a hopeless bundle of depression, which angered Bradford beyond reason. He told her over and over he had no sympathy for anyone with depression and to snap out of it. The more he complained about her or ignored her, the more depressed and desperate she became. The demons were winning.

She had her tennis friends, but it was strictly tennis around them. She couldn't confide in any of those ladies. If you weren't playing tennis or talking tennis, teammates would have little interest in you. A perfect example was when she had to drop out of league tennis when they adopted Landon. Stella Ann got socially banned from league tennis for a while. Another time years later was when she had surgery. She had been on a team for seven years. They played three times a week, traveled to fun destinations together for tournaments and clinics, and went to state playoffs three times. The captain, a girl who had been her doubles partner for three years, called Stella Ann to inform her the team decided she was no longer needed on the team because of her health status. Stella Ann's doctor cleared her to play, and she was fine. League tennis could be brutal.

After a call from the Chattanooga Tennis Association, Stella Ann humbled herself and joined a new, young team with members who could have been her daughters. It was the best decision she had made in a long time. They beat the team that dropped her and went to the state playoffs their first season. Three years later while playing on a senior team, she sustained a bad knee injury. She won the match but had orders from her doctor to hang up her racket. She could no longer play tennis. Losing her ability to play tennis was something she grieved for years. It was part of her identity.

She was invited to meet the team for dinner a couple of times and was invited to a pool party. Eventually, she was dropped from their social roster. She loved the tennis ladies but understood the underlying theme of competitive league tennis. If you don't play, you don't stay. Stella Ann remained in contact with two of her tennis friends through social media, but never saw them in person again. She accepted it was the nature of the game.

When they attended the annual Children's Charity Ball, Bradford never sat with her, nor did he dance with her. He never introduced her to anyone and worked the room again like a politician, hugging and kissing all the ladies and blessing the men. He had always had a dream to run for the U.S. Senate. Stella Ann thought he was laying some groundwork.

She went to the restroom and water fountain at least ten times to have something to do and to not look abandoned. She glanced at herself in the full view mirror as she left the ladies' room. She looked pretty in her long, red, size eight evening gown, and her blue eyes sparkled. Her hair stylist had done a wonderful job helping her grow out her short brunette style to shoulder length.

She thought to herself, "Why didn't Bradford love her? She had tried so hard to be what he wanted."

A little voice inside her head replied, "Stella Ann, he has never loved you. Give up."

She wandered downstairs to the piano bar. She knew she wouldn't be missed in the ballroom. No one was playing the piano. She sat down and started playing some of her favorite songs. After fifteen minutes of playing, the bartender asked to see her musician's union membership card. Her impromptu concert ended. He apologized and said she was a good pianist, but only union members could play the hotel instruments.

On the way home, Stella Ann asked, "Bradford, why didn't you sit with me or dance with me tonight? Was I that much of an embarrassment to you?"

"No, Stella Ann, you looked beautiful tonight. You know I love it when you wear red. I had to make sure I got around to talk to as many doctors as possible. I am up for the chief of staff position at the hospital again this year."

"Bradford, you weren't talking to many doctors. Almost every time I caught a glimpse of you, you were kissing a different woman on the cheek or dancing with her."

"Stella Ann, women talk to their husbands and influence them. It is a way to get favor for a vote in the spring. Plus, I can't help it if women love me."

Stella Ann shot back, "And I can't help it if men love me, Bradford."

She had no clue what she was talking about, but she had enough of his ego trip for one night.

Out of painful loneliness, she started exploring chatrooms. She joined in a couple of chats but signed off when things got ugly or irrelevant to the topic. She decided to do some research about the daily stress a physician faces and how stress affects their family. A simple search for doctors online brought up a list of hundreds of people claiming to be doctors.

Stella Ann knew enough to understand there were many imposters in the dark silent world of the internet. She became skilled at asking the right questions to verify their claim. She thought if she had a better understanding of the daily routines and struggles a doctor encountered, she could better understand Bradford's behavior.

Bradford did not allow Stella Ann at his clinic unless it was an emergency, so she had no idea about his office environment. It never occurred to her his behavior stemmed from other things beyond his profession. She thought if she understood what he dealt with daily she could change, and he would love her. She carried the whole burden of his behavior. Bradford told her repeatedly everything was her fault, and she believed it. She would fix it.

She talked with dozens of doctors. They were approachable, kind, and willing to answer questions. Most gave her their credentials. She talked with men and women physicians. Her questions centered around the stress of the job and how it carried over into their home life. Most were concerned by how she was treated and urged counseling. Others indicated factors beyond the profession contributed to aggressive behavior, but none would make suggestions about what those factors could be.

All the doctors she communicated with were careful not to make any judgment. It was an unspoken fact that doctors take care of doctors. It was a tight-knit group of professionals. Others explained how a hospital was like a small town rampant with gossip and inappropriate behavior. Then there was a category of doctors so dedicated to their mission and families they would never entertain impure thoughts or deeds. It was refreshing to learn their perspective.

One doctor explained a physician was always walking an ethical tightrope and doing the right or wrong thing was one decision away. Many got away with inappropriate behavior; others got caught and reprimanded or helped by colleagues. They confirmed what she already knew. Divorce was rampant within the profession, and affairs happened. It was the nature of the environment and status of the profession that could create unhealthy families. Some spouses endured and looked the other way to keep their family together; others left. Stella Ann was in no position to leave, and she didn't want to leave. She wanted her marriage and family to stay together. But she continued to keep her attorney on retainer.

She became chat friends with several of the doctors and enjoyed online conversations with them. One was a cardiologist from Pittsburgh, and another was a pediatrician from Atlanta. There was another cardiologist from Miami and a lung specialist from Nashville who also shared a musical interest. It never occurred to Stella Ann she was participating in a form of marital cheating by having conversations with other men. She never even tried to justify what she was doing because she didn't realize she was contributing to her marital problems. She was trying to find a solution. She wanted to fix it. The saying was true, "desperate people do desperate things in desperate times."

Bradford resumed his pattern of threatening to "leave her ass" and had anger rages. He threatened to leave a lot throughout the marriage, but this time he made sure he used divorce in the threat. He got angry about a trip they had planned for spring break. There was a simple solution, but he would not entertain a discussion. It was a simple scheduling issue that could have been resolved with a phone call but escalated to a full-blown fight.

The next evening after dinner, Bradford pointed his finger at Stella Ann and said, "Tell me you don't love me, Stella Ann. Tell me. Tell me. Tell me, dammit." Then he pushed his finger into her chest and pushed her into the kitchen cabinets.

"Why do you treat me this way, Bradford? Why? I hate the way you treat me."

She couldn't tell him she didn't love him because she did love him.

It frightened Stella Ann so much she started to run toward the bedroom. He grabbed her. She tried to push him away, and she started to cry. "Bradford, I do not love what you are doing to our family. Why do you get so angry? We can change the reservation or cancel."

He pointed his finger at her again and said, "We are divorced. You hear me, bitch. We are divorced." He slammed the kitchen door and screeched tires as he left the house.

She washed her face and went upstairs to check on Landon.

"Mom," he said. "What set him off this time? Why is dad so mad?"

"He's under a lot of pressure at work. Landon, never treat a woman or girlfriend the way you see or hear your dad treat me." She was always doing clean up to guide her son to treat women with dignity and respect. Landon learned mixed messages at home. He saw anger flares followed by gifts and empty apologies.

The next day she canceled their spring break trip. It wasn't worth it to go anywhere, and if she was honest with herself, she was scared to go anywhere with Bradford when he was so angry.

She started talking with lawyers online to get legal advice. Some of her doctor connections continued to check on her. She had retained an attorney but never made an appointment to talk about divorce, divorce laws, and procedures. She had to be careful how she used her attorney retainer because her access to money was limited, and she hired the best divorce lawyer in the city.

Lawyers were a bit more skeptical about talking with her online. It was the nature of their profession. Why give advice away when they could be on the billing clock? The ones who did talk with her were kind and wanted to be helpful. She talked with an attorney from New York, who listened and gave her legal advice. She remained friends with him for many years, and he was always patient and kind, offering sound advice. A former state attorney general from a southern state advised her and gave her encouragement to make her marriage work. A man who was a doctor and a lawyer in Louisiana offered an attentive ear, but Louisiana laws were so different from other states he could not offer her much legal advice. There was an attorney in Alabama, and another in Mississippi who helped her understand divorce law and legal jargon. She gained a wealth of knowledge about divorce from them and by reading. She learned she had rights. She spent hours in the library and bought many books about divorce as well as about healing a marriage. She did not want a divorce but realized she needed to be prepared because the threats toward her intensified.

Beyond the legal information the online attorneys gave her, all of them encouraged her to seek individual counseling and try to make the marriage work because divorce was awful for everyone, especially the kids. She started seeing an individual therapist months earlier. He was an expert in women's issues that included depression, relationships, marriage, and divorce. Her minister referred her to him.

Her therapist told Stella Ann she needed to learn strategies to live in the marriage if she was going to stay, and if she was going to leave, she needed to start making serious plans. After three sessions, her therapist told Stella Ann she was in a sick marriage that included a sick extended family. He said she needed to make a life changing decision before she got sick. Unfortunately, it was too late. Stella Ann had been struggling for years trying to keep her marriage together and hoping her husband would love her. She was defeated and sick.

She developed consistent online friendships with the lung specialist/musician in Nashville, the attorney in New York, and the doctor/attorney in Louisiana. They became friends she could trust, and she believed they would not betray her. At any point of the day, she could find someone with whom to talk. She was no longer alone and started to feel the rebirth of her self-esteem and self-confidence.

Many months after her informal research study, she was contacted by an attorney from Alabama with whom she spoke briefly. He asked if her situation had been resolved and indicated he was having marital issues of his own. They had several conversations in which Stella Ann made a valid and sincere plea for him to work out his issues with his wife. Shortly after the encounter, he asked if he could call her. She declined.

For spring break, Bradford had to work and said he would like to send Stella Ann and Landon on a cruise. It was the last thing Stella Ann was interested in, but Landon got excited about it. Bradford showed them a brochure he got from one of his patients who was a travel agent. It was a new, nonsmoking, family ship, and the pictures were fabulous. They would stop at three islands with excursions available to explore each island. Unlimited food including ice cream and delicious desserts got Landon's attention. He was at the age where he couldn't get enough to eat and never gained a pound. Stella Ann could read a recipe and gain weight. She agreed the amenities were impressive, and the trip was set.

On the day they left for their cruise, Stella Ann failed to check the status of parking at the airport. She and Landon missed their flight to Fort Lauderdale because there were no available parking places due to construction. As a result, they also missed the boat. They spent three days in Florida before they could fly to meet the ship. What started off as a rocky trip ended up being a wonderful experience for Landon and an enjoyable time for Stella Ann.

Landon made friends with other young teens, and the ship had many things he could do without supervision. Stella Ann was lonely, but the trip was more for Landon than her. Families did not offer a mom and young teenage son a seat at their table, so she ate in their cabin most of the time while Landon ate with his new friends.

She played the piano at a designated area and time each day and picked up about $25 in tips. People thought she was an employee of the ship, and explaining she was not proved too complicated. It was a good trip, but the downside was she had vertigo for two weeks after they returned. She decided a cruise was not her ideal choice for any future vacation.

Later in the spring, she had an appointment with her doctor for her yearly physical. He had operated on her many times, placed Landon with them, and attempted to engage in small talk during her visit. He said he and his wife and kids went to their lake house for a few days over spring break. He said he saw Bradford and his sister at the marina one day having lunch. Stella Ann thought it was strange and asked him what the girl looked like. He said she was about Stella Ann's height with red hair.

Stella Ann kept her mouth shut but knew the young woman was not Bradford's sister. Liza was tall and beautiful with long brown straight hair. What a plan! Bradford sent her and Landon off on a boat trip thousands of miles away while he went on a weekend rendezvous to Center Hill Lake with a petite red-headed woman. What Bradford didn't know was Stella Ann knew the identity of the mystery woman. People back home had already told her about his new love interest.

Every time Stella Ann was online, the attorney from Alabama contacted her. She did not know how to block anyone from contacting her but knew it was something she needed to research and learn how to do. They continued a brief conversation and signed off. He assured her he was making progress getting his marriage back on track. It made Stella Ann feel useful by helping him refocus on his wife and family. She was aware he could be lying. They were chatting one day, and he asked to talk on the telephone again. This time Stella Ann agreed.

She felt awful, guilty, and dirty for talking with a man she did not know. Even though the conversation was benign and only lasted two or three minutes, it was not right. She had always maintained a pristine reputation and was conscientious about doing the right thing even in the worst circumstances. She decided she would talk to Bradford about it. He was her husband, he was supposed to help her, support her, and make her feel safe and protected. He agreed to meet her on the deck for a glass of wine after dinner.

"Bradford, I have been so lonely and isolated. Is there a possibility we could start spending more time together?" she asked.

"Stella Ann, you know how busy my schedule is, and I have a lot of obligations. Don't start whining now. Go out to lunch with your girlfriends, go shopping, play more tennis, take an art class. You could even get involved in Wednesday night church and teach a class. We can go somewhere in July." Stella Ann was already teaching a Wednesday night class at church. His suggestion confirmed how out of touch they were with each other.

"Bradford, we have a family trip to Sullivan's Island planned for July. I can find things to do, but I need and want time with you. Even if we go out to dinner and to a movie, I would love it. We have never had date night."

When her tennis friends talked about going on business trips with their husbands or when they bragged about their husbands surprising them with a special night out, even taking care of securing a babysitter, Stella Ann reeled with envy. Some of the girls described pleasure trips they took with their husbands. What was wrong with her? Why didn't Bradford want those experiences? His partner and his wife took trips together, and they had three kids. She knew not to mention her feelings and jealousy of her friends. Nothing angered Bradford more than comparisons.

"We will work something out soon, but don't get your hopes up. I have a lot on my plate right now."

She wanted to scream, "You sure do. I am sure you have a lot planned with Melissa, the petite redhead at the lake." But she didn't go there.

"Bradford, I have a confession. Please don't be mad. I have started visiting chatrooms online. I am talking with people I don't even know, and I talked with someone from Birmingham on the phone. I feel terrible about it, and I am so sorry."

"Stella Ann, you are an attractive woman. You have needs, and I am busy. You did it; do not do it again," Bradford said without emotion.

What followed was devastating to Stella Ann. It confirmed he didn't care about her.

"Stella Ann, if you want to have an affair, go ahead. Just do not tell me. Do not bring another man into our home and use protection. Don't bring home any diseases."

Tears welled up in Stella Ann's eyes, and she got dizzy. She wanted to scream or throw up. Her stomach churned, and her heart raced. She got her wine glass, went into the house, and said nothing.

Stella Ann stood at the kitchen sink thinking. "Who says those kinds of things to their wife?" She was hoping for a different outcome, and she for damned sure was not looking for a green light from her husband to have an affair. It never entered her mind. What she wanted was for him to care, to tell her they would recommit to their relationship and family; to assure her he would talk with her more and spend more time with her.

She didn't get what she so desired, what she asked for, what she needed. She didn't get her husband and never would. She had never had a husband who loved her, and she needed to accept it. She got elaborate gifts to include jewelry, furs, designer bags, and signed porcelain collectibles, but none of the gifts had their origin in love. Bradford was generous to her and others. She got plenty materially, but her heart was lacking the gift she always wanted, love and a best friend. The saying was true. You can't force love. Begging made her pathetic.

Their physical attraction never wavered, and they made passionate love that night. Bradford professed his love and promised to spend more time with her. He left early to make weekend rounds at the hospital, and Landon was upstairs watching cartoons. He would never outgrow cartoons.

When Stella Ann pulled herself out of bed, she noticed a check for $500 on the nightstand made out to her and a note written on it to buy herself something pretty. He was being generous, but she felt like the resident whore. She felt he was getting ready to leave her and erased his guilt by leaving a check on the nightstand. She didn't need a check from him to buy herself something. She had access to the checking account.

She surmised an emotional connection was not worth it to him, and he bought her off. She was his wife! Couldn't he even show her respect?

She knew she was headed right into a nervous breakdown magnified by depression, and there was little she could do about it. She felt defeated. They never talked about Bradford spending more time with her again.

Bradford threatened to have Stella Ann committed. She retreated to herself and cut off most interaction with family and friends. She was in a robotic state and went through the motions of daily life. She went to all her therapy sessions and maintained her tennis schedule. When Bradford threatened Stella Ann, he told her she would never see Landon again. He angrily reminded her he had the power to make sure she was put away in an institution for a long time. He prescribed her antidepressants and Ritalin, which she did not take. She added walking to her tennis schedule and limited carbohydrates in her diet. She also eliminated wine. Something clicked in her, and she was determined to snap out of her severe depression without medication despite Bradford's threats to take her son away. No one would ever take her son.

She increased her communication with her doctor /musician friend from Nashville and even helped him at times with songs he was writing. He would call and pitch melodies to her as she sat at the piano and played them. It tapped a part of her brain that gave her purpose and ignited her creativity. She no longer painted or did needlework. Sewing made her nervous because she was afraid she would make a mistake. Fear of failure and fear of disappointing those whom she loved were lifelong demons. She never felt like she was outstanding at anything, just adequate.

She talked with the attorney from New York and the attorney general from a southern state regularly as well as her friend from Louisiana. None of the men mentioned anything inappropriate, nor did they suggest an in-person meeting. Somehow, she had found people who cared, and all had a protective interest in her situation. Maybe chivalry wasn't dead.

The attorney from Alabama jumped in and out of her instant messages at the oddest times. It made Stella Ann feel like he was a fake or a predator, but he was always nice to her. He suggested they meet for lunch halfway between Chattanooga and Birmingham. He lured her by offering legal advice. Stella Ann resisted but was convinced a simple lunch could do no harm, and she needed legal advice. She was desperate to learn more about the divorce process and her rights. Bradford told her constantly she had no rights.

She agreed to meet the man for lunch. It was an experience no woman should have, and she replayed in her own life what had happened to Norma years earlier. What transpired was awful, violent, and terrifying, and her instincts were right. He was a clever manipulator and liar. She made it to her car and pointed her car toward Tennessee. Her tears clouded her sight, and she was an emotional wreck.

She made a conscious decision to meet him. What had she done? What was she thinking? Maybe she would die in a car accident, and she wouldn't have to deal with the consequences of her actions. On the way home, she stopped in Scottsboro, Alabama, and tried to buy a gun but did not know there was a waiting period. The worst thoughts ran through her mind. She would end her life. She felt she was a miserable person and didn't deserve to live. She didn't know the process of buying a gun, and it saved her life. She told herself to keep her mouth shut. When she got home, she took a scalding hot shower, threw her clothes away, started dinner, and figured out how to block people online.

She knew she had to continue life as usual and stay quiet and isolated, but the incident haunted her every minute. She knew she would forever regret the awful choice she made. She was at the depths of depression and reeling from rejection, but there was absolutely no excuse for the choice she made to meet someone. She was pathetically desperate and convinced herself she was the despicable person Bradford had been telling her she was for years.

They went to Sullivan's Island in July and took Michael, Landon's best friend. Tension mounted at the beginning of the trip when Bradford kept rearranging the luggage in the midsized rental car. When Stella Ann suggested sizing up, he cursed and told her to shut up. The boys stayed quiet and watched. The tension eased when they arrived at their cottage. It was a good trip, and Bradford and Stella Ann spent quality time walking on the beach and talking.

During their conversations as they walked the beach, Stella Ann shared her communication with the lung specialist from Nashville and how she helped him with some songs he wrote and recorded. She said he would send her a tape of the recordings once he finished it. Bradford seemed to be interested in Stella Ann's music, and he was always the first one to suggest she play the piano at a party. They had good times with friends when they gathered around the piano to sing. Playing the piano was one way she didn't have to interact with others. She was safe when she played. She knew she would not accidentally tell a family secret when she was at the piano.

Stella Ann signed up to take a study class for the LSAT to prepare to apply for law school. She decided the best thing for her was to move forward and stay busy. She focused on studying, playing tennis, and family. She had always wanted to go to law school, and it was a good time to put her dream into action. She felt the way to cope within the marriage was to stay busy, be a dutiful wife and attentive mother, keep her head down, and get out of the way when tempers flared. She never filled the empty space in her heart where a loving relationship with her husband was a healthy reality.

An invitation from her Nashville friend late in September offered Stella Ann an opportunity to be backstage in the green room during a concert that featured a famous musician from Nashville. He invited her and Bradford to be his guests in Kentucky. Her friend had been invited to play a couple of the songs Stella Ann helped him write. The famous musician was his patient and one of the best guitarists in the world. She didn't think Bradford would accept the invitation, but she wanted to attend. The doctor called Bradford at the office, and as Stella Ann thought, Bradford declined the invitation but offered Stella Ann the opportunity to attend. Stella Ann got to see inside the music industry from backstage and in the green room, and the experience was a pleasant, exciting, cherished memory.

When she returned to Chattanooga, she had a lot to share with Bradford and Landon. Only Landon listened. Bradford wasn't around. She thought she had thrown an earring in the trash and went outside to check the large trash bins. She discovered many empty bottles in the trash, and a wave of sadness shrouded her. Was there a party without her? Was there a party with Landon there? Her year of silence continued. Sometimes it was best to look the other way. Stella Ann realized she was a big part of the problem for several reasons. She decided not to buy any beverages or cigarettes for Bradford from that day forward. He would have to shop for himself.

For the bulk of the months that followed, Stella Ann focused on studying for the LSAT for law school. She continued her chats with a handful of online friends, both men and women. During Princess Diana's death and funeral, she became friends with a young British woman. Her name was Ellen, and she described the massive sea of flowers everywhere and the sweet yet overwhelming aroma that filled the air.

As ironic as it seemed, Stella Ann felt like her online friends threw out a protective safety net by checking in with her periodically. It never entered her mind that her chat friends had ulterior motives. She had already experienced the worst. She never heard from the Alabama attorney after their meeting.

Stella Ann was alone when she experienced a hot stabbing pain in her abdomen along with unstoppable nausea. She called Bradford for help. He was at the clinic, and it was a while before he came home. When he saw her condition, he arranged for Landon to stay with the neighbors and rushed Stella Ann to the hospital. There was one thing consistent with Bradford. When someone was in need, hurt, or sick, he could step up and be attentive, decisive, and gallant. The agony she experienced in the emergency room was beyond anything she could imagine, and Stella Ann was no stranger to pain. By early morning, her doctor transferred her to a room, and she was able to get some relief and rest. She had a ruptured ovarian cyst which brought her to her knees in pain. Fortunately, the event subsided about as quickly as it started, and she was released within 48 hours. She had the weekend to recover. She also had some strong pain pills to help her manage further pain.

Bradford offered to take Landon and Lindsay, Landon's friend from church, to a movie and to get a hamburger afterward. Stella Ann was grateful for the offer because it would provide a quiet house so she could get some rest. It was midnight when the telephone rang.

"Where is my daughter?" a distraught father yelled.

Stella Ann was awakened from a deep sleep. "Who is this?" she asked.

"Where is my daughter? You said she would be home by 10:30 p.m., and it is now after midnight. This is Derek Warren, Lindsay's father."

"You mean she isn't home yet?" Stella Ann asked and added, "Excuse me, Mr. Warren, but I got out of the hospital this morning and am a bit groggy. Let me check with my husband and get back with you." She got out of bed and checked the house to see if Bradford and Landon were home. They weren't. Panic set in.

"Mrs. Taber, I have already notified the police."

"Thank you," Stella Ann replied trying to get her bearings.

What direction to take next was fuzzy for Stella Ann, but there was one thing for sure, she had to hurry and try to keep the incident private. Before she could decide, the phone rang again.

"Mom, can you come and get us?" asked Landon.

"Oh, my gosh, Landon, where are you? Are you and Lindsay safe?" Stella Ann asked frantically.

"Mom, we don't know where we are. We are in the playroom of someone's house, and Dad brought us some snacks and told us to stay up here until he was ready to go home. Mom, it is after midnight. Lindsay's parents are going to be so angry and worried about her."

"Where is your father, Landon?"

"He is somewhere else in the house. He said he was invited to a Christmas party and was going to stop by there for a few minutes, but that was a long time ago. I have asked him twice to take us home, but he told me to go back upstairs. He said we would go when he was ready."

"Landon, I can't track where you are, and even if I could, I can't drive yet. Go down and tell your dad, Lindsay's father called me, and you all must leave. Tell Lindsay I have talked with her parents, and she is not in trouble."

"I will never be able to ask Lindsay to go anywhere again. Her parents thought we were going to a movie and to get a hamburger."

"Landon, that is where you were supposed to go. It is not your fault. I promised the Warrens that Lindsay would be home by 10:30 p.m. I love you, Landon. Reassure Lindsay she will be home soon."

Stella Ann was beside herself. She could not get Bradford to answer his beeper signals, and Mr. Warren continued to demand answers she could not give him. She was in pain but dared not take anything for it and walked the floors looking out windows and checking doors for any sign of them. Nothing.

It was 3:30 a.m. when they arrived at the backdoor, and Landon used the back stairs to go straight to his room. Stella Ann could tell by the way he walked he was furious and tired.

Bradford came into the kitchen where Stella Ann was standing expecting an explanation. He said nothing.

"Excuse me, Bradford," Stella Ann said. "Aren't you going to explain to me what happened? Did you apologize to the Warrens?"

"I don't have to explain anything to you, Stella Ann. I can take my son where I want to without asking you, and I have nothing to apologize for," he shot back with an arrogant attitude.

"Bradford, you do have an apology to make. You were responsible for someone else's child, and you can't act irresponsibly with Landon. He is my son also, and I deserve an explanation about where you took the kids."

"I took them to a hospital Christmas party. So there. Are you satisfied?"

"What party? We did not receive an invitation in the mail. Was I not invited?" Stella Ann asked.

"A nurse at the hospital gave the party and only invited hospital staff. I stopped by to say hello, but she insisted I stay."

He stayed true to form. It wasn't his fault. He was so popular he had to stay. Obviously, the hostess served drinks.

"Bradford, this was not all about you. You made a promise to have Lindsay home by 10:30 p.m. Your son trusted you would keep your word. You disrespected Lindsay and her parents. You drove when you should have called a cab or asked someone to bring you and the kids home. You told no one where you were going. You also jeopardized your standing in the church."

"Get out of my way, Stella Ann, I am going to bed," he said as he pushed her aside. "I don't owe anyone anything."

A week after the incident, Stella Ann was back on her feet and on the tennis court. On his way to get in the car to go to school, Landon asked Stella Ann if she could start taking him to school and picking him up. It was understandable. Landon was uneasy being in the car with Bradford after the late-night mystery episode he experienced. Stella Ann knew there was more to Landon's request, but it was not necessary for him to tell her. Her mother's instinct kicked in. She was happy to take him and pick him up.

Their minister called Stella Ann a couple of weeks following the Christmas party incident and asked her to give Bradford a message that the committee voted to dismiss him from the elder ministry at the church. Stella Ann told Dr. Marshall she could not deliver the message and suggested he tell Bradford or have him attend a meeting so the other elders could voice their concerns. She knew Bradford had missed numerous meetings and had stopped teaching Sunday school. Bradford never mentioned his dismissal to Stella Ann. They simply stopped going to church.

CHAPTER 12

Fight or Flee?

After the new year, Bradford told Stella Ann it was their turn for a spring break vacation since his partner had spring break off the year before. They started discussing where they would like to go and asked Landon for suggestions. Stella Ann's British friend, Ellen, was getting married during their spring break. She wanted to go to Ellen's wedding but was hesitant to suggest England. After dinner, she took a chance and asked if Bradford would consider England, and he was agreeable to the suggestion. He said he had always wanted to see Stonehenge and other British landmarks and told Stella Ann to start planning the trip. He even agreed to go to Ellen's wedding. Stella Ann worked hard to make their trip special.

The next day, she went to the office of a travel agent they had used for two other trips. Stella Ann thought it best to have help with plans for their first European trip, and their agent had visited England many times. She told Stella Ann she would put together a package to include sightseeing tickets and a day trip to Paris. She promised to contact Stella Ann by the end of the week with the details. From there, Stella Ann went to a department store and purchased all three of them a large piece of luggage with wheels and a trolley handle. Then she went to the women's department and purchased a new raincoat.

After all the plans were set and the trip purchased, a sense of dread came over Stella Ann about the vacation. Bradford was not an easy traveler. In the weeks that led up to their departure, he said things like, "I am anxious about this trip, and I do not like the feeling of not being in control." The statements were red flags to Stella Ann. She had purchased trip insurance in case something happened, or Bradford decided he did not want them to go to England.

Stella Ann checked and rechecked their itinerary many times. She made a packing list for each of them. Their new passports came on time, and she had a list of suggestions and tips from friends who had been to England. Regardless of her efforts to avoid any issue that might upset Bradford on a trip, she would always slip somewhere. It didn't matter how small the issue was; her mistake would ruin the trip.

The international flight was long, and they got little sleep. It seemed like all they did was eat. Stella Ann felt she needed a do not disturb sign around her neck. Each time she drifted off to sleep, she was awakened by a flight attendant with another meal in hand. Halfway across the Atlantic, a flight attendant made a call for a doctor on board. During the flight Bradford was called three different times for in-flight emergencies. He got irritated because he was on vacation but was happy to help someone.

They arrived at Gatwick Airport on time, gathered their luggage, and walked to the train station to make their way to Victoria where they were staying. Bradford and Landon boarded the train first. Stella Ann had trouble lifting her luggage up the steep steps of the train. Bradford made his way to help her and was irritated she could not take care of her own luggage. He grabbed it forcefully by the toggle handle, and it broke even though it was an expensive piece of name brand luggage. He picked it up and threw it on the train in time for them to get to their seats before the train pulled out of the station. Stella Ann thanked him and sat down.

Bradford was already upset and exhausted from the trip and nagged all the way to the hotel. He called Stella Ann a few choice expletives and told her how stupid she was to get luggage she could not handle. Stella Ann and Landon looked out the window and said nothing. A family sitting across the aisle looked at them with disdain.

When they got to Victoria Station, they were able to walk to their hotel because it was so close. Stella Ann was fascinated by the activity and the mounds of beautiful fresh flowers available in the train station. It was cumbersome trying to drag her luggage with a broken handle, but she did not say a word. She tried to keep up. When they got to the hotel, they had enough time to freshen up, change clothes, and find their way to Ellen's wedding at the Brydon Room in the Chelsea Old Town Hall Register Office.

They arrived at the wedding venue as the doors were being closed for the wedding. Ellen was in the hallway and hugged Stella Ann. She looked beautiful. She wore a yellow silk suit she had made in Bangkok with a matching hat from Harrods. Her shoes were the same color, and she carried a small bouquet of lilies of the valley, myrtle, yellow roses, and miniature English ivy. Bradford and Stella Ann stood in the back of the room, and Landon was asked to manage the CD player and music. Ellen's two children were much younger than Landon and stood beside Ellen during the ceremony. Ellen thanked them for coming and invited them to the wedding reception and party at a restaurant nearby, but they declined.

Ellen was a good friend to Stella Ann despite the distance and age between them. Ellen was quite a character with amazing determination and a free spirit. She was also accomplished and successful in her career and sensitive to her friends.

When Stella Ann was at a dark point in her life and needed to make some life-changing decisions, Ellen sent her a Harrods teddy bear. Ellen stated in her thick British accent, "Having something to hold during difficult times can be a comfort and evoke familiar positive memories." The cute little bear with Harrods embroidered on its foot has a special place of honor amongst hundreds of books and other special bears Stella Ann has on her bookshelf. Her relationship with Ellen confirmed people come into one's life for a reason.

Jet lag was real, and they decided to take a nap when they returned to the hotel. Stella Ann and Landon slept longer than they should have, and Bradford wandered around the area close to the hotel. When they finally adjusted to the time, they ventured out for fish and chips and smashed peas. Their meal was delicious, and they took a night ride on a double-decker bus. They cut the evening short because they were tired. About midnight, Landon woke up.

"Mom, Mom, where is Dad?" he whispered.

Half asleep she raised up and said, "He is asleep, Landon, go back to bed."

"No, Mom, Dad is not asleep. He is not in here."

"Check the dresser, Landon, and see if he left a note."

"Mom, there is nothing on the dresser. Dad left us here." Landon lunged for the door and looked down at the long hallway. "Mom, we have to find him."

"Let's get some street clothes on and see if he is in the building. Do you know where the workout room is?"

"Yes, I do," Landon said. "Dad and I found it and the pool when you were getting dressed to go to Ellen's wedding. Maybe Dad went swimming."

They were like detectives as they sleuthed to all the public areas of the hotel looking for Bradford. It was not surprising when they located him at the Irish Pub connected to the hotel. He was having a grand old time chatting with a group of Irishmen, boozing, and running up a hefty bill. Stella Ann and Landon watched from behind a huge indoor palm plant at the entrance.

"Mom let's go in and get him," Landon said.

"Landon, it will make him angry. He will be fine, and I will notify the hotel desk clerk to check on him. While we are down here, I will check to see if I can arrange for my luggage handle to be repaired. Then we need to go back upstairs. Do you want a snack to take with you?" Stella Ann said.

"No, Mom. I am fine, but I would like a soda to drink."

"We'll get one out of the vending machine on the way up to our room. I have some money in my pocket."

"Mom, can we get a flight and go home? It looks like this is going to be another bad trip."

"Landon, we can't leave now. I promise I will do what I can to make sure I don't anger your father, but he is already mad at me about my luggage."

The desk clerk told Stella Ann to bring her luggage to the desk the next morning, and they would send it out for repair. She and Landon went back to the room. Bradford came stumbling in close to dawn from his party night and slipped into bed. It was Sunday, and they decided to stay close to the hotel to rest and take it easy to prepare for some serious touring the next few days.

It was going to be a long Monday packed with sightseeing. The first stop was breakfast in the hotel restaurant. The plan was to visit Buckingham Palace to see the Changing of the Guard, the Tower of London to see the royal jewels, Westminster Abby, Big Ben, and Harrods. Bradford offered to buy Stella Ann a hat at Harrods, but they were ridiculously expensive. Stella Ann declined. The memorial to Princess Diana and her boyfriend in Harrods was impressive and quite moving. They grabbed dinner on the way home and fell into bed when they got back to the hotel. It was a good day.

The next day, they took a bus tour to Stonehenge, Bath, Somerset, and the countryside. Stella Ann bought some antique lace at a shop in Bath, and they had lunch at an outside café overlooking the city. The views were beautiful. Bradford snapped pictures all day, not realizing the film had not been loaded into the camera, which was, of course, Stella Ann's fault.

Wednesday was another rest day and a day to catch up on seeing things they missed. On Thursday, they planned to take The Chunnel to Paris.

Before boarding The Chunnel train on Thursday morning, they looked for a restaurant to have breakfast.

"Mom, I saw a fast-food place across the street," Landon said. "Can we go there? I am hungry, and the food here is not good."

"Landon, ask your dad," Stella Ann replied.

"No, Mom, you ask him."

"Landon, he won't get mad at you. He will be furious with me if I suggest fast food for breakfast."

"Please, Mom."

"Let me see what I can do."

As they crossed the street from the hotel, Stella Ann decided to ask Bradford about breakfast.

"Bradford, I see an American based fast-food place across the street. Do you think we could have a quick breakfast there? Landon is hungry."

"We are not in England to have a fast-food breakfast, Stella Ann," Bradford responded disgustedly.

"Bradford, we can get Landon's meal to go. He can eat it in the restaurant you choose," Stella Ann said compromisingly.

Bradford stopped walking, turned to Stella Ann, gestured with his arm, and said, "Get away from me."

"From now on while we are here, you keep your bossy ass behind me and stay at least ten feet away," Bradford said angrily. "I don't want people to know you are with us. You are an embarrassment."

Landon turned to look at her apologetically and mouthed, "Mom, I'm sorry."

A huge set of tears drizzled down her cheek. Stella Ann was devastated Bradford treated her that way, especially in front of Landon and in front of people on the streets of London. He never hesitated to humiliate her and would forget about it or apologize later with a fancy gift. She wanted to return to the hotel room and hide, but she wanted to make sure Landon had a good time in Paris.

They had breakfast at an upscale English pub before boarding the Chunnel. Stella Ann was required to sit at a different table. It was worth it to Stella Ann to sit at another table for breakfast rather than try to sit with Bradford and Landon and risk causing a scene.

Landon and Stella Ann sat together on the Chunnel train, and Bradford hung out in the bar car. Maybe he would calm down before they got to Paris. When they arrived at the train station, Bradford apologized for his morning behavior and lifted the restriction she had to walk ten feet behind him when they were in Paris. He offered to buy her a purse while they were there. Stella Ann thanked him but declined.

The walking pace was more like a run in Paris. People bumped into them without apology and had little regard for visitors meandering their streets. Communication was difficult for Stella Ann, Bradford, and Landon. When they asked for English menus, the body language of the employees they encountered at one restaurant visibly showed their disgust. One waitress threw the menu across the table and knocked over Landon's iceless soda.

They planned to go to the Louvre, but it was closed for renovation. In place of the Louvre, they substituted the Museum d'Orsay. They saw many fabulous well-known paintings and sculptures and stopped for pastries at La Mie d'Orsay. They enjoyed delicate pastries and coffee and bought extras to take back to London with them. They walked or rather ran the Avenue Champs-Elysees and went into a few shops. Little was affordable, so they kept moving. The fruit and vegetable stands were charming, and they were surprised public restrooms cost a quarter to use.

They had a late lunch at L'Arc Café and loved their meal. Stella Ann was allowed to sit with them even though Bradford said she was disgusting the way she attacked her food. No one had ever pointed out to her she attacked her food, and he couldn't shame her for her weight. She was down to her high school weight. Bradford decided to hire a driver for the rest of the day, so they could see as much as possible before boarding the Chunnel train back to London. It turned out to be a wise choice. Not only did the driver get them to the Eiffel Tower and the Pont de l'Alma tunnel where Princess Diana's car wreck happened, but he took them to many places in the city they would have never thought to go, giving them a tour guide rendition of the sights. Bradford tipped him well as he dropped them at the Chunnel station. Stella Ann and Landon slept all the way back to London, and Bradford returned to his seat in the bar car.

Their last day in London included Trafalgar Square, Piccadilly Circus, and The British Museum. They took a quick side trip to Windsor in the afternoon and had an early dinner at Windsor Grill. They packed before going to bed and made their way to Gatwick Airport via Victoria Station early the next morning. By the time their flight took off, they were exhausted and ready for a flight nap. Bradford never noticed Stella Ann had her luggage repaired.

It was the trip of a lifetime in many ways, and Stella Ann made sure she talked with Ellen when she returned to Chattanooga. They remained friends for a long time, and Stella Ann went back to visit her with Landon and Conner a few years later. Ellen even visited Stella Ann in Chattanooga when her husband was in the States working. Then life got in the way, and they lost touch with each other. Stella Ann tried to find Ellen many times but had no luck. Letters were returned unable to be delivered.

Stella Ann was in the laundry room ironing and listening to talk radio when the telephone rang. Her heart almost stopped when she heard the voice. She hadn't heard that voice in almost a year and pushed what happened to the deepest recesses of her mind.

"Hello, Stella Ann, we haven't chatted in a long time," said the attorney from Birmingham in a smooth, confident voice.

"Leave me alone," Stella Ann said.

"Stella Ann, how do you think your husband would feel if I called him and told him about our encounter?"

"How do you think your wife would feel if I told her you were a predator and a jerk? Furthermore, it wasn't an encounter. It was a nightmare, and my husband would stand by me and help me. He knew I was not myself for months, and I was depressed."

"Oh, I doubt it, Stella Ann. He won't stand by you. No man wants to know that kind of information about his wife," he said.

"Look, leave me alone. I want to forget you and try to forgive myself for my lapse in judgment. You took advantage of my vulnerability, and I almost took my life because of it.

"What a pitiful plea, Stella Ann. My wife wouldn't care what you tell her. She has filed for divorce, and I think your husband would do the same if he knew. But a divorce could be avoided at a price."

"What are you talking about?"

"For a price, I could keep silent. Your husband is a doctor. You have money. Let's say you send me $5,000 by the end of the week. My divorce legal fees are mounting up along with the maintenance and child support I must pay. My private legal business has been off lately. I have your husband's office number and know the hospital he uses. I could have him paged within minutes and tell him what you won't. I have a second line and could do it right now as a matter of fact."

"Why do you want money from me? You are an attorney, and your wife is wealthy. I don't believe for a minute you are in financial trouble.

Leave me alone!"

Stella Ann hung up on him. Her heart was racing. She started pacing and fell into a puddle of tears. She was terrified about what she faced but called Bradford to come home from the hospital. She told him it was important, and she was in trouble. She had to tell him. She needed help. She had no intention of paying the scum bag any money. He wouldn't hesitate to call Bradford at work.

Bradford did not come home immediately, but when he got there, she asked him to meet her in the sitting area of their bedroom. She was wearing shorts, a tennis tournament t- shirt, was barefoot, and had red eyes from crying. She told him what happened, every painful bit of it. Bradford was kind and hugged her and said they would work through it. He could compartmentalize and be understanding in difficult situations. Bradford heard what he wanted or what he thought he heard. What stuck in his mind was he heard her say, "that man didn't even apologize for what he did to me." Bradford took it to mean Stella Ann condoned what happened, was a willing participant, and only wanted an apology. What she meant was he violated her and didn't even care about what he had done.

She learned later Bradford called him. She didn't know what was said, but Bradford assured Stella Ann, he would never contact her again. Bradford fought for her. Maybe he did love her. However, nothing could make her feel better. She deserved to feel awful. She deserved every bad thing thrown her way. Bradford reprimanded her for allowing herself to be a piece of meat for a man. Allowing? It was confusing and extremely demeaning but true. She made the choice, the unbelievably bad choice, to do something she knew was wrong and would pay for the rest of her life.

She knew there would be a delayed rage from Bradford. Ever since she was thrown out in the winter cold, she always had a bag for herself, a bag for Landon, and money in the trunk of her car. She was prepared if they had to flee, and they did many times. Her main motivation was protecting Landon, and her reality was she didn't care if she lived or died. She was a broken wreck.

Rage kicked in with Bradford a week later. When she came home from running errands on Bradford's afternoon off, he was sitting in the formal living room with a gun across his lap. It was a gun he had purchased from Burt a few years earlier. It would be ironic if he killed her with her father's gun. He had amassed quite a collection of new and vintage guns. Landon was with friends. Thank goodness, he was safe. Bradford didn't see Stella Ann. She backed out of the dining room through the kitchen and got to her car.

Stella Ann called a police friend of Bradford's and their minister. Each told her to leave immediately. She checked into a hotel and waited. Fortunately, they were able to intercept anything unfortunate from happening and promised Stella Ann they would keep the incident quiet. The policeman said he would check on her daily at the hotel and instructed if she was going out to leave a note at the desk for him.

The days that followed were terrifying. She wrote pages and pages of notes on hotel stationery. Taking copious notes was something she learned as a teacher. She contacted her attorney who told her not to go back into the house until she felt like it was safe and then have someone accompany her. Landon was in a safe place with Claire and her family. Stella Ann was scared to go home, but after a week she agreed to meet Bradford at a counselor of his choice.

When she got to the counselor's office, Bradford had already been with the counselor for about fifteen minutes. It was an awkward first few minutes because she and Bradford had not seen each other in days. Bradford had already told the therapist their background and described the most recent events. What ensued was a two-hour session with many appointments to follow.

When they left the office, they went to a nearby restaurant to have lunch before Bradford went to the hospital to make rounds. Stella Ann ordered a salad and iced tea. Bradford ordered a hamburger and a glass of wine. Stella Ann stared at him without a word. The counselor told Bradford never to drink any social beverages, but she stopped short of labeling him.

Bradford said, "Stella Ann, no woman is going to tell me what I can and can't do. My butt is pinned to the wall with her list of requirements.

If I want a glass of wine, I will have a glass of wine."

Stella Ann had reservations about the marriage counseling process working but remained silent. They had each done their part to destroy each other and their marriage. She didn't even recognize herself. She had compromised every virtue and core value she ever possessed. She wanted the old Stella Ann back. She and Bradford were emotionally sick and needed serious individual therapy even if their marriage was beyond repair. Sadly, they were too self-absorbed to even entertain the possibility of what their demise was doing to Landon. When the damage to Landon was revealed years later, she was ashamed and apologetic.

After three weeks of intensive counseling and setting boundaries and rules each had to follow, they made a commitment to do what was necessary to save their marriage. Stella Ann and Landon went home escorted by their minister. Bradford could not drink. Stella Ann was instructed to get Landon and leave if he had a drink. Stella Ann could only use the computer with permission from Bradford, and if he wanted to sit with her when she was on the computer, she had to let him. She stopped visiting chat rooms and blocked anyone from contacting her.

They made efforts to be together more and to take family trips to the lake to get out of the city and relax. What was sad and brutal for Stella Ann was she realized she had become Bradford's sexual experiment. There was no love, only anger. Things he requested in the bedroom were bizarre. Behavior she had never heard of or thought of before was required, demanded, and ordered. She had sold herself into inappropriate marital submission. Who would believe her if she sought help? Afterall, Bradford was a respected doctor in the medical world and beloved by his patients.

Their family trip to Sullivan's Island was a vacation they always enjoyed, and Stella Ann hoped it would provide a temporary escape from the stress of her situation. Ron, Jenny, and Conner joined them. It was the third time they had shared a cottage in Lighthouse Circle, which was a quiet area near Sea Grass Market and a short walk to the beach. As they unpacked each car, the boys were quiet and watching tv. Suddenly, Jenny ran to the living area and stood in front of the tv. The boys discovered a pornographic video someone left in their bedroom, and they decided to check it out. Stella Ann could still hear Jenny stuttering when she discovered the entertainment. It went something like, "Ooo, Oh, No, Uh," and then she bellowed, "Boys, go outside!"

They spent most of the week on the island and at the beach, but it was sweltering in July. The trip to Sullivan's Island was not complete without historical sightseeing. They spent an afternoon in Charleston. They ate lunch at The Icehouse restaurant in the market, took a carriage ride, and visited The Battery. The rest of the time, they ate fresh seafood at the cottage or ordered take out at one of the restaurants. Ron, Stella Ann, Conner, and Landon played a lot of tennis, especially at night. There was no place Stella Ann felt more comfortable and in control than on a tennis court.

Jenny asked Stella Ann to go to Charleston to enjoy girl shopping one afternoon. Jenny bought an adorable sundress and an evening gown at a store on King Street. They ended up in an upscale mall connected to a hotel. Stella Ann bought a purse and large brimmed sun hat. Before they called it an afternoon, they ended up in a fancy lingerie shop with lovely items made of beautiful, silky fabric. The items in the store were elegant, but Stella Ann was not the fancy lingerie type. She was more the big t-shirt or flannel night gown type.

"Stella Ann, if you buy some of these silky, little lingerie pretties, you might spice things up in the bedroom," Jenny said teasing.

Stella Ann thought to herself, "If she only knew."

Jenny and Ron sensed things were tense between Stella Ann and Bradford but knew little about the details of their troubles. They gauged most of their assessment from Bradford's condescending remarks and aggressive behavior toward Stella Ann.

The comment shocked Stella Ann because it was out of character for Jenny. Jenny was reserved and ladylike. Stella Ann had never even heard her say a bad word. Stella Ann, on the other hand, could spit select swear words out comfortably at times.

Stella Ann responded, "Jenny, I doubt if any of these things will save my marriage." She didn't dare tell Jenny how she was being treated in the bedroom and thought about the comments years earlier when Bradford referred to exotic sex partners and threesomes.

"Well, you don't know until you try," Jenny popped back. "Let's see if we can find something you like that will turn Bradford's head."

Stella Ann ended up purchasing a leopard baby doll number with matching French cut panties and a baby blue flimsy nightgown with a matching wrap around bath robe. Stella Ann was not comfortable but was willing to give the lingerie a chance. She knew she was setting herself up for rejection. She was right.

In late July, Stella Ann and Norma took a walk at the lake and saw an adorable vintage lake house for sale not too far from the Taber's family lake house. Stella Ann begged Bradford to go with her to see it, and within a week they purchased it. To Stella Ann, it represented a new chapter or beginning for them.

Stella Ann had visited the Taber's lake house many times from the time she was 13 years old and loved it there. It was a place of good times, good food, and laughter. It was a happy place for a family who had many unhappy things happen and constant conflicts brewing. Hopefully, their house would represent the same good times and laughter without conflicts.

They spent the better part of what was left of summer refurbishing the house and decorating. It was small, but it was a place Stella Ann loved from the minute she saw it. She felt safe there. She put her touch on it with pictures and decorating items from their attic and surplus furniture from the moves they made. Norma helped her with furniture placement and decorating ideas, and they compiled a list of things needed. Norma's husband helped Bradford tame the overgrown yard, and he generously offered to maintain the yard and check on the house when they weren't there.

Stella Ann spent a week making white ruffle curtains for the bedrooms and bathroom, and red and white checked curtains for the kitchen. She used the quilts her grandmother and Bradford's Grammie had made on the beds and added white ruffle shams and pillows she made. It looked like a quaint country cottage straight out of a magazine. Lou and Burt made bookshelves and many pieces of primitive furniture to help with the cottage look. The bench and chairs they made for the front porch were perfect for Sunday morning coffee and conversation sessions. The house had a tin roof, and raindrops sang peacefully on it during southern rain showers. Life was good and improving.

Stella Ann spent a week in Columbia when Landon was at camp. She, Lou, and Burt went to many antique and thrift shops gathering items for the house to make it cozy and comfortable. They bought an adorable vintage pie safe with glass panes in the doors which was perfect to hold extra dishes, bowls, and flatware in the kitchen. An old English pub table pulled out to seat at least six people and was perfect for the kitchen. They purchased end tables and a coffee table with a lift top which served as a small dining table in front of the sofa instead of using tv trays. Burt was driving again, and he and Lou came to the lake often to help them put the house together. They also loved it there, and a cautious friendship blossomed between the families. Stella Ann was hopeful for many reasons.

In the fall, they helped Ron and Jenny host a fiftieth wedding anniversary party for Lou and Burt. It was a lot of fun, and Lou and Burt had a good time. They tried to include every detail to make it a special evening for them. Jenny arranged for a professional photographer to take formal family pictures, and Conner and Landon were given cameras to take candid pictures. The event reminded Stella Ann of the fun times spent at her grandparents' house years before. Aunts and uncles on both sides came to support Burt and Lou as well as many friends who had stood by them through the years.

It was a fun, elegant night. Jenny and Stella Ann made sure they covered every detail to make the night special. The flowers were yellow roses, beautiful, and plentiful, and they got Lou a corsage and Burt a boutonniere. The three-tier cake was stunning, and Burt had fun trying to feed it to Lou. She was determined he was not going to mess up her makeup or hair and kept pulling her head back. Everyone laughed at their efforts to feed each other. Bradford made a beautiful toast to them, and Jenny wrote a lovely poem she had framed.

They went to the lake for a long weekend in October to get the house prepared for winter. Norma, Stella Ann, and five-year-old Sophie, Scott's daughter, made plans to go grocery shopping and to get Sophie a winter coat. Bradford, Scott, and Landon stayed to rake leaves and go fishing.

When Norma and Stella Ann returned from shopping, they saw Bradford and Scott swinging fists, kicking, throwing each other on the ground, and shouting at each other. Norma jumped out of the car and didn't miss a step to get between them. She blasted them for their immature, silly behavior, and she was especially disgusted they acted like idiots in front of Landon and Sophie. Bradford and Scott exchanged choice words and sat down at separate ends of the deck to cool off with a beer. No one knew what prompted the fight, and the men did not volunteer an excuse. Scott was playful and funny, which was not a good thing if Bradford was in a bad mood

When Bradford, Landon, and Stella Ann left on Sunday to return to Chattanooga, they made plans to celebrate Thanksgiving at the lake. Landon was going to be in Colorado on a ski trip with his youth church group. It would be a chance for Stella Ann and Bradford to spend some time alone. Stella Ann invited Bradford's family to come to their lake cottage for Thanksgiving dinner.

Stella Ann worked for a couple of weeks making and freezing casseroles to include cornbread dressing, corn pudding, green beans, squash, sweet potatoes, and broccoli, pumpkin and pecan pies, and homemade rolls to take to the lake for Thanksgiving. Norma's husband, Charles, was going to fry a spicy turkey and another one without a lot of spices. Stella Ann selected the perfect wine to enhance the food and made sweet tea, a Southern requirement at any table. She brought eggnog and boiled custard in case anyone wanted those treats with their dessert. Stella Ann was looking forward to making Thanksgiving special.

She decided to go to the lake two days early after she dropped Landon off at the church for his Colorado ski trip. She purchased mums to plant around the house and gathered up pumpkins to make the porch look festive. She made sure she packed the Pilgrims and Indians she used on their Thanksgiving table each year and was sure to pack plenty of candles to add another level of holiday spirit to the occasion. All of Bradford's siblings and their families confirmed they were coming, and Grandpa even agreed to join them for dinner. Stella Ann brought folding tables and chairs from their house in Chattanooga. She purchased festive tablecloths and napkins and made sure there were enough dinner plates and flatware. She didn't want anyone to have to do anything but come and have a blessed Thanksgiving.

Stella Ann cleaned the house thoroughly and changed the bed sheets in the guest room and Landon's room in case anyone wanted to sleep at their house. She knew Bradford liked things to be clinically clean, so she made sure the house sparkled.

The plan was to have their Thanksgiving dinner at noon. The night before Thanksgiving, Bradford called and said he would not be able to get there that night and would come early Thanksgiving morning to help Stella Ann. She took care of all the details so he could look forward to enjoying his family. She did not ask why he couldn't be there and thanked him for calling. He hung up without a word. She used the time to relax, assess her accomplishments, read, and turn in early. She always slept better at the lake. There was a certain peace Stella Ann couldn't explain when she was in the little house. It was like it wrapped its walls around her and made her feel safe.

Norma arrived by 11a.m. Thanksgiving Day to help Stella Ann get casseroles heated and ready to serve. Bradford was not there, and Stella Ann was inwardly worried. Norma kept asking if he was on call or if he had an emergency at the hospital. He was not on call, and his partner was taking all calls and emergencies. Stella Ann assured Norma he would arrive soon.

"Keep in mind, Norma, Bradford runs every morning. He may have gone on a long run and let the time slip up on him." She continued her loyal defense of him.

"I hope he gets here soon, Stella Ann. You know there is a killer on the loose in East Tennessee, and they think he may be hiding in the wooded area around the lake. The authorities have been trying to locate him for days and have put out all kinds of cautions for the public. He escaped from Northeast Tennessee Penitentiary in Mountain City a few days ago," Norma said.

"I am sure Bradford is fine," Stella Ann said trying to reassure Norma.

Bradford arrived before the family gathered, and Stella Ann and Norma noticed his demeanor. He was distant and visibly angry, cutting Stella Ann off at anything she said. Norma suggested they give him some space to cool off.

"Why do you think he is so angry?" Norma asked.

"I have no idea, Norma, but he was curt and direct on the phone last night. I did not ask him any questions. I do know he and his partner are having disagreements about documentation and filing procedures at the office," Stella Ann offered.

Norma said, "I hope he puts that aside and takes the time to enjoy this holiday and his family."

"He will," Stella Ann said. "He loves nothing more than to be around family. We don't get many opportunities to visit family with his busy schedule."

"I miss Landon," Norma said.

"So do I, but I know he is having a blast in Colorado with his friends. This will be the second time he has gone on a ski trip. He doesn't like to ski as much as he likes snowboarding, and Colorado is beautiful."

"Stella Ann, we are going to have a good Thanksgiving and make the most of it. We have much to be thankful for this year."

Norma and Stella Ann had developed a nice friendship since she and Bradford bought the lake house. Lou never hesitated to remind Stella Ann to be cautious about getting too close or trusting Norma too much. Stella Ann had been tricked many times before, but she was optimistic and wanted to be friends with Norma.

Liza, Bradford's sister, called at the last minute and said she and the girls would not be able to get there until late in the afternoon the next day. Alex, his brother, and Charlotte and their kids needed to stay in Columbia to help Charlotte's parents. Her mother had been ill, so Charlotte cooked their dinner and invited Hank and his girlfriend to join them. Their celebration was dwindling. It was typical for things to come up and plans to change with many families involved. Stella Ann learned over the years to be flexible if she was going to have any peace in Bradford's family. Thanksgiving would still be special. Stella Ann didn't know it would be her last time to be at their lake house.

Bradford refused to say the prayer before dinner, so Stella Ann offered a blessing for family and food. They enjoyed a delicious meal and visiting. It was like old times when Grammie was alive. She was the best cook in the world. Before Norma and Stella Ann could take up the plates and serve dessert, Bradford stood up and told everyone to leave. Stella Ann was shocked, and Norma and the others were bewildered by Bradford's demand. They thought he was joking.

"I said get out of my house. All of you, get out." Bradford said. "Leave, now."

"What on earth are you doing, Bradford?" Norma asked in dismay. "We haven't even had dessert."

"Mom, I said for you all to leave. This is my house, and I want you to get out."

Norma turned to Stella Ann, "Do you know what is going on? Are you going to be all right?"

"He must be tired. I will bring you all casserole leftovers, turkey, and a pie later this afternoon." She didn't share she had a foreboding feeling and didn't want to be alone with Bradford.

It was sad to see Norma, Charles, Grandpa, Scott, and Sophie quietly file out of their house as Bradford stood by the fireplace entertaining a scowl on his face. No one said a word.

Stella Ann cleaned the kitchen and put everything back in order in solitude. She was too afraid to say anything. She was confused and embarrassed. Scott returned later that afternoon to ask if he could watch football with Bradford. Stella Ann took food to Norma. When she returned, she retreated to the bedroom to read and stay out of the way. The first half of the game was not over before Scott and Bradford were fist fighting and tumbling in the middle of the living room floor. Bradford ordered Scott out for the second time. Again, Stella Ann had no idea what prompted the scuffle.

The next day, Stella Ann and Norma went Christmas shopping and had lunch at a cute café in Smithville. It was fun to have Sophie with them. She was at the age to get excited about Christmas and squealed at all the trees and decorations they saw at the small shopping mall. The town was having their Christmas parade, and many streets were cordoned off. It was an added surprise for all three of them. While they were shopping, Norma asked Stella Ann if she and Bradford would like to come to their house for dinner on Saturday night. Stella Ann readily accepted.

Friday night, they had Thanksgiving leftovers for dinner and watched a movie. Then, Stella Ann put on her warm, well-worn flannel nightgown and went to bed. She did not want to talk about Thanksgiving Day, and she didn't want to fight. She was disappointed because there was no appreciation from Bradford for all the work she did to make Thanksgiving special, but she would never verbalize it. Bradford started watching another movie and said he would come to bed when it was over.

At midnight, Stella Ann heard shouting and someone bumping into the stairway wall. There were five steps down to the bedrooms, and it sounded like more than one person making a commotion. She could not understand what was said, and Bradford burst into the bedroom, grabbed her by the shoulders and shook her repeatedly mumbling something she couldn't understand. Stella Ann started crying.

"Bradford, what is it? Please stop," Stella Ann cried. She thought he was having a heart attack or stroke.

"You worthless bitch. I am going to kill you." Bradford said with fire in his eyes.

As quickly as he came into the bedroom, he left, shouting obscenities as he walked down the hall.

Stella Ann was shivering and scared but was eventually able to fall back asleep.

It happened again. Bradford came lumbering back to the bedroom, knocked the door in with his foot, and told Stella Ann to get up. Stella Ann dove deeper under the covers and was still. She hoped he would go away. He flung the covers off onto the floor and threw Stella Ann on top of them. He kept saying he was going to kill her, and she was worthless.

All she could do was kick and scream until he finally left. Bradford carried out the same procedure two more times until dawn. When things got quiet, Stella Ann, without a sound, crept to the living room. He was asleep on the sofa with an empty bottle lying on the floor next to him. It looked like a cigarette made a hole in the new carpet and burned itself out.

She was grateful Landon was in Colorado. She knew she had to get through the day. She would say she had a headache and send Bradford to have dinner with Norma, Charles, Scott, Sophie, and Grandpa. As soon as he drove off and was out of sight, she would throw what she could in the car and head back to Chattanooga. He had promised many times to kill her the night before, and she was not going to be a sitting duck so he could follow through on his word.

Her excuse worked. As soon as he cleared the road, Stella Ann got to work. She knew she didn't have long to make her escape. She threw her clothes and anything that meant something to her into the car. She didn't have time to pack the blue Yorktown dishes her mother had given them when they married. Burt had made many furniture pieces, and Lou helped to stain and finish them. Stella Ann would have to leave them. They would understand. She never gave a thought to the fugitive on the loose in East Tennessee.

All she thought about was getting out, leaving, staying safe. The theme of her life became "run to live." There were only two people in her life she was afraid of, Bradford and Norma. Together they could be dangerous.

When she got back to Chattanooga, she immediately moved all the things she would need into an upstairs guest bedroom. She was shivering, scared, and finally fell into bed to sleep a few hours before the telephone rang.

"Stella Ann, why did you leave the lake?" Bradford questioned angrily.

"Bradford, you scared me, and I thought the best thing I could do was to get out of the way."

"Stella Ann, don't you realize how dangerous it was for a woman to drive from here to Chattanooga alone with the police looking for a fugitive?"

"I didn't think about that, Bradford. I was taking care of myself. I was not afraid to drive back. I am more afraid of you than the fugitive."

Bradford went on. "You have upset everyone at the lake by leaving with no explanation. I am going to stay another night."

"Why don't you tell them you threatened to kill me repeatedly?" Stella Ann asked.

"What are you talking about you lying bitch?"

"Tell them what you did all night Friday."

"I don't know what you are talking about," Bradford said.

It was typical for Bradford not to remember what he did when he was so angry, which gave Stella Ann more reason for concern.

"When does Landon get back?"

"This afternoon. The flight gets in at 3 p.m., and the kids will be loaded onto the church bus at the airport and brought to the church parking lot for parental pick up." Stella Ann said.

"I will be home tomorrow night," he said and slammed the phone down.

When Stella Ann picked Landon up, she was thrilled to see him and wanted to learn all about the trip. It was obvious he was too exhausted to talk. He wanted to go home and get some sleep. Stella Ann managed to tell Landon she had moved back upstairs for a while but never mentioned a thing about what happened at the lake house over Thanksgiving weekend. She only explained Bradford stayed over to take care of some maintenance at the house.

When Bradford returned the next day, he never acknowledged anything had happened and barely spoke to Stella Ann or Landon.

Stella Ann started decorating for Christmas right after Thanksgiving. It was a big house to decorate, but she had already made the decision not to put as many decorations up as usual. They had no plans to entertain. It was going to be the three of them. Even though she took Christmas decorations to the lake, she knew she would not be back to decorate.

She continued therapy sessions. Bradford had long since stopped going. He thought the counselor and Stella Ann were plotting against him. She refused to admit nothing was going to save her marriage, but she knew it was over. She never had a marriage to save, and suspected Bradford stayed at the lake during Thanksgiving an extra day to plot his divorce strategy with Norma's help.

Stella Ann updated her resume and went to see a career counselor to help her with self-esteem, wardrobe, and interview strategies. She had several interviews before Christmas but wasn't offered a job for lack of experience and time lapse in her work history. Bradford helped her secure an interview with a major drug company, but that fell flat. At forty-six, she was too old, even though companies could never use age, religion, or gender to keep one from a job. She knew she was not considered because of her age. She could see the young recent college graduates line the room to wait their turn for an interview. It couldn't be more obvious she was in the reject group.

She had given up her original dream of law school. Her circumstances had dramatically changed. Stella Ann thought if she got back into the working world, Bradford would appreciate her and love her. He measured a person's worth by work and money. She was offered a job as a flight attendant for a major airline, but there was no way she could spend five weeks in Minneapolis training. She would never leave Landon that long, and she gladly and proudly accepted the bulk of parental responsibility. She renewed her teaching license and signed up to take a class to get her travel agent license after the holidays.

Their anniversary was in December and quickly approaching. Stella Ann didn't mention it or get a card or gift for Bradford. Her heart wasn't into it. She sensed he had checked out, and the calendar was a ticking clock on their relationship. To her surprise, Bradford invited her to dinner at one of their favorite restaurants, The Train Station Grille, a lovely, renovated old train depot which was an upscale establishment. It was quaint, romantic, and the food was delicious. She always ordered roasted salmon with ginger sauce, a baked potato, and house salad. The bread was always fresh and hot, and dessert was always crème brulee. Stella Ann made every effort to look her best and dressed up in a little black dress, pearls, heels, and full-length mahogany mink coat, which was a trend among area housewives at the time. It wasn't a must for Stella Ann, but it was a gift from Bradford a few years earlier.

The restaurant was busy. It was Christmas, and many people were gathering for celebrations and to see friends during the holidays. They were seated in the fireplace room next to a group of older women celebrating their friendship and Christmas. As soon as Stella Ann and Bradford received their glasses of wine, Bradford lit a cigarette.

Stella Ann leaned over and whispered, "Bradford, you might want to put your cigarette out or step outside to finish it. I noticed the smoke drifting toward the table next to us. It is bothering the group of ladies sitting there." Stella Ann had overheard one lady ask their waiter if they could be moved.

Her suggestion ignited a response in him that caused the guests in the whole dining area to take notice. He stood up. Stella Ann thought he was going outside to finish his cigarette.

"Who are you to tell anyone to do anything? You slept with another man!"

He slapped a $100 bill on the table, grabbed his coat, and left.

Stella Ann sat there unable to move for a few minutes. She collected her coat and purse, looked for their waiter to give him the money and cancel their order, and left into the dark, cold night. Bradford was gone. Their car was not where they parked. He left her, and there was no taxi service on the mountain where they lived.

She started walking down a dark road that led to the main road toward the mountain. Fortunately, she had a house key. It was going to be a long walk home in the cold, but she was not going to call anyone to help her. She did not want anyone to know, and she was humiliated enough. Tears started falling down her cheek. She was thankful Landon was at Claire's to spend the night with Michael.

She was almost on the main road when she heard a vehicle motor behind her. It was Bradford. He demanded she get in the car.

"Get in the damn car, Stella Ann," he yelled.

She ignored the demand and kept looking down.

"I said for you to get in the damn car," he demanded again.

Her heart was pounding. Then she heard him race the engine and get

265

closer to her. He bumped her with the car and knocked her into a soppy wet ditch. She got up and kept walking. He stopped the car and got out.

"Stella Ann, get in the car. I am not going to hurt you. We don't need someone to call the police."

Stella Ann quietly got in the car, but she was terrified and clung to the door handle. When they got to the house, she ran up the back stairs and locked herself in her room. Bradford knocked and begged for an hour assuring her he would not hurt her, but she didn't trust him. He finally went downstairs and left her alone. She was exhausted and fell asleep across the bed still in her dress and wet shoes.

The next day, she was accused of provoking him into inappropriate behavior. It was her fault—everything was her fault. She knew half of their marital trouble was her fault. She could not control his temper or erratic behavior. He made those choices.

She learned rumors were floating around about her. She protected Bradford; he threw her to the gossip wolves.

CHAPTER 13

Nails and No

It was the worst anniversary Stella Ann could have anticipated. How could Bradford say such a vile, private, humiliating thing in public? Their marriage was reduced to flight and fear instead of celebration, healing, restoration, and joy. Stella Ann knew she expected too much considering everything that had happened, but she was hopeful. She decided it was best to forget what happened on their anniversary and move forward.

They stayed in Chattanooga for Christmas. It was a quiet Christmas, and they got along well despite the anniversary disaster. The saying "the calm before the storm" became real during the holidays. January provided time for more healing and kindness. Stella Ann moved into the bedroom again, and their lovemaking activity became more loving and less demanding and forceful.

Stella Ann had hoped her prayers were being answered for restoration of their marriage and keeping her family together. Maybe a vow renewal, a constant movie of her daydreams, was in their future. Hopefully, Bradford wouldn't reject the idea this time. Stella Ann didn't want a divorce, but there was a nagging question she asked herself, "How could she continue to love someone so deeply despite the indifference she experienced?"

She heard the phone ringing in the kitchen as she got out of her car from her morning tennis clinic. Bradford never said a word about how much time or money she spent playing tennis if it kept her skinny. When she answered the phone, there was an odd silence, and a man asked to speak to Dr. Taber.

"I am sorry; he is not here right now. May I take a message?" Stella Ann said.

"He gave me this number to call, and I told him we could take care of the spyware installation on his computer over the phone."

"Can I help you? I know more about the computer than Dr. Taber."

"Are you his secretary?" the man asked.

"No, I am Dr. Taber's wife. Why is he installing spyware onto our computer?"

Stella Ann knew what Bradford was doing. He was going to track her computer activity. Her heart sank as she realized the reconciliation honeymoon during the holidays and the new year was fake. Bradford was planning to gather information on her and track her. He probably had a tracker on her car. She would have to get the car checked.

He replied, "Uh, I am not at liberty to discuss details of an order. Goodbye."

Stella Ann found out it was a company in Florida, and they installed computer spyware for private citizens. Most of the time, the spyware was like a private eye, and it copied a footprint of every stroke of the keyboard. Some offered more sophisticated information gathering devices and software. Stella Ann knew it was no mistake, and Bradford had arranged it. Later, she saw where he had started the installation process by checking their credit card statement. The reply message in the identification tagline on the transaction stated, "installation aborted, refund to follow." What Bradford didn't realize was a footprint of each keyboard stroke was already recorded on the hard drive.

Bradford had given her permission to chat with three of the friends she made online. One was Ellen, her friend in England, another was the musician/physician, and the other one was an attorney in New York. Bradford sat with her or exercised on the bike or treadmill while they chatted. Why was Bradford tracking her? Was he looking up things she was researching?

It wasn't long after the spyware caper when Stella Ann saw Bradford had a chat with a woman online and forgot to shut down the computer. As Stella Ann started reading, she realized Bradford was talking negatively about her, said he was unhappy, was filing for divorce, and planned to meet the woman at The Read House in downtown Chattanooga. He told her how tall, dark, and handsome he was, described his eyes as bedroom eyes, and claimed to be an athlete and real jock, which made Stella Ann want to vomit. He told her what he did for a living, what his interests were, and stated his age as ten years younger than his actual age. As she continued to read, she learned the woman was a young nurse from St. Louis, and Bradford offered to pay for her airline ticket to spend a day with him and show her Chattanooga. Stella Ann immediately hit print. The chat ended up being thirty pages long. It was possible he was having the spyware installed to cover his own butt.

She started her travel agent class after Christmas. It was not unusual for Stella Ann to be late to her night class because she picked Landon up from soccer practice at 5:30 p.m. and made sure dinner was ready before she left for class. Bradford did not offer to help her with Landon's soccer pick-up on the day she had class. Thus, she would be from 10 to 30 minutes late. Her teacher was nice, and other students shared their notes.

Bradford invited Stella Ann to dinner for Valentine's Day, but she offered to make a favorite meal for them. She made her signature Mexican casserole, tacos, and Grammie's Rocky Road fudge brownies for dessert. When Bradford came home from work on Valentine's Day, he stumbled through the back door. Stella Ann suspected they had either had an office party, or he stopped at a local bar for a Valentine's Day drink with a friend or friends. She was reaching for something in the refrigerator when he bumped into her and closed the door. He was wearing his long gray dress coat and pulled a black velvet jewelry box from his pocket pushing it into her face.

"Oh, Bradford, I thought we agreed no gifts for Valentine's Day," Stella Ann said.

"That was not the gratitude and thanks I expected," Bradford said.

"No, Bradford, I didn't mean to seem ungrateful. You know it has been a rough year, and it seems a display of gifts and romantic love today seems phony and dishonest."

"Stella Ann, if I want to give my wife a gift, I will do it. Now, open the damn box."

Stella Ann opened the black velvet box to discover a beautiful diamond and sapphire tennis bracelet. It was stunning and brought tears to Stella Ann's eyes. She thanked him and hugged him for being generous and thoughtful. Bradford always loved to buy jewelry and rarely missed an opportunity to purchase another expensive and extravagant piece. She amassed quite a lovely collection. She wore the bracelet daily for a week when she noticed an oval sapphire missing. She showed it to Bradford, and he said he would take the bracelet back to his jeweler and have it repaired. She never saw the bracelet again.

When Bradford came home from work a few days later, he made a drink, straightened the items on the kitchen counter, and sat down at the kitchen table as Stella Ann finished making dinner.

"Stella Ann, we need to talk," Bradford said.

Here we go again, thought Stella Ann, but she agreed. "Do I need to sit at the table, Bradford?" I am almost finished making dinner."

"No, it's fine. Finish making dinner. We can wait until after dinner to talk."

It seemed every time she made spaghetti, Bradford wanted to have a serious conversation. She sat down at the table, and they ate dinner in silence. Stella Ann cleared the table, Landon went upstairs to study, and Bradford lit a cigarette.

Returning to the table, Stella Ann said, "Are you ready for our conversation?"

"Stella Ann, you know we have had a rough time of it for several years, and this reconciliation is not working for me."

"What do you mean not working for you?" Stella Ann said.

"I am not feeling it, Stella Ann. I want out. I can forgive you for what you have done, but I can't forget it and never will. I want a divorce, and I want you to file."

"What? Not feeling what? For what I have done? What about what you have done over the years?" She knew she should not have gone there, but self-preservation took over. "I guess I misread how things were going for us lately. Our relationship seemed to be improving these last few weeks. Is there someone else again?" Stella Ann asked. She knew it was. It was always someone else.

"No," he said. "Do what I asked you to do. "Call your attorney and have the papers served at my office. I want people to see what you have done to me."

Stella Ann didn't even respond. She decided she would call her attorney the next morning. When she was studying for her travel agent class in the playroom, her emotions took over. He wanted out and wanted her to take the fall. What was worse than the brutality of her taking the fall was his cold, heartless delivery. She had never cried so hard in her life, and she could not stop the tears.

Landon entered the room, patted her on the shoulder, and said, "Mom, please don't cry. We will be fine."

She grabbed him and held on tight. He was an amazing young man with empathy beyond his age.

"He doesn't want me, Landon. He never has."

The next day, she called her attorney and directed her to serve divorce papers. She told Stella Ann she would notify her when the papers had been delivered to Bradford. She asked again to make sure Stella Ann wanted the divorce papers served at the office, and Stella Ann confirmed it telling her those were Bradford's instructions. It was not going to be an easy divorce. Stella Ann knew she would be fighting the whole family, and they were ruthless.

"Yes, serve the papers at his office. It was what he requested."

She started making lists of things that needed to be accomplished. She needed to get a job, she needed to meet with Landon's teacher, and she needed to find a place for her and Landon to live. Time was of the essence, and attorney meetings seemed endless. Bradford didn't care how long the divorce took. He would carry on with his girlfriends and be seen in public with them humiliating her, but Stella Ann was bound legally not to see anyone since they did not have a legal separation. It was financially better for him to keep Stella Ann in limbo and suspended in life. It was also an example of continued control and manipulation.

The first person she called after her attorney was a teaching colleague who had moved into an administrative position. She had always liked her and knew she could relate to Stella Ann's situation. When she answered the phone, Stella Ann shocked herself and burst into tears. Then she collected herself and told her friend what was going on and asked if she knew of a teaching job there or at any other private school for the coming year. It was still early because contracts were not issued until mid-March, but maybe someone had already made the decision not to return. It was a chance Stella Ann had to take. Stella Ann's friend said she would keep her in mind and would call if she heard of an opening for the next school year. She assured Stella Ann she would keep their call confidential and told her not to worry about the tears.

When Bradford came home, the reception was icy, and the mood was tense.

"Stella Ann, I hope you are happy. You proceeded to humiliate me yet again in front of my staff and patients by having the divorce papers served at my office."

"Bradford, you said many times you wanted to be served at the office."

"Stella Ann! I didn't think you would do it!" he screamed.

"I asked you three times if you were sure that was the procedure you preferred. I was afraid not to follow your instructions."

"You are afraid of me? Why are you afraid of me, Stella Ann?" Bradford demanded.

"I have been afraid of you for years because I never know how you are going to respond. I can't trust what you say, and you get tongue-biting and fist-clenching angry if I step out of my box and push back."

"Plus," she continued, "I didn't think we would ever be getting a divorce! I thought our bond was stronger. I thought we could work through our issues. I know I made a huge mistake. I have looked the other way many times when you faltered. I thought we could overcome the hiccups in our marriage."

"What makes you think I believe you only made one mistake, Stella Ann? Do not ever say another word to me. You do not exist. You are of no use to me, Stella Ann. You are dead." Bradford stomped to the bedroom and slammed the door.

He terrified Stella Ann. She went upstairs to her room and locked her door.

By the end of March, she received a call from her teaching friend about an opening to teach literature and reading strategies in the upper school. Stella Ann taught fifth grade reading in the afternoons early in her teaching career, so it would be a familiar subject. Her friend helped her arrange an interview with Dr. Stafford. Because he was retiring, she would also be interviewed by the new administrator, who was coming in for a few days to meet the faculty and interview new teachers.

Stella Ann realized getting the job was going to be a challenge and was prepared by Dr. Stafford to expect the process to be different. Dr. Stafford was wonderful, and Stella Ann always loved talking with him. He made her feel like he had all the time in the world, and he seemed interested in any topic up for discussion. She respected him as a man of honor and integrity.

She felt during the Dr. Stafford era of her teaching career that teachers were appreciated. He advocated for them. She never felt underrated but understood and admired for her natural teaching style and God-given gifts and talents. She was pushed to do more and helped with music when needed or asked. She helped coach tennis and loved it. She was more than a faculty member, as was the rest of the faculty. She was seen as a professional who had much to contribute to the school. It was a good feeling for Stella Ann. It was important to feel like she was a viable member of the team and the faculty family.

The educator, who many wanted to take Dr. Stafford's place, decided not to move his young family to Chattanooga. Many were disappointed because they thought he would bring a new vision and solid, steady growth to the school. The next in line for the job seemed distant and focused on his mission rather than on relationships. The fact that Stella Ann had been part of the school and church community for years offered her no favors. The direction of the school appeared to be moving from a classical, traditional education, which was the foundation of the school, toward more progressive ideologies.

Stella Ann rose above what she perceived as immature questions and an ivy league attitude during her conference. She remained confident and positive throughout the interview. The new administrator made it abundantly clear Stella Ann's job offer was out of respect for Dr. Stafford. The delivery was direct and clear. Stella Ann was at the bottom of his list of desirable candidates for the job. The main reason she was not a top pick was she lacked extra degrees and went to a state school. In the same breath, she was told Dr. Stafford would extend her a formal contract, but her status would be probationary. She had never heard such formality or intimidation in her profession before, and it concerned her for about a split second. She simply wondered why it was necessary. Posturing had to be the reason. She was grateful and made up her mind to be loyal and supportive of the new principal regardless of her instincts.

Stella Ann quickly learned in her new work environment the worth of a person depended on the number of degrees behind their name and the school they attended instead of one's ability to do the job and have a strong work ethic. Experience meant nothing. She had been out of the workforce for seven years, and a lot had changed. She made a mental note to herself to stay current and relevant in her career. She let a glimmer of disgust filter in because women were penalized for being stay-at-home moms. It was obvious the years she was taking care of her family and running a home did not count toward her ability or skill set.

The next month was busy as she studied for her travel agent class, took care of Landon, answered phone calls, fielded letters from her three attorneys, prepared discovery for trial and tried to find a place for her and Landon to live. Landon went with her on weekends to visit possible homes for sale or rent around the area. Nothing seemed to work for them. The space would be too small or the rent too high. Without a downpayment, negotiations stopped. If she took money from the marital funds, it would be used against her in court.

Bradford became increasingly elusive and verbally condescending. At times, Stella Ann and Landon received "the silent treatment." Bradford refused to move out of the house, which made life even more difficult. She could hear him talking with women on the phone through the master bedroom door. It was devastating and added to the tension in their living environment.

She was in the study reading when tears and wretched crying consumed her. Her grief and fear caused emotional distress regardless of where she was or what she was doing. She would be in the grocery store, driving, reading, cleaning, cooking, or playing tennis and become overwhelmed with tears. They weren't quiet tears either. They were messy tears that caused heaving, a runny nose, and streaks down her face. She had to leave whatever she was doing to retreat to a bathroom or to the car to collect herself. She knew they were tears of fear, but they were also tears of grief for her marriage and her family and of dreams that divorce splattered into a dark hole. She couldn't bury her emotions.

On her way to get Landon from school, she stumbled into a new zero-lot-line development tucked into a quiet area. It was a gated community, and many houses were being built. Stella Ann stopped at the model home and talked with a nice real estate agent. He took her through the model home and showed her other plan options available. The beauty of the area was the location and safety factors. She and Landon would be behind a coded security gate. She could choose a plan to meet their needs and alter the plans as necessary to accommodate privacy for Landon and herself. She could also choose the finishings like the flooring, cabinetry, and fixtures.

She would need a $1,000 deposit to start building. To Stella Ann, it might as well be a million dollars. Knowing she did not have a penny to spare, she did not let that dampen her spirit. Somehow, someway she would produce the money. She could sell her jewelry. She and Landon went back to the building site after she picked him up from school, and he approved. If they started the house by the first of April, it would be ready for them to move in by August before school started for both.

She went through every purse she owned, gathered the money from the laundry room she collected from pockets, and grabbed the cash she kept on hand for incidentals like candy kids sold door to door, fruit orders from the high school band, Girl Scout cookies, and the cleaners. She sat on her bed and counted it. She had less than $200.

She got out her jewelry box and inspected each piece of jewelry she felt she could sell. She decided most of the jewelry Bradford had given her would go, including her wedding rings. She collected thirteen pieces of jewelry and made plans to see a broker the next day to see how much money she could get for them. She also decided that many of her designer clothes could be sold and put an ad in the newspaper.

Landon knocked on her door to tell her goodnight, and Stella Ann noticed his hands were in his pockets.

"Mom, I came to say goodnight and to tell you everything will be OK."

Stella Ann felt terrible, she had put Landon in a position to be her strength and optimism. He had saved her life on more than one occasion when Bradford had been out of control and angry with her. He bounded down the entry stairs twice and knocked Bradford off her when Bradford had a choke hold on her.

"Landon, you are right. Everything will be OK. We must find a place for us to live. I must figure out how to find the money we need to start the house."

Landon emptied his pockets onto her bed. The bills covered her duvet. Dollar bills, tens, twenties, fifties. The money was from the savings he kept in a plastic trick-or-treat jack-o-lantern in the attic located at the end of his closet.

"Mom, I counted the money. It should be about $800. With that money and with what you have, will we be able to get out of here?"

Stella Ann sat there unable to move. It was an unbelievable scene. They were living in a million-dollar house and scraping together what they could to start building a small house, a home.

"Oh, Landon, I can't take the money you worked for, received as gifts, and saved."

"Mom, you can pay me back when we get settled into our new life, and you have a paycheck. Right now, we need to start the house."

Landon was fourteen years old and well beyond his years in

intelligence, maturity, common sense, and kindness. He was compassionate and had a heart.

"Landon, I will call the real estate agent tomorrow morning and see if we can meet him after school to pick out a lot among the three left and sign the papers to start the house."

Stella Ann gave him a hug as he walked down the hall to his room. They had $1,000 and a copy of her teaching contract. They were going to start a new life in a safe place. Stella Ann called her attorney to get guidance about marital property and building a house in her name only. The test would be if Bradford would sign a release not to claim any part of the new property. He gladly signed to get rid of her.

Stella Ann and Landon selected a lot for their home at the back of the development on the small lake. The huge backyard would offer privacy and safety for them. It would be a peaceful place for them to sit by the bank and watch the ducks and turtles play. Another beauty of the area was that it was close to Landon's school.

They picked out a small two-story plan and altered the upstairs to change two small bedrooms into a large bedroom for Landon. They decided to turn the space above the garage into a TV room for Landon. They picked out light hardwood floors, tile, and paint, and Stella Ann decided to splurge and spend extra money on a small screened-in porch. She thought it would be a lovely place to grade papers and have a glass of wine in the afternoon as she looked out over the lake. The house would take four months to complete depending on the amount of spring rain in the area. They started the house and had until the first of August to produce the closing costs.

The most she could get for her jewelry was $1300. The array of jewelry included a gold chain with a diamond drop, pearl and diamond earrings, a sapphire and gold necklace slide, a diamond necklace slide, diamond stud earrings, an emerald ring, two gold bracelets, a gold and diamond broach, a diamond tennis bracelet, and her marquise cut two-carat diamond engagement ring and gold wedding band.

The broker told her a cubic zirconia was worth more than her engagement ring because her diamond was filled with black spots and yellow flaws. He showed her the flaws with his magnifying equipment and lights and showed her the value scale of the diamond from his reference guide. It was the lowest grade diamond that could be purchased. He offered her the value of the gold setting. She did not have a choice, and let all the jewelry go, but she was plenty upset she had been sporting what wasn't much more than a fake diamond for years. She realized her whole life was fake.

She had to have money for the closing costs in August, or they would lose the house. She got permission from Bradford to have a couple of yard sales. The school contacted her to teach the first session of summer school, and she did not hesitate at the opportunity. She needed yard sale money to put food on the table as well as pay bills. The legal steps for her to receive child support and maintenance would take a while to complete. She and Landon needed at least $4,000 for the closing cost of their new home. She had to do this herself. She had no one to turn to for help.

The house needed to be listed for sale, or Bradford would need to buy her half out. Bradford was not cooperative as they talked with the real estate agent, and it was obvious something was amiss with him. He was usually cordial and polite when he met someone, but not this time. It took a long time for Bradford to join them in the dining room.

As they sat at the elaborate dining room table, waiting for Bradford to join them, the agent leaned over to Stella Ann and said, "Mrs. Taber, do not be embarrassed. I know you two are going through a hard time."

"I am humiliated at how disrespectful and difficult he is being. Did you see him fall up the foyer stairway?"

"Mrs. Taber, I have seen it all, but I will have to say, I feel sorry for you. People develop emotional ties to their houses, and your husband thinks his house is the best and biggest home in Chattanooga. It is not. We need to get him to agree to a reasonable price today."

They had the outside of the house painted and made repairs at the suggestion of their real estate agent. After two more meetings, they agreed on a starting sale price. The agent made it clear the price continued to be an extremely high starting point.

She was studying for her travel agent exam late in April when the phone rang. It was Norma.

"Stella Ann, this is Norma. I know we are not supposed to be talking with each other because you are in divorce proceedings with Bradford, but I want to talk with you about my jewelry."

"What jewelry are you talking about, Norma? It is not an appropriate time for me to be talking. I am studying for my travel agent exam."

"You will talk to me, Stella Ann. I want my jewelry back."

"Are you talking about the jewelry you gave me several years ago when you gave Bradford Grammie's silver?"

"Yes, that is the jewelry, the rubies and diamonds. I want it back."

"I thought it was a gift, Norma, but Bradford has it in the lockbox at the bank. He said it would be something from you for Landon someday. Tell him to give it to you. I don't have it."

"Yes, you do, and you will talk with me. I will get my jewelry back."

"I am studying. Please leave me alone."

Within minutes, Scott, Bradford's brother, called. "Stella Ann, why are you being so mean to my mom? She hasn't done anything to you."

"Scott, I am not being mean to your mother, and I am not discussing this with you. Call Bradford to get what she wants."

As she left the building where she took her travel agent exam, Stella Ann got a call from her attorney.

"Mrs. Taber, this is Matt, an associate at the law firm, where are you right now?"

"I am just leaving the testing site. I took my travel agent exam. I am excited that I passed and am meeting a girlfriend for lunch to celebrate."

"Can you come to my office after lunch? Something has come up in your case, and my partner turned this part of your divorce over to me."

"What are you talking about, Matt?"

"Mrs. Taber, we have just received a letter from your mother-in-law's attorney that you are being sued for some jewelry. I need to ask you a lot of questions. It will be a separate legal process from your divorce."

"I will be there by 1:00 p.m."

Stella Ann was livid. She called Bradford.

"Your mother is suing me, Bradford. What is she thinking? At the most vulnerable time for us, she is inserting herself into our lives again and making more trouble. You know the jewelry is in the lock box at the bank. Give her the jewelry!"

"Stella Ann, I told her not to get this started. I will sign a document stating I was present when she gave you the jewelry. It was the weekend they came here for my birthday, and she gave me Grammie's silver."

"Thank you, Bradford. I know things are tense for us, but I do appreciate your help with this. I would never steal anything from anyone, and you know it."

Stella Ann thought the matter was resolved, and Bradford was going to get the jewelry from the bank and give it to his mom. She thought Bradford would convince his mom to drop the lawsuit. It wasn't a horrible day. She passed her exam, and she had renewed trust in Bradford that he would convince Norma to drop her frivolous lawsuit against her.

They sat on the front porch one afternoon in mid-May and, in conversation, commented about how they were getting along better than ever. They even questioned the divorce, but Stella Ann knew those were only fleeting thoughts. Their marriage was over.

She excused herself to take Landon to meet his friends at the movie and to pick up a few groceries on the way back. When she returned, she was putting groceries away, and what came next was out of nowhere. It caught Stella Ann off guard. She never got used to Bradford's verbal and emotional ambushes.

"Haven't I told you over and over to never wear red?" Bradford said in a commanding voice.

"Excuse me? You have never told me not to wear red. I can wear red whenever I want to wear red. It's my favorite color."

Stella Ann ran errands that day and was wearing a red linen dress with a hem right above her ankles, a white short-sleeved cardigan, and red sandals.

Bradford continued, "Dammit, I have told you when you wear anything red, you look sexy and catch the attention of men. For now, you are still my wife and will do what I tell you to do."

She walked past him to go to the family room to watch the news when he came up behind her and grabbed her. He had a steel lock grip on her. He was a strong man. It was hard to fight him off.

"You have given me an erection, and dammit, you are going to take care of it!"

"Let me go, Bradford. You are hurting my arms."

"Oh, come on, Stella Ann. You know you want me. You know you like rough sex. Come on, let's go to the bedroom and make love one more time for old time's sake."

"No!"

He grabbed her and dragged her to the bedroom ripping her dress. He threw her on the bed, kissed her hard, and was determined to have his way with her. She was kicking and screaming. He hit her between the legs and on her upper thighs, then he held her down by her shoulders. She was still kicking and screaming for him to stop.

"Let me go, Bradford! Let me up." After a mighty struggle, Stella Ann broke away, ran to the kitchen, grabbed her purse, fled out the kitchen door, and got to her car. She was crying so hard she could barely see to drive but made her way to the theater parking lot where she was going to pick Landon up after the movie. She always made sure Landon was safe.

She looked down at her wrinkled dress where it was torn, and her tears made big burgundy wet spots down the front. She straightened the dress out as much as she could. Her glasses were broken on the side, and the places on her arms and legs where Bradford grabbed and hit her were sore. She looked at her face. No signs of a fight were evident. Bradford stopped hitting her in the face when people started noticing she was wearing sunglasses when they weren't needed.

She hoped in the dark Landon would not be able to see the evidence of Bradford's demands. Demands orchestrated to use against her in the divorce. Bradford knew sexual relations between them would negate any divorce proceedings in progress. It was all about money, alimony, and child support. Stella Ann decided to take the necessary steps to get Bradford to move out of the house.

The next day, she had a big tennis tournament which determined the teams that made it to the state playoffs in Memphis. It was important to her. Most players had their families there for support. She wished Burt could be there. He watched her play often in high school when he picked her up and waited for her practices to end. In all the years Stella Ann played tennis, Bradford never saw her play. Landon came to a lot of her matches. She would miss him. He brought her good luck.

Stella Ann planned to go home to Columbia for her nephew's graduation after the match. Bradford and Landon were going to spend the weekend at the lake to prepare the property for the summer. It would be good for Stella Ann and Bradford to have time away from each other, and Landon needed some time with his father. Stella Ann wanted Bradford and Landon to have the relationship they enjoyed when Landon was little. She would do nothing to prevent their time together.

The lineup showed she was playing with a girl she didn't know well, but she was a steady player with a calm demeanor. She would offset Stella Ann's tendency to lose focus. When Stella Ann walked to the court, her doubles partner pointed to her legs and arms.

"Stella Ann, did you have a car accident? What happened to your legs and arms?"

Stella Ann had not paid attention to the deep purple bruises up and down her legs and arms. She was busy trying to get Bradford and Landon off to the lake and get to the tennis court on time.

"Oh, you know how clumsy I am. I was moving a piece of furniture and bumped into the wall and anything else in the way."

She thought to herself, "Damn these short tennis skirts!" She had to giggle to herself though. Landon demanded she change out of her tennis wear before she picked him up at school. She had to remember to cover her legs more. As serious as things got in her life, Stella Ann counted on her sense of humor to gloss over the deep hurt.

Their team captain came up to Stella Ann and asked if they could talk off the court.

"Stella Ann, this is more than an injury from moving furniture. Come clean. How did you get those bruises? The girls have seen bruises on you before. We must report these things."

"Please," Stella Ann said with tears starting to stream. "Please don't pressure me to talk about this now. Please don't report anything. I want to win this match and get on the highway to Columbia for my nephew's graduation."

They won within a short time 6-2, 6-0, and Stella Ann went to the house to pack the car to leave for Columbia. She got the mail, took a shower, and loaded the car. As she walked through the kitchen, she stopped at the counter and thumbed through the mail. There was a letter from the county courthouse where the lake house was located. Stella Ann thought it was something about the water bill, which was always late, and opened it. It wasn't the water bill. It was a warrant for Bradford's arrest for having an open container in his car during the time she and Landon were on the cruise. He had missed the court date more than once. She immediately tried to call Bradford's cell phone, but the cell connections in the area were awful, so she called Norma.

"Norma, this is Stella Ann. Have Bradford and Landon arrived at the lake, or have you heard from them this morning? I can't get Bradford to answer his phone or his beeper."

"Stella Ann, I am not supposed to talk with you. No, I haven't seen them."

"Norma, please, if you see them or talk with them, tell Bradford to have Landon drive the car this weekend. Landon has a hardship license. He can drive to school and back home, but this is an emergency. If the county police stop Bradford, he will end up in jail, Norma."

"What? You are lying! You are trying to pull anything to get Bradford in trouble so you can take everything in the divorce."

"No, Norma, you are wrong. If he is stopped the police will automatically take Bradford to jail. You know how aggressive law enforcement is in that county. Please, I am trying to keep Bradford and Landon safe."

"You have stooped to a new low this time, Stella Ann. Do not ever call this house again."

Stella Ann tried to intercept what could be a very bad situation and had to trust Landon would take care of himself. She pulled out of the driveway to get to the safety, comfort, and peace of her family in

Columbia. She hadn't been home in months. Bradford didn't return her call.

When she got to Columbia, Burt was sitting on the back porch in one of his favorite spots. He immediately saw her bruises and had Lou get his camera. Burt was livid as he took at least twenty pictures of the bruises scattered all over Stella Ann's legs and arms. Neither asked for details of what happened, as they sensed Stella Ann was upset and tired. It was a conversation best left for the next day.

The following Tuesday, Bradford left for work later than usual and was wearing a plaid shirt with no tie instead of his usual dress slacks, white or blue heavily starched shirt, designer tie, leather cordovan dress shoes, and fresh lab coat. Stella Ann mentioned his dressed-down look, and he didn't respond. She didn't push the issue but saw it as a red flag that something was amiss. Landon was still asleep since it was exam week, and he only had to be at school for the exam he was scheduled to take that day.

Later in the morning, Landon was in the study off the upstairs gallery preparing for his afternoon exam when he leaned over the banister and called to Stella Ann in the kitchen that he saw police cars in front of their house. Stella Ann told him they were probably looking for Jack, a young man who lived across the street and was suspected of selling drugs. Living in their upscale neighborhood was a cover-up for Jack. No one in the neighborhood interacted with Jack, but teenagers from high school gathered information about him. He had Rottweiler fight dogs in the backyard that got out occasionally and proved to be a danger to residents and pets in the area.

Four deputies came to the porch and rang the doorbell. Stella Ann answered it, thinking she was going to direct them to Jack's house. They came into the large foyer, and Stella Ann backed up to the staircase. Landon leaned over the banister to see what was happening.

"Are you Stella Ann Langston Taber?" the big burly deputy asked.

"Yes, I am. Can I help you?"

"Mrs. Taber, you have been served," as he pushed a large document envelope in her face.

"What are you talking about? My husband and I have already taken care of divorce papers."

"Do you know Norma Elizabeth Clark Bailey Taber?"

"Yes, she is my mother-in-law."

"She has filed a lawsuit against you. I need you to sign your name on this clipboard document indicating you have received the papers."

"Are you kidding me?"

"Mom," Landon yelled from the banister. "Are they taking you to jail?"

"No, Landon, they are not taking me to jail." Stella Ann said as she ushered the men out of the house.

"Mom, are you in trouble? Why is grandmother suing you? Does dad know?" Landon was loaded with questions.

"No, Landon, I am not in trouble. Please concentrate on studying for the exam you have this afternoon."

Stella Ann went to the kitchen and was shaking as she opened the envelope. Norma was suing her for theft of three pieces of jewelry. Stella Ann sat there in disbelief but knew she had to kick into action. She began to realize it was a plan Bradford and Norma may have concocted at the lake.

Stella Ann suspected Bradford and Norma planned to have her served with papers as a distraction from the divorce. Bradford knew what was going to happen that morning. Bradford must have gone to his attorney's office instead of work. It explained why he was dressed so casually. Stella Ann thought about all the names Bradford had thrown out as his attorney. She called each office to see if he was there.

"This is Mrs. Taber. We are having a little emergency at home. Dr. Taber mentioned he might see Mr. Roberts today when he left the house. May I speak with him?"

"Yes, ma'am, Dr. Taber just went into Mr. Roberts' office. I will put you through."

Bingo! Stella Ann had figured out the identity of Bradford's attorney by elimination.

"Bradford, I wanted to alert you to the fact you and your mother are responsible for scaring the hell out of our son. Having me served with papers by four huge sheriff deputies in two cars while Landon studied for exams was beyond cruel."

"What do you mean, Stella Ann?"

"You did not give the jewelry to your mother over the weekend. You two plotted to have me served with papers for a lawsuit today. You collaborated to get Norma's frivolous lawsuit started. Where is the letter you were going to write saying that you knew for a fact, I did not steal anything from your mother?"

"I don't remember telling you I would write a letter for you. I forgot the circumstances that surrounded you getting Mom's jewelry. You may have taken it from her bedroom when we were at the lake. Maybe Mom loaned it to you, and you forgot you had it."

"You were sitting right next to me on our den sofa when she pulled the jewelry out of her purse six years ago and gave it to me. You told me to accept the jewelry, or your mother would have her feelings hurt. She gave you Grammie's silver flatware at the same time. Oh my gosh, Bradford! You have been brainwashed for three pieces of jewelry not worth over $1500. I had it appraised six years ago before you took it to the lockbox at the bank. You said we would give it to Landon someday, so he would have something from his grandmother."

She had to get Bradford out of the house. She didn't feel safe, and now she had confirmation she was fighting the whole family in the divorce.

The next day after she dropped Landon off at school for his exam, she went to the police department to get information about how to get Bradford out of the house. She took the red dress and the pictures Burt took of her bruises to the police station. The police took just as many pictures of her as Burt. If she filed a report, police would escort Bradford off the premises. If she filed a complaint, they would arrest him. She didn't want Bradford arrested even though he deserved it, so she filed a report and was advised by the department to stay in a safe place in the house. They would escort him to the house to collect some of his belongings and make him leave.

Within an hour, they arrived at the side entrance of the house. Stella Ann watched from the playroom window. There was a police car in front of him and a police car behind him. Four police officers escorted him to the door. She couldn't help but have a twinge of sadness in her heart as she saw them help Bradford load his belongings into his car. She didn't know where he would go. She didn't care. He was ordered to stay away from her and Landon.

She told Landon what happened when she picked him up from his exam.

"Mom, you and dad should have divorced a long time ago when I was ten."

There were many things to arrange and sell before they could move into their new house. When Bradford left, he left financial obligations as well until the court ordered him to pay child support. She would get no spousal support until the divorce was final. She and Landon went regularly to check on the house construction, and each time the building was on schedule. It looked like they would close on the new house the first week in August. She had a lot of money to gather before they could close.

One afternoon in mid-July, there was a loud knock on the kitchen door. Landon was not at home, and Stella Ann was startled to see an angry Bradford at the back door.

"Hello, Bradford, what can I do for you?"

"I came to bring you the child support money I have been ordered to give you. I went to the bank, and instead of depositing my check the stupid teller cashed it. Here."

When Stella Ann reached out her hand, Bradford looked at her with angry eyes and pierced lips, slapped her hand, pointed his finger at her and said, "I hate your guts, bitch. You think you are going to destroy me, but I always come out smelling like a rose. Don't you ever forget that. I always come out smelling like a rose. I will rise above this, Stella Ann. You will be the fool. I can't wait to get you out of my life forever!"

There was an awkward silence, and Stella Ann said nothing.

Then Bradford threw the money inside the door onto the kitchen floor behind her. He turned abruptly and left.

Stella Ann started picking the money up like it was manna from heaven. It was cash. There was enough money along with the money she and Landon had accumulated to pay their closing cost. They were going to be able to move into their new house. She cried tears of joy and said a quiet prayer of gratitude.

It was a busy summer. Their yard sales kept them afloat until they could move. They closed on the house at the end of July. Landon went with Stella Ann to the closing, and both were nervous. To have Landon by her side meant the world to Stella Ann. Without his unselfish generosity, getting a place to live was not an option.

Bradford wouldn't hesitate to put them out in the street. Along with his caring and gentle bedside manner, he had a cold, harsh streak few recognized. When he was through with someone or they could no longer do anything for him, he threw them away. Over the years, Stella Ann saw how Bradford tossed friends, family, and co-workers out of his life never looking back. She never thought she would be one of his castaways. She had totally misread their relationship. But had she?

She and Landon sat in the car in silence taking in the closing experience and the relief of having a place to go. They were going to be OK. Then they decided where they wanted to go to dinner to celebrate. They decided on a great burger place in the North Shore area and enjoyed every bite of their burgers and fries. They even tried their hand throwing sandwich picks at the ceiling to see if they would stick. It was a tradition at the restaurant. For the first time in a long while, they were laughing and carefree.

The closing costs were not as much as she thought, so there was money left to arrange for a mover, buy a sofa for the living room, a bed for Stella Ann, and a chest for Landon. Along with the furniture she inherited, they would be comfortable. It was ridiculous for them to be required to buy furniture because the big house was filled to the brim with designer pieces and antiques, but Bradford refused to let them take things they needed. She didn't care about things anyway. She wanted peace and safety for herself and her son.

Even though Burt was in poor health and mobility was difficult, he and Lou came to Chattanooga to help with the move. They stayed until Stella Ann and Landon got settled in their school routines. There was so much to get done, and having Lou and Burt there to greet landscapers, drapery hangers, the piano tuner, and to hang pictures was a tremendous help. Landon and his friends moved their clothes and small items. They had four days to get things in place before school started.

The day before school started, they were preparing to eat lunch, and someone knocked on the door. Stella Ann thought it was the washer and dryer delivery, but it was Bradford. He was charmingly polite and asked if he could come in and see where his wife and son would be living. She hated it when he continued to refer to her as his wife. He had tossed her out of his life years ago. Exhausted and not wanting to cause a confrontation in front of Landon, Lou, and Burt, she allowed him in. Lou and Burt took their sandwiches to the patio to eat. Burt especially did not want to see Bradford. The images of Stella Ann's bruises were still fresh in his mind.

Bradford asked for a tour of the house, and Landon joined Stella Ann. Bradford looked in every nook, cranny, drawer, and closet for anything they may have taken without his permission. As he left, he reminded Landon of their dinner plans for the following Wednesday night. Stella Ann and Landon stood at the closed front door, took a deep breath, and agreed it was an awkward encounter.

"Come on, Landon, let's finish lunch. We have a lot to accomplish today." They joined Burt and Lou on the porch.

Lou said, "Stella Ann, Bradford cannot come over here whenever he wants. This is yours and Landon's house, and he is not supposed to be around you."

"Mama, I don't think he will come over here again. He wanted to see what we took from the big house more than anything. He is moving back into the house tomorrow, so we need to go over there tonight to clean and get the last of the items we left. Our house was the last one to be finished, and the real estate agent said the gate code would be effective starting next week. I will contact my attorney and tell her what happened here today."

She started her new job the next day, and it was comforting knowing Lou and Burt were at the house because Landon had not started classes.

She was walking familiar halls and reconnecting with many friends she taught with before and with those who taught Landon. She was excited to be back in the classroom again. The members of her teaching team were wonderful and kind, which gave Stella Ann a sense of security and confidence.

Before she left for school, she got a call from one of her dearest friends and former tennis partner. Her friend, Gwen, unloaded on Stella Ann for getting a divorce and for moving. Stella Ann could not handle her disrespect and lack of understanding, especially since she was getting ready to start a new job in minutes. The rationale Gwen gave Stella Ann for staying in a horrible marriage was that Bradford was a good provider, bought her jewelry, fur coats, and a big house, and took her on nice trips. Stella Ann could not understand her reasoning, but her friend had always been taken care of by her husband and her father. She had never earned a paycheck in her life. Stella Ann had enough on her plate without being chastised by someone she thought was her friend. Obviously, Gwen was not her friend. Stella Ann decided to distance herself from such negativity.

Stella Ann was not shocked when she got a letter from Bradford's attorney. Bradford changed his mind about things he authorized her to take from the house, which proved the reason he stopped at the new house was to itemize what he wanted back. They went through the big house together and tagged what each of them wanted. Stella Ann asked him to review the list of what she wanted four different times. He would never be specific about what he wanted her to leave. He repeated over and over it was only stuff, and he did not care what Stella Ann took.

He demanded she return four dining room chairs. She kept them. He wanted the piano; he didn't play. Landon asked for a picture and a chair, and Bradford would never give him an answer. Landon took them to the new house. Bradford maintained the division had not been done fairly but would not give specifics of his complaint. Stella Ann ignored the letter and didn't bring up the fact Bradford was getting the lake house and all its contents, which included things that had been made by her parents and things that had belonged to her grandmother.

Answers to discovery questions were due by October, and their court date was set for the first of November. Stella Ann visited her attorney's office many times to prepare for the proceedings. She hated to have to take off work since she had just started, but she had no choice. It was a cold, rainy day as she made her way downtown to her attorney's office. She was told to meet her attorney there, and they would walk to the courthouse together. They waited and waited. After two hours, the judge's office called and said the proceedings were canceled because Dr. Taber did not show up at his attorney's office.

Bradford was manipulating the system. Manipulation was something he mastered years before. Not only was she stressed about the divorce, but she faced the lawsuit by Norma and mounting legal bills from three attorneys. Her jewelry lawsuit attorney was trying to keep the jewelry suit out of court because it could be used against Stella Ann in the divorce case even if the whole thing was a lie.

It was a rainy evening in October when she got another phone call from Scott, Bradford's brother. He demanded the jewelry, which Stella Ann did not have. He said his mother was not in good health and did not need the stress of the lawsuit.

"Scott, Norma brought this on herself. I don't have the jewelry she gave me. Bradford has it, so you need to talk with him," Stella Ann said. "Now, I need to go because I should not be talking with you about this."

"Stella Ann, you better do what you are told. Mom's jewelry better show up, or you might be found at the bottom of the lake behind your house tied to cinder blocks," Scott threatened.

Stella Ann hung up without saying a word. She took him seriously. The next day she informed her attorney of Scott's call.

Eventually the judge ordered the bank lockbox to be opened. The jewelry was there. Norma was ordered to pay Stella Ann's legal bills and issue a formal written apology. Bradford paid the legal bills, and Stella Ann never received an apology.

Some of her friends felt the need to tell her what Bradford was doing before, during, and after the divorce. When she started teaching again, her divorce had just begun. Before chapel one Monday morning, a longtime friend told her she had seen Bradford the weekend before at the

291

Chattanooga Ball with a young blonde woman. She said they were dancing and showing a lot of public displays of affection. She thought Stella Ann needed to know. What it did was send Stella Ann into the ladies' room heaving among a flood of tears. She was an emotional wreck, and school was a place of peace, joy, and safety for her. When she asked the messenger if she would testify in court, she answered with a loud no. No one wanted to get involved in another person's divorce, but they sure did want to get involved in the gossip.

Friends, family, and acquaintances back home had the best intentions. They told her about sightings of Bradford and a girl from a nearby town. Stella Ann knew he had already been seeing her during their marriage. She was the petite redhead he entertained at the lake when Bradford sent her and Landon on a cruise. He brought her out of the closet to meet friends and family as well as help set her up in business. Stella Ann and Bradford were not yet divorced, but things were different for men than for women in the divorce world. Men were free to carry on their lives and do whatever they wanted. Women weren't.

The mother of a student Stella Ann taught and was in Landon's class stopped her in the church hall one morning to chat. She told Stella Ann outlandish stories and lies were being told about her in Bible study class. She included she had been at a cocktail party where Bradford had the full attention of a large group as he was making accusations about her. Unless she was told who told the lies and what the lies were, the information was of no use to Stella Ann. There was much she had to let go, let fly, and let others determine what junk they would believe or discard. Apparently, they didn't learn much about the Bible in the class. Stella Ann was at her capacity for burden and responsibility. She ended up in the restroom in tears again.

A court date no show by Bradford happened twice. Stella Ann knew why he kept delaying even though he wanted the divorce. It was all about control. Her attorney explained it benefited Bradford not to settle because alimony would be added to his child support payments. Every time a court date was canceled, it cost each of them $1400, which was an added financial burden for Stella Ann. Bradford had plenty of money, so court costs didn't matter to him.

After years of divorce games, they agreed to mediation. It took two different long sessions for them to come to an agreement, and a court date was set for the judge to put the final nail in the marital coffin.

Stella Ann would never forget the divorce morning as long as she lived. Landon offered to go with her, but she felt like he did not need to be exposed to the divorce court process. Her brother, Ron, called the night before and offered to drive from Columbia to go with her. It was a reasonable drive, and she appreciated the gesture but declined. In hindsight, she wished she had said yes to Ron.

She went to her attorney's office, and they walked to the courthouse together. As they entered the courthouse, her attorney directed her about her responses and briefed her about what to expect. When they went into the court room, Stella Ann was overwhelmed at how many people were there. It seemed each person who had a ten o'clock court appearance appointment brought their whole family. She had no one.

She was the only person on her bench. It was lonely. A strong feeling of abandonment washed over her. She had felt the fear of abandonment over the years with Bradford's threats, but this time it was a painful feeling wrought with reality and despair. She sat there for over an hour. She wore a red blazer, black turtleneck, houndstooth slacks, and leather flats, which was her typical conservative style and an outfit approved by her attorney.

Bradford never showed up. It took about six minutes for her to be sworn in, answer a handful of questions, and be directed to step down. It was bewildering for Stella Ann that twenty-eight years of marriage counted for nothing in less than ten minutes, but the divorce process took over three years. She was divorced, a word she couldn't even say when the nightmare started.

Her attorney walked her out of the courthouse and back to the office, where she would need to sign some papers. The whole process took less than two hours. Her attorney offered to walk her to her car. Stella Ann declined and assured her attorney she would be fine.

As she walked over the breezeway to the parking garage, she started shaking, and her tears streamed like a raging waterfall down her cheeks. When she got to the garage, she collapsed on the steps in a heap of brokenness. A nice gentleman offered to walk her to her car then took her keys and opened the door for her. He offered to stay until she was steady enough to drive, but she convinced him she was fine. She needed to make some phone calls before she left the garage. The first call she made was to Burt and Lou to tell them the divorce was over.

Before she went back to class, she stopped at Bradford's house to leave an inspirational book for happiness and a heartfelt note in her handwriting. All the note contained was that she hoped he would find the happiness he desired. She meant it when she wished him happiness. She wanted happiness, too. Then she called Landon's school and asked for a note to be delivered to him that read, "Your mom is fine and back at school. She will see you tonight and loves you very much."

Walking back into school was hard. She wanted to hide but knew she couldn't. She went up the back stairwell to her room. When she got to the second floor, she was relieved the students were not there. Her three teammates came into the hall and gathered around her, hugging her without a word. They let her cry. She had half an hour to collect herself before her next class started. In all her brokenness, it was the first step toward stitching her life back together. She faced a long process of reconciling anger, grief, and acceptance. Stella Ann felt like a failure of varying degrees for years.

She was determined to rebuild her life and reclaim her core values. For too long, she lived in an environment where the attitude was "anything goes" with a family who harbored values and morals far below what Stella Ann believed to be normal or acceptable. Rebuilding was not going to be easy. Her identity had been linked to Bradford ever since eighth grade. She had been absent from her own life for a long time. It was time to reintroduce herself to the Stella Ann she was at the core of her being and to introduce herself to the woman she wanted to become on her own.

PART FIVE:

Renewal

CHAPTER 14

Rips and Realization

She was three years into her teaching job and never forgot the kindness extended to her by Dr. Stafford in helping her get back into the workforce. She adapted to the grade level and enjoyed the subject she taught. The students were smart, eager, and active. She enjoyed her colleagues in her division and grade level, and two became loyal friends. She worked hard and thrived on the demands of the job. She volunteered to serve on a variety of committees. She was always willing to travel to learn new teaching strategies to share with the faculty. Stella Ann's focus was her rebooted career and her son.

She and Landon were on their own in many ways and had been since the beginning of their mother-son journey. Stella Ann knew Bradford wanted a family, but she accepted too late in her own life the family of his desire was never meant to include her.

She encouraged Landon to keep trying to have a relationship with his father. Stella Ann knew Bradford loved Landon, but the relationship was strained from the time he was nine years old. Landon became aware of happenings around him and started asking difficult questions. Bradford never answered his questions. Stella Ann hoped Bradford would find the family he wanted and treat them well.

One of her greatest regrets was the rips in her life tore Landon's young life into pieces that would take years to resolve. The sun would eventually shine for them even though it would take longer than they could imagine.

Although he gave it his best shot and after three years of trying, Landon couldn't find his path at the prestigious private school he attended. The administration was cold and disinterested during Stella Ann's meeting explaining Landon's home life situation that included the divorce. Her request for a mentor to help Landon navigate the extreme alterations in his life was ignored. For the over $18,000 tuition fee they paid each year, Stella Ann expected some compassion and simple, uncomplicated mentoring of her son. She could afford counseling, but Landon needed an adult mentor or friend he could trust and talk with during his daily life.

Since his life was being turned upside down, Landon wanted to be in school with Michael, and Stella Ann understood. He had known Michael all his life, and they were more like brothers than best friends. Stella Ann decided changing schools was a doable request, and Bradford agreed.

At his new school, a mentor was assigned to Landon. He called before school started to arrange to take him to dinner. Landon became interested in drama and participated in theatrical productions. He played on the indoor soccer team and continued to play baseball. The teachers at his new school took a genuine interest in him. His English teacher was paramount in nurturing Landon's gift for writing, which led to several college scholarship offers. Another positive resulted from his transfer to the new school. His social life flourished.

Stella Ann did not have a social life but adapted to staying home. She was used to being alone. Friends did not include her in social gatherings or offer to set her up with dates, and it was fine. There was no one in her age group to date. Everyone was part of a couple. It was true many of her friends dispersed and took Bradford's side. She was of no use to them. At least he could write them a prescription, make a house call, or see them in the office on short notice. Stella Ann could offer them nothing but free piano playing at a party or a laugh or two. She had one true friend who stood by her, listened to her, and was honest and direct when Stella Ann needed grounding and focus. Claire was a friend of a lifetime she would always cherish.

She spent a lot of time in her closet, where her computer was located. Most of the time, she worked on lesson plans and read. During lonely weekends, she chatted with the friends she made online, went home to Columbia, increased her time on the tennis court, and went shopping. It appeared like a pathetic little life, but she was safe.

She knew enough about computer dating for it to be a huge danger to her well-being. Predators were rampant, and vulnerable older women with few interpersonal life experiences were clear targets of such despicable people. She almost got caught in the web of a couple of ill-intended men even though she was careful to request an introduction meeting in a public place. She withdrew from internet dating after three introductions. Her need to be desired or attractive to the opposite sex was not worth the hassle. She realized she wasn't ready to test midlife dating. She knew nothing of the real world. For years, she was isolated as a stay-at-home mom and as a teacher in a classroom filled with children.

Several months after her divorce, she met a man in the communication industry. He was quite a few years older and was one of the most elegant, interesting, and mannerly men she had ever met.

Robert insulated her and made sure she was safe. He respected her boundaries and introduced her to new people, places, and things. He had a lot of social events to attend through his job and liked nothing more than for Stella Ann to be beside him. They went to parties, openings, and cultural events. Stella Ann met celebrities and local status figures. She especially enjoyed meeting the radio personalities she had listened to for years on the station Robert managed.

Robert and Stella Ann saw each other a lot, but they never discussed an exclusive relationship or moving in together. The only person Stella Ann had ever lived with was her husband. Cohabitation was a boundary she was not about to cross. Without a ring and a long-term commitment, no one was going to move in with her regardless of their manners and status. Stella Ann was not ready for such a relationship and made up her mind she would not entertain the possibility of marriage again for a long time, if ever.

She was still reeling from the three-year divorce process and had her hands full raising a teenage boy. Her priority was Landon, and she wanted to be a good role model for him. Robert came into her life at a perfect time and protected her from the "newly" divorced dating disasters many women experienced. She had a lot to learn about men, and she was naive and vulnerable. Not all men were self-centered and ill-mannered, but those men sported wedding rings. Homewrecker was not a title she would ever consider.

In the winter of 2005, Stella Ann's world came tumbling down again. It was after dinner when her brother called.

"Stella Ann, I am at the house with Lou. There is no easy way for me to tell you what I need to tell you." His voice cracked, "Burt passed away about an hour ago."

Stella Ann sat there frozen as she gripped the phone. It was like she was spinning on a carousel and couldn't get off. She couldn't breathe. She wanted to faint.

"Stella Ann, are you there?" Ron shouted into the phone and snapped Stella Ann back into reality.

"Oh, no, Ron, what happened? He was doing so well when I was there a couple of weeks ago."

"Lou was at the nursing home this afternoon. Burt told her to leave at about four o'clock to miss the traffic and get home before it got too dark. She made him a snack and left it on his tray table and kissed him goodbye. We got a call about eight o'clock from the head nurse that he passed away. They think it was a blood clot."

Stella Ann was crying but tried to be stoic. "How is Mama?"

He responded, "She is doing better than we are, Stella Ann. When do you think you can get here? We need to make funeral arrangements."

"I will be there tomorrow, Ron. Make the appointment for early tomorrow afternoon."

"Be careful coming home."

She stood in the kitchen and then started walking in circles and from room to room. What was the first thing she needed to do? She didn't handle these kinds of situations well and crumpled into tears. She did not need to be alone.

Landon was in college nearby and could be home within an hour. She called him first. Then she called Robert who also came to her house. They made a list of things she needed to do and helped her pack, insisting she get a decent night's sleep. She called her grade-level colleague, her division head, and her principal. Then she made lesson plans. She was going to get to school as soon as the doors opened at 6 a.m. to leave lesson plans and notes for a substitute. She was on the road to Columbia within an hour. Landon had a test and would leave later in the day for Columbia. He needed to talk with two of his professors about missing class for a few days.

Stella Ann was in a lonely place during her drive home. It was the same feeling she had sitting on the courtroom bench waiting for her divorce to be final. She hoped if she drove slowly, the news wouldn't be real, and her daddy would be alive when she got there. She would never forget the day. It was overcast, gray, and dreary, with spatters of rain pockets along the way. She never saw the sun, and she reminisced, cried, and screamed. She could. She was alone. Again.

She was directed to go straight to the funeral home to meet Lou, Ron, and Jenny to make funeral arrangements. Afterward, she and Jenny went to the flower shop. Ron and Lou went back to the house to collect pictures of Burt for the slideshow during visitation. Each of them had a special song they wanted played at the service. Stella Ann had not been involved in making funeral plans before, and it was foreign territory to her. Thank goodness for Jenny, who knew more about those things and had impeccable taste in planning anything from a wedding or shower to a funeral. She left no detail unturned. Stella Ann was scattered. It was going to be a stressful time with long days ahead. Her principal told her to take as long as she needed to get through the funeral and take time to help her mom. Stella Ann gave him credit for sympathy and compassion at a difficult time for her.

The funeral was difficult yet filled with nice comments and tributes to her daddy. Both grandsons wrote an essay about Burt for school during elementary and middle school. The essays were read during the service leaving the congregation visibly moved. Burt had been a public servant and was always ready to help during an emergency. He was a man of modest means and limited formal education, but he always felt he was rich beyond a bank account. He always told Stella Ann and Ron if someone had friends, they were richer than any millionaire. Her daddy had plenty of friends.

The procession from the funeral home was touching as all traffic lights stopped, people stood along the street to show respect, two fire engines were draped in black, guns were fired, and a bagpiper played "Amazing Grace" from under a tree on a hill at the cemetery. Her mother gave the flag draping Burt's casket to Ron instead of keeping it herself. Stella Ann thought it was an appropriate gesture.

When she got back to Chattanooga, it took days for her to get back in the swing of daily life and teaching. She was grieving and could not seem to get beyond it. She would go home after school each afternoon exhausted and would crawl into bed. She slept more than usual and burst into tears at the most unexpected times. The most important man in her life was gone. God needed him home, and Stella Ann had to get on with life.

Robert could not have been nicer and gave her the space she needed to grieve the loss of her daddy. She spent a lot of time going to Columbia on the weekends and during school breaks. She agreed to another year of teaching in Chattanooga. Each time she was home, it became evident to her that she needed to move back to Columbia. It was a move she had wanted to make for over thirty years.

Stella Ann decided in the late fall to start planning her move. She decided to tell no one. Landon was well on his way to completing college and rarely came home. She knew he would be fine. He planned to spend the last semester of his junior year studying in England at Oxford. She would be back in Columbia by the time he returned to the States. She enlisted the help of a real estate agent in Chattanooga to sell her house and another real estate agent in Columbia to help her find a home. She looked at homes to buy and apartments to rent. The prices seemed to push her further north or south of where she wanted to live.

She instructed each real estate agent not to contact her during the day at school and not to use her school email address. She had a landline at home and a private email she instructed them to use. She didn't trust getting any personal communication at the school. She had given her heart and soul to the school for seventeen years, and she wanted to exit there and Chattanooga with the dignity and accolades she had earned and deserved. She wanted to leave of her own accord.

Not only was finding housing in Columbia tricky, but she needed to start working on her resume to apply for teaching jobs. She needed to make sure her resume was impeccable by January, so she could start the application process. She learned she was not a candidate for a county or city teaching position back home because even though she had seventeen years of experience, she was not considered a master teacher. All her experience teaching in Chattanooga was in the independent school system. She only got credit for four years of experience. It was disheartening since she taught in one of the most prestigious schools in the country. By the end of January, she sent out many applications and resumes. She was on her way home.

Stella Ann and her teammates received glowing professional development and performance reports early in the second semester. All four of them expected to be invited to return by being issued a contract for the next school term. It was common knowledge within the school community that their team was strong. After the contracts were issued, Stella Ann planned to request an appointment to explain her situation and her need to return home to be available to help her mother. However, one's best plans are sometimes turned upside down.

After chapel on a Wednesday morning in early March, Katy, their grade-level chairperson and teammate, told Stella Ann and the other two teachers they had a meeting with their division head in her room after lunch.

"Do you know what this could be about, Stella Ann?" she asked.

"Not at all. It could have something to do with the argument he and

Stacy had in Tina's room this morning."

"What argument? I had early duty in the gym this morning."

"I was in Tina's room asking her if her doctor's appointment went well and if she was feeling better. Stacy and Mr. Burgess came bursting through the door, screaming at each other about a student she caught cheating on a test. She gave him a zero, and Mr. Burgess demanded she give him another test. She refused. Stacy was against the wall in Tina's room, and he was pointing and screaming at her. She was crying screaming back at him. Tina and I said nothing and kept the students out of the room. Would a team meeting be necessary about that?"

"He wants everyone on the team in a meeting in my room at noon. We need to be on time."

At noon, all four of them gathered in Katy's room. Mr. Burgess was already there. He told them to listen to him and say nothing until he finished reading a document he had prepared after chapel.

The document contained the most despicable things he could say about them as a grade-level team. That disgusting diatribe was followed by individual personal grievances he had against each one of them. It was a damning document riddled with anger. It was the most unprofessional, embarrassing thing any of them had ever experienced. The question of why he would do something like that after all four of them got glowing professional review reports from him kept surfacing within each of them. They never received an answer.

All four of them had supported this man and tried to help him feel welcomed in his new position. They went to bat for him with parents and students. He was teased endlessly about a misspelled word during a presentation, but they stood by him. They supported him when he made demands of students that were beyond their level of understanding. They tolerated him when he ranted on and on in division meetings and prattled about nothing of importance.

Stella Ann forgave him when he left her and a student in Atlanta at the children's hospital while on a school trip to the Children's Museum. As soon as they got to the first exhibit, a student came up to her, complaining of not feeling well. She ended up in the infirmary with the student all day.

The child slept most of the day, but the museum required an adult to stay with the child. The infirmary nurse suggested transferring the child to the children's hospital because the student seemed too sick to travel on a bus to Chattanooga.

Mr. Burgess sent Stella Ann and the student in a taxi to the hospital in downtown Atlanta. Stella Ann had to sign her life away to get the child admitted. The mother told her to get a commercial flight back to Chattanooga and leave her child at the hospital because the father was on his way in his private plane. He had been on business in Charlotte and planned to fly to Atlanta. Stella Ann thought it was a terrible waste of resources because Atlanta was not far away. She couldn't understand why the mother didn't get in the car and come to get her child.

"I will not leave your child alone in a hospital in an unfamiliar town. Can't I fly home with your husband?"

"No, he will not have room in the plane for all three of you. I have secured you a ticket on the last flight out of Atlanta to Chattanooga. You must leave now."

"I made myself clear. I will not be leaving until I know your child is safe with a parent."

When the father arrived, the doctor on call was in the room and explained the child had severe stomach pains due to a virus and dehydration but agreed to discharge the child since the fluids had helped. It made Stella Ann wonder if the child was sick before coming to school that day.

"How are you going to get home, Mrs. Taber?"

"I am going with you and your child."

"I don't have room for all three of us."

"I suggest you make room or rent a larger plane," Stella Ann replied.

"I flew my own plane. I am not renting a plane. We can make a pillow bed in the back, and my child can sleep there on the way back. I'll ask the hospital for more pillows. You can sit in the cockpit with me."

They took a cab to the small airport and boarded the plane. As soon as they settled in, the child's father handed Stella Ann a headset.

"What is this for?" Stella Ann asked.

"If you want to hear me, you need to wear these headphones," he replied.

Stella Ann put them on as they took off. They had ascended when Stella Ann asked a question.

"Excuse me, how long have you been flying?"

He replied, "It is a little late for that question, but I have been flying for 15 years. I need you to look out of your window. See those green blinking lights down there? If something happens to me in flight, you will need to land this plane in an area where you see those lights."

"Oh, hell!" Stella Ann had never given a thought to that possibility. It shut her up for a while. Then she asked, "How long will we be circling Atlanta?"

"That is not Atlanta. That is Dalton, and we will be in Chattanooga in about fifteen minutes. How are you going to get home from the airport?"

"I guess you will take me to the parking lot at the school to get my car."

"I will need to stay and get the plane in the hangar and check out in the airport office."

"My wife is coming to pick up our child. I will tell her to take you to your car."

When they landed, the mom was waiting in her car. She got out and practically threw her child in the backseat like a sack of potatoes. Then she told Stella Ann to get in the front passenger seat. When they got to the school parking lot, the gate was locked, and only one car was there: Stella Ann's.

"Would you mind taking me to my house? I don't live far from here, and my son can bring me to get my car tomorrow."

The mother was not happy but asked Stella Ann for directions to her house.

Stella Ann had never been so glad to see her little house and to be back in Chattanooga. She never got a thank you from the child's parents then, later, or ever. Stella Ann thought if people knew all the extra things teachers did for students, they would be more grateful for their service and dedication.

The administrator called the next morning to cover his tracks, apologize for leaving them, and thank Stella Ann for taking care of the situation. She covered for this man, and in turn, he called her and her colleagues vile, despicable things in a written document after giving them glowing yearly reviews. They were refused a copy of the document.

The following Monday, all four teachers received an email informing them their contracts were being held until the principal read and assessed the content of Mr. Burgess's document. This meant they would spend two weeks wondering if they had a job or an offer of a job for the next year. The rest of the faculty had already received contracts.

A sweet supportive mom of a student passed away before spring break. The faculty was notified if they wanted to go to the funeral to let the office know. The child was in Stella Ann's grade level at the time, and all the teachers had become close to the family. All four were denied the opportunity to attend the funeral. They were left to sit with the students of the teachers who were cleared to attend. Stella Ann thought it was the most despicable thing anyone could do to the child and to the teachers. All the students in the grade level went to the funeral, but their teachers were denied.

It was a decision beyond anything Stella Ann could define as fair or moral. The student had nothing to do with the administration's feelings toward the teachers, but they were being made examples of what happens when you are not in the administration's groupie gallery. They had no clue what they had done. What was the origin of the administration's vendetta against them?

Stella Ann thought there was a traitor in the division. She had a good idea who betrayed them. It was a good guess the person told the administration a policy with which they disagreed. They took note other colleagues were ostracizing them; no one would talk with them. It was a typical response. Teachers didn't want the stigma or the perception of being sympathetic to them. They acted to save their own job.

By the time the funeral ended, all four teachers got an email saying the principal wanted to see each of them before they left for spring break. One by one, they were called before the man who held their fate. Katy and Stella Ann were refused a contract renewal; Tina and Stacy got contracts that included an unusually nice raise for the coming year and their silence.

They never knew the reason for the decision. Stella Ann tackled each extra task she was given. She worked with others to develop a new reading program. She traveled anywhere her principal wanted her to go to learn new teaching methods. One absolute remained. He never wanted her from the beginning, an echo from her marriage of 28 years. She was familiar with not being wanted.

Something was said to her in the contract denial meeting that confirmed her suspicion that her email was intercepted and read. The phrase "word on the street" was used in reference to her property search in Middle Tennessee. She had told no one, not even her teaching team, about her plans to move, but her real estate agent had accidentally sent her an email to her school email address. She responded that "word on the street" constituted gossip and was unprofessional. She was advised to finish the year strong and leave quietly to protect her teaching career. The implication was daunting.

True colors were revealed when power came into play. She was glad she had already sent her resume and numerous applications to schools where she hoped to get a job. Folded into the heartbreak of recent events, Stella Ann realized she would not be leaving with the dignity and accolades she had earned.

She sold her house and bought a townhouse fifteen miles north of Columbia. She bought the model home because it would be finished by the time she needed it, and she still had the option to make a few changes. It was another gated community in a safe area and included a beautiful pool complex, which Stella Ann would enjoy during the summer.

With the help of a childhood friend, she was able to get a job at a nice private school in a nearby town. She drove a lot to and from school each day. It was about sixty miles round trip in heavy traffic. The fact that she was alone made the decision to buy a house far from work easier. Plus, it was affordable housing. She started her day at 4:30 a.m. and, if she was lucky, got home at about 6:30 p.m. She was in bed by 9 p.m. She enjoyed being out in the suburbs on the weekend and felt she was able to maintain a certain sense of autonomy.

Stella Ann had five days left in Chattanooga before a moving van arrived, and four men would empty the contents of the little home she and Landon built. For six years, it represented a place of peace and safety for her. She had mountains of things to get done in the five days she had left.

After over thirty years in Chattanooga, she decided to take a day to have lunch on Signal Mountain, an area where she, Landon, and Bradford lived for seven years. She wanted to say goodbye to people in businesses she still frequented even though she had moved out of the area. There was her favorite grocery store, her hair salon, her manicurist, her florist, and various shops in the mall. She also needed to return a dress to her favorite dress shop. She was going to miss all her business friends as well as the products and services they provided, but she had new friends to make back home.

When she walked into the dress shop to return the dress, she saw the mother of a student she taught years earlier. They exchanged a quick conversation about their sons, and Stella Ann asked a sales lady if she could try on a few items. She forgot her store credit card and asked if the sales associate could look up her account while she tried on the items she selected. Stella Ann handed the associate her driver's license.

Nothing she tried on seemed to work, so she asked for account credit. When the young woman handed her license back, she stood there as if contemplating something. Then the girl asked her a question.

"Is your husband, Bradford Taber?"

Stella Ann redirected her by saying, "He is my ex-husband." Then, Stella Ann took a deep breath. She only had five days left and hoped she could avoid any further scandals or humiliation.

"Would you mind meeting me outside the door in a few minutes? I have a break and would like to talk with you."

Stella Ann sat down outside and waited for the young lady. Within minutes, she was there, and Stella Ann stood up against a column, hoping the meeting would not last long.

310

The young lady looked at her and said, "You can't imagine what was going through my mind while you were in the dressing room. I heard you tell your friend you were leaving Chattanooga in five days."

"Yes, it is time for me to return home. I have nothing further to accomplish here now that I am divorced, and my son is finishing college next year. I need to go home to help my mom since my dad died last year. How can I help you?"

The young lady said, "I felt like I needed to talk with you because with your time limit it was now or never. I am your son's birth mother."

It was a good thing Stella Ann was leaning against a brick wall, or she would have been reduced to a puddle of middle-aged blubber. She felt her knees shaking and on the verge of buckling.

"What?" Stella Ann said.

"I am your son's birth mother. I have a few more minutes left in my break. Would you mind having a glass of tea with me at the restaurant around the corner?"

Stella Ann responded, "I would love to have a drink with you, but it is going to be stronger than iced tea."

Stella Ann realized she was babbling when she got a telephone call from Bradford. They rarely spoke anymore, and he was ranting about Landon's car insurance. She finally changed the subject and asked Bradford if he could guess who she was sitting with.

"Well, you are probably with one of your many boyfriends," Bradford said sarcastically.

"Bradford, I am with Landon's birth mother."

There was an abrupt and long silence. Then Bradford asked if she would talk with him. They had a few brief exchanges, and the young lady handed the phone back to Stella Ann.

Bradford seemed to see this new revelation as a threat. Stella Ann felt the circle of people who loved Landon get bigger. She thanked the young lady for the precious gift she had given them and told her Landon was in England studying at Oxford. The young lady asked many questions about Landon's childhood and accomplishments, and Stella Ann was happy to share the joy Landon had brought the family. Stella Ann promised to give

Landon her contact information when he returned from England and asked that she not contact Landon herself.

Stella Ann made it clear she wanted to be the one to tell him. She explained that Landon was a thoughtful young man and processed things completely before acting. Stella Ann was direct, explaining it would be up to Landon to determine if he wanted to meet with her at some point. The young lady was gracious and promised not to contact Landon.

Stella Ann went home that afternoon, and instead of packing, she dug through boxes, gathering baby items and pictures. She put together a baby book filled with some of Landon's baby pictures and milestone achievements, as well as some of his elementary artwork and papers. She mailed it to her before she left Chattanooga. Stella Ann invited her to Landon's college graduation the next year, and she attended from a distance.

When Landon returned from England, he landed in Nashville, and Stella Ann and Lou picked him up at the airport. He was going to spend a few days in the Middle Tennessee area before going to The University of the South in Sewanee to start his senior year of college. Stella Ann missed him beyond measure and was thrilled to have him home. She heard all about his trip and planned a family dinner at their new house. The second day Landon was home, Stella Ann shared with him the encounter with his birth mother. She gave him her contact information. He listened intently.

"Mom, didn't it freak you out when she asked you to meet her outside the store?"

"At first, my heart skipped a beat, but she seemed nice and genuine. After she identified herself, I could see the resemblance between you two. You each have dark, thick, wavy hair and deep blue eyes."

"Mom, I don't really know how to respond to this information. For years, I have wondered about who she might be as well as my birth father, and now I have this information, I am not sure I want to meet her. You are my mom."

"Landon, the way I look at this revelation is the circle of people who love you got larger. It is a miracle that our paths crossed before I left

Chattanooga. You have the information and can do with it what you feel is best. I told her not to contact you and informed her you would take your time to digest her identity and determine if you wanted to have a meeting. Put the information in a safe place."

They hugged, and Landon went to his new room upstairs.

Stella Ann started her new job a few weeks later. She met a lot of nice people who welcomed her with kindness. It was a much different teaching environment with a competitive atmosphere instead of the new Ivy League social vibe of her previous school. There was a lot to learn. One of the most obvious procedures she had to learn was tempering discipline. From her observation, there was no defined discipline plan. Students needed boundaries to learn to trust their teachers and respect them and each other. Stella Ann learned promptly she would have little backup regarding discipline.

There was no one she could turn to for help with her adjustment. There was no mentor program for new teachers or students in the school. She was reprimanded regularly and wondered if she was going through a hazing process. She got in trouble for throwing out old stuffed animals in her closet and how her students walked back to class after chapel. She was chastised for assigning homework and asking students to lower their voices in the cafeteria. She would have to manage the best she could. She knew how to look the other way, but it rattled her to the core.

Stella Ann lost count of the times she was summoned to her division head's office or the number of times she was invited to take a walk around the track with her principal. She was given "the look" when she declined to take a walk around the track the first time she was asked. She quickly realized "the look" meant there was no option to decline. She was eventually befriended by three teachers who sensed her frustration, and they gave her encouragement and support to make it through the first year. She decided she could trust them. It was a complicated place. It took Stella Ann two years to adjust to the school climate and three years to get a tight grip on the two levels of subject matter she taught.

A competitive spirit permeated the faculty, parents, and students. Stella Ann didn't have time to worry about competition and left that inner drive on the tennis court. She put her nose to the grind to delve into the two different grade levels she was teaching. She was charged with doing a job best suited for more than one teacher. She had no written curriculum for any area and few materials, so she carved out a program based on the needs of her students.

Her goal was to improve reading comprehension and help students discover writing skills that would improve their confidence and tap their critical thinking skills. It was refreshing to have the opportunity to develop the curriculum, but it was going to be a monumental task. The kids could handle more. They were smart and eager. It was true that when much was expected, much could be accomplished. Her students rose to the challenge.

Stella Ann appreciated the final school of her career, but she never felt like she was in an environment to reach her full potential as a leader or contributor. Her opinion was sought on occasion, and she gave it freely and honestly. It accounted for some form of respect for her educational experience and status in life. But if she were honest, Stella Ann felt like a workhorse with student, parental, or colleague requests piled higher than she could reach. She always put aside her work to listen to and address their concerns. She arrived early and stayed late by necessity. She took work home working well into the night and on weekends to try to catch up. There was no time for anything else but work. She gave her heart and soul to her students. She often retreated to the storage closet in her room to take a deep breath, shed a few tears, or regroup.

She learned much about her students through their writing and their journey learning more advanced writing skills. Her goal was to make sure students felt confident with the written word and with their own written expression. Many thought she didn't care about the kids or her job because she was not socially visible. There was no time for Stella Ann to attend games, recitals, plays, or parties. What many didn't know was she spent hours on the weekends reading and grading student papers. Any small planning time she had in her schedule was quickly absorbed with parent meetings, grade level meetings, and responding to email as well as returning phone calls. Burnout was inevitable. Stella Ann knew her students better than most teachers because she got to know their young, tender hearts. She admired her principal. He was a dedicated, honorable, and brilliant person, and his family was remarkable. Stella Ann loved teaching his children.

Reflecting on her career some years later, she accepted with an unexplainable sadness and childlike disappointment that she would never receive recognition for her contribution to the schools or students she taught. To some, it was a job, but to Stella Ann, it was her life. After her self-imposed, split-second pity party, humility shook her back to what was most important. It wasn't superficial awards or accolades.

When she retired, Stella Ann's own words from her most recent professional development plan were used to describe her. The speaker didn't take the time to produce a few original words. It stung and sent her into a puddle of tears before she got back to her room to complete the last checkout task of turning in her computer. She could not get in her car quickly enough and continued to cry as she drove home. She thought to herself, "Twenty-nine years of some of the hardest work mentally, emotionally, and physically, and her own words were used to say goodbye. She didn't need to sit through that stupid luncheon to send herself off." It was like she wrote her own obituary and heard it read aloud by someone who didn't know her.

There were a few parents who saw a positive shift in their child from her influence. They were gracious and thanked her, which Stella Ann appreciated. The letters of appreciation she received from a student or parent were limited, but she cherished those letters. She kept them in her memory box for reflection. The reality was she was merely a fleeting shadow in the wings of the lives of her students and colleagues to fade and disappear as time passed.

CHAPTER 15

Reasons
and Real Love

Growing up and during her marriage, Stella Ann recognized and admitted her periodic temper issues and impatience. Most of the time, she ended up with temporary episodes of depression and frustration followed by a string of apologies she had to deliver. As a child, she had tantrums that landed her a session at the end of her daddy's belt or her mama's switch. Like Bradford, she had thrown clothes out of her closet and stuffed animals at her bedroom door. The difference was her temper tantrums terminated by her teen years, and her frustrations took an emotional shift to defeat and depression sprinkled with tears.

As an adult, she became a master at managing depression and frustration through tennis, music, humor, and self-deprecation. She started therapy in 1996 to learn how to cope in her marriage and continued therapy over several intervals for years to reconcile and manage other issues. Years later and long after her divorce, a therapist asked her if she had considered ADHD as a diagnosis.

Stella Ann replied, "No, I have never given it a thought. My son and ex-husband would say I had ADHD and laugh. I thought they were being silly. Maybe they were right. I seriously doubt anyone my age has ADHD. I am with kids all day, and I know what ADHD looks like."

"You seem agitated, Mrs. Taber," the therapist responded. "Why are you so upset?"

"For one thing, you gave me a mountain of books to read. If I had time to read those books, I wouldn't need to be here with you. I teach two levels of Language Arts to include reading, writing, vocabulary, grammar, and spelling. My workday starts at 4:30 a.m. and doesn't end until 6:30 p.m. I don't have time to read books. I pay you to read the books and tell me what I need to do."

The therapist was surprised by Stella Ann's direct and blunt response and asked, "Would you mind taking an informal test for ADHD? I can't diagnose you, but I can get an idea of the therapy you need and determine if you would benefit being referred to a psychiatrist who specializes in women's issues."

"Sure, I will take a test. How long will it take?" Stella Ann asked.

"It shouldn't take over thirty minutes for the test and another fifteen minutes for me to evaluate it. Let's get started."

The informal results showed Stella Ann was on the Adult Attention Deficit and Hyperactivity spectrum. An appointment was made with a psychiatrist who could formally assess her and prescribe medication. It didn't take the doctor five minutes talking with Stella Ann to determine she had ADHD and most likely had it as a child. After many tests and meetings, she was officially diagnosed with ADHD and PTSD. It was a relief to learn there were medical reasons for her anxiety, and she would learn coping skills to manage both. The diagnoses of ADHD and PTSD explained many things about her life. Her doctor tried many medications, but none seemed to agree with her. At least, she had information she could work with to improve her life.

Stella Ann thought she was incorrectly perceived as aloof, distant, and arrogant. Classmates, administrators, colleagues, and parents confirmed it. She was told she was "stuck up" or "hard to get to know." In school, she couldn't see classmates' faces and avoided speaking for fear she would call the wrong name. She didn't wear glasses until she was sixteen when she got her permit to drive. The labels attached to her were off target. She felt she was always misunderstood.

She was often outside a circle of classmates or colleagues looking in, and upon arrival at a meeting was not included in a conversation. Being in a situation where more than one conversation was in process at once was frustrating to her because she felt like she missed out due to her inability to focus. Group projects or breakout sessions drove Stella Ann crazy. Sitting in a class or meeting and listening to someone speak was pure torture to her. She was always asking for an update, ultimately ending up confused. Stella Ann described her experiences as frustrating, and she felt like rockets or fireworks were repeatedly going off in her head in different directions.

She was a cheerleader for years and jumped and yelled herself into exhaustion. It was a coping mechanism she didn't recognize at the time. For Stella Ann, being a cheerleader was more about her ability than popularity because she wasn't particularly popular. Stella Ann did not see herself identifying with any group. She was considered the enemy through high school because she dated a boy from their rival school. It was Bradford.

She liked everyone but fit in with no one, and such difficulty would follow her all her life. She had two close friends from fourth grade forward, but they lost touch during their senior year in high school. Most of her friends were older because they were the kids she grew up with in her formative years, and most were friends of her brother. Ron was always reminded to take care of Stella Ann when they were in the neighborhood playing. It was a lot to expect of her brother, who was just four years older, but her parents knew she would get into trouble or wander off.

She was a pleaser and often compromised herself by taking on too many projects. Then she would have a meltdown, and Lou would come to her rescue. People didn't realize her appearance of snobbery was insecurity and shyness, and her isolation was a lack of self-confidence.

Being in a large group social situation sent her into a panic because she did not feel comfortable. She was an actress. When necessary, she could socially work a room like a charm, and it would take days for her to recover from her performance. Other insecurities were hidden with her humor which was quick and clever.

Swatting a tennis ball was another way of helping her deal with the characteristics of ADHD and depression, even though they had no clue about such a diagnosis at the time. She was considered overactive and talkative at times or quiet and distant at other times. Staying active, engaged, and busy was an organic, nonpharmaceutical way of behavior and focus management. The diagnosis and medication for ADHD was not available when she was growing up. She was simply labeled scattered or flighty. She procrastinated leaving for school or starting homework. She was often told she could accomplish so much more if she paced herself. The truth was she could not organize herself adequately to pace herself. She spent most of her time getting organized to get ready to get on task. By the time she accomplished getting organized, she was too exhausted to study. It was a good thing she was smart and had a good memory.

Her late-in-life ADHD diagnosis helped to explain why she never had recess in second and third grade and why she had to serve after-school detention at least twice every week when she got older. One thing that helped keep her out of trouble was her love of reading. She would lose herself in books. She always got good grades and seemed to work harder than others. A strong work ethic was instilled in her early in life, but her drive to be better triggered her obsession to excel.

The decision to move back home to Columbia brought more changes in Stella Ann's life. Her daddy reminded her as a teenager she had to learn to adjust. Adjustment proved to be a pattern and a constant struggle.

She broke up with Robert six months before she left Chattanooga. Although she missed him, she knew her decision was in her best interest. He couldn't leave Chattanooga, and she couldn't stay.

The last thing she needed to do after moving home was join a dating site, but she discovered a few sites targeted toward older adults and signed up. She was lonely and gave it a try. She had scattered coffee dates and a few dinner dates.

There were men who grieved the loss of a wife and men who saw her as a sounding board for their true confessions. Some men left her with the dinner bill, did not show up, or misrepresented themselves. One thing she became good at detecting in conversation was when a man was married and seeking a playmate on the side. She studied the signs of a player and became a questioning expert learning to sense when most were lying. It was a sad commentary at her age to be a detective of poor behavior in men. She had years of practice in her marriage doing just that.

At school, Stella Ann was targeted for daily reprimands by her new, inexperienced supervisor. When that person showed up at her door, she knew an apology was expected. Most of the time, she had no idea she had done anything offensive. It didn't matter what she did right or wrong, she simply was not liked. The new supervisor was condescending and rude in front of colleagues anytime she asked a question or expressed an opinion in meetings. She spent much time in her classroom closet in tears caused by being misunderstood.

There was a hometown man she knew from high school who pretended interest in her for a few weeks, and it was a nice diversion. They went to dinner a few times and played tennis together on Sunday afternoons. She realized he was not the least bit interested in her when he redirected the conversation over and over toward one of her best friends. He asked countless questions about her. Stella Ann was a means to an end. Again.

Stella Ann told him over and over that her friend was engaged. Within a few weeks, he and her friend were a couple. Her childhood friend called her and told her she had broken off her engagement. Stella Ann warned her to be careful because she saw him as an opportunist.

Following the stressful and negative chain of events, someone she dated for a while disappeared from her life for months at a time. They were never a couple, but Stella Ann thought his periodic disappearances were odd. He showed up in her life after a lengthy disappearance and without an explanation. He asked her out to dinner. She thought he was sick during his long absence. Stella Ann helped him through a difficult time medically while they dated. At dinner, he apologized for his erratic behavior and led her to believe all was well. Stella Ann thought she would hear from him again because he gave her no reason to think otherwise.

It wasn't long after their dinner date, she learned he was married. Stella Ann counted backward to the date when they went to dinner and calculated he was either married or engaged when he asked her out. It was a humiliating blow to Stella Ann, and she was livid for falling for such a trick for him to clear his conscience. She wished he had left her alone. She didn't even care to confront him about his manipulative behavior. She was abandoned again, but this time she didn't care. Anyone who would treat a person so poorly didn't deserve the time of day from her.

She called her therapist for an emergency session. Situations had piled up so high that she didn't know how she was going to handle her day-to-day life. It was common for her to get overwhelmed. She was about as low as she had been the day her divorce was final and when she learned her daddy had passed away. She was beginning a depressive crash. She was afraid. It seemed the harder she tried to work out of her difficult situations, the worse things became.

Her son left to teach English overseas and would be gone for many months, work was overwhelming, disrespect was rampant, and several people she trusted betrayed her. She was in a dark place and was isolating herself even more. It was decided in therapy she would no longer date and would shut down any dating apps. As she started shutting the last of two dating apps down, the picture of a handsome man with a dynamic smile came across her options feed that read, "before you go." At first, she thought it was a bait scheme to keep her on the site. She was right. Out of curiosity, she sent a hello icon and went to bed, knowing she would shut down the site the next morning.

The next day, when she checked her email, she had an eloquent, sincere, well-written letter in her box from the handsome man in the picture. She spent more time than she should have to determine if it was a form letter. She assessed it was a real letter. Several letters were exchanged between them, and he asked if he could call her. The first phone call lasted four hours and was followed by another four-hour phone call the next day. She was excited but cautious.

By the third telephone call, they realized they had not discussed their locations.

"Where do you live in Tennessee?" Stella Ann asked.

"Tennessee? I am not in Tennessee," Doug replied. "I am in the Fairfax, Virginia/Washington, D.C., area for now. I have been here almost a year working on an assignment."

"Oh, you are not in Tennessee?"

"No, for now, I live in Fairfax, Virginia."

"I see. Well, it has been a pleasure exchanging emails and chatting on the telephone, but I am in no position to travel. I am not interested in a long-distance relationship. I hope you find the love interest you are seeking. Goodbye, now," Stella Ann said with disappointment. It was confirmation that a relationship was not something she needed in her life. She realized her therapist was right.

"Wait a minute, Stella Ann. Please don't hang up. I can travel and am willing to see what we can work out."

Stella Ann listened with caution, thinking that if it was too good to be true, it probably wasn't. She put up her guard. She had learned that men usually were not interested in traveling more than ten or fifteen miles to have a cup of coffee or dinner, but she was willing to give him a chance.

"You mean you would travel all the way to Tennessee to see me?" Stella Ann asked.

"Yes, I am leaving to visit my family in Wisconsin for Christmas and could leave a day early to have dinner with you."

"Are you kidding?" Stella Ann questioned.

"I am serious. I love to drive, and it is no problem for me to leave early for the holidays."

As suspicious as it sounded, Stella Ann was thrilled and said nothing to dissuade him.

This was the last thing she needed. She did not need to dig her dark hole of despair deeper. She was in her late fifties. She was just getting resigned to being alone. It was also further proof of her ADHD diagnosis and her impulsive behavior. Doug was different or seemed like it anyway.

He stayed in a hotel outside of Nashville and planned to arrive at Stella Ann's house by 11:00 a.m. It was two weeks before Christmas. Stella Ann was a nervous wreck getting ready before they met on Saturday morning. She changed clothes at least three times. She never accepted her middle-aged curvy figure and looked frantically for something to wear that would make her look slimmer. She ended up settling on a black cowl neck sweater and black pants, adding a belt and boots. She didn't want to overdress, but she didn't want to look dowdy either.

The doorbell rang, and Stella Ann's heart skipped a beat. Should she answer it? The guidelines about online dating included a warning about letting someone come to one's home. They should have met at a coffee shop. It was too late now, and she opened the door to find a tall handsome man holding a bouquet of roses. Her heart melted.

She invited him in and ushered him to the living room, where they exchanged a hug and a kiss and talked about his trip from Washington through the hills of East Tennessee. They laughed and laughed, and the conversation flowed freely except for a few dialect bumps and colloquialisms for each of them. Stella Ann offered to make lunch before they ventured out for a tour of Columbia and a simplified history lesson about the area. While they were eating lunch, Stella Ann got a call from Ron.

"Hey, Stella Ann, I am at the hospital with Lou. We are in the admissions area waiting for a room."

"What is wrong, Ron? Has Mama seen a doctor?"

"Yes, she has seen a doctor, but they have not made a diagnosis. It looks like she will need to stay a few days."

"I am on my way."

Stella Ann turned to Doug and said, "It has been a treat meeting you and spending time with you, but I have an emergency. My mama is at the hospital with my brother, and I need to go. You are welcome to go with me, or you can go ahead and leave for Wisconsin."

Doug replied, "I am going with you, and I will drive."

Stella Ann was speechless. He had just met her face to face and was willing to go with her to the hospital to join her mother and brother. She wasn't ready to include the family. She had just met Doug, but she extended the invitation, and Doug accepted.

When they got to the hospital, she introduced Doug to her brother and mother. Doug did not skip a beat engaging in sincere and lively conversation with her brother as Stella Ann sat quietly by her mother.

Ron and Jenny offered to stay with Lou until she was settled in the hospital to allow Stella Ann and Doug to continue with their date plans to have dinner at an upscale restaurant. Stella Ann returned to the hospital early the next morning to be with Lou. Doug continued with his plan to go to Wisconsin. He asked Stella Ann if he could return to her house to spend more time with her after Christmas. She agreed, but there was a thought in the back of her mind that he just may not return. She had been left and stood up too many times to genuinely trust he would be back. She couldn't help her cautious thoughts, but she was also as giddy and silly as a schoolgirl. This was special. What a Christmas gift!

After five days in the hospital, Lou was released to spend her recovery at Stella Ann's house. Landon came home for the holidays. He and Conner offered to make their family Christmas Eve dinner which was going to be at Stella Ann's house. Stella Ann was happy to turn her kitchen over to them. It promised to be a nice holiday season. She felt like she was beginning to fit into a new life, a positive life, a life of acceptance for the first time in years, and Lou recovered seamlessly.

Landon stayed until December 28, when he returned to Chattanooga to visit with his dad and friends. She was not ready for Doug and Landon to meet. Doug returned from Wisconsin on December 30. This relationship was extremely different from anything Stella Ann had ever experienced.

When Doug returned, they went out to dinner with Ron and Jenny, went to Nashville sightseeing, and ended the visit with a big band concert at the theater. Stella Ann didn't watch much television and only had a discarded TV set from Landon's dorm room. Doug bought her a large, flat-screen television. Stella Ann thought it was an extravagant gift and unnecessary, but she later learned Doug always wanted to make someone's life better if he could. Stella Ann was hopeful yet sad when Doug had to return to Washington. What followed was a whirlwind courtship, with Doug traveling to Columbia three times as much as Stella Ann traveled to Washington. It didn't matter. They wanted to be together, and they were willing to do what was necessary to keep a long-distance relationship alive.

Thirteen months into their relationship, they got engaged. Stella Ann and Doug went ring shopping many times without finding the ring or stone that suited them. On a whim one Saturday in August, Jenny, Stella Ann, and Lou went to a nearby city to a jeweler friend of Jenny's while the men played golf. It was an unplanned visit to Jenny's jeweler, and Doug approved of Stella Ann looking at rings without him. Lou picked out the perfect ring. She always had impeccable taste, and the ring was stunning. Stella Ann and Jenny had overlooked the beautiful Asscher cut diamond halo ring when they were looking in the cases. It didn't have the size diamond she and Doug chose, but the overall look and feel of the ring was perfect. Jenny saw a wedding band to fit the ring, and an added feature included sapphires, Stella Ann and Doug's birthstone.

They bought a fixer-upper house in Columbia. It was an example of the horrible home decorating trends of the seventies with avocado green and orange mushroom wallpaper, harvest gold appliances, and orange and green matted shag carpet throughout the house. The owners had not updated one thing through the years. Doug was a visionary and imagined how the house could be transformed. Stella Ann couldn't get beyond the harvest gold kitchen. Doug started renovating the house when he came to Columbia on the weekends. He made a promise to her she would get to return to Columbia, and he made it happen. With grit, determination, time, and talent, Doug made the old house into a beautiful, customized home for them.

Before she put her townhouse on the market, a new neighbor moved into the townhouse next door to Stella Ann while she was out of town on school business. The original owner moved, and no one had lived in the townhouse next door to Stella Ann for a couple of years.

Stella Ann turned into her driveway and saw her new neighbor in the yard. She jumped out of the car and said, "Hi, I am Stella Ann Taber. Welcome to the neighborhood."

"Are you the person who owns a radio that knocks me out of bed every morning at 4:30 a.m.?" the woman with blazing red hair snapped in a grouchy voice.

"I guess I am. I am so sorry about that. No one has lived in your townhouse for a long time. I did not know I was getting a new neighbor. I have been on a school trip to Florida and forgot to turn the volume down on my alarm clock. I will be more careful now that you are here."

"Well, I will tell you one thing; I will take it once, but I won't take it again. I will report you to the homeowner's association or the police. You had better watch yourself."

Stella Ann didn't know what she meant by, "take it once but not again." Take what?

Later in the week, Stella Ann was watching one of her housewives shows, and there was a knock on the door. She was already in her pajamas and robe. In her childlike mindset, she thought it might be the neighbor coming to apologize. Maybe she was bringing cookies as a peace offering. To Stella Ann's surprise, it was the police.

"Ma'am, we were called about a loud party going on at this address. Are you having a party?" the policeman asked.

Stella Ann could not help it and started to laugh.

"Party? I am not having a party. I am just watching my housewives show. Come in, and I will show you." He started laughing. "I live alone, and I have never had a party here. Did that lady next door call you?"

"The complaint lodged was disturbing the peace. Just turn your TV down a little. We must respond to all calls. The station is getting an interesting and thick file of complaints toward several of your neighbors from the new resident. I have been to the neighborhood three times since she moved in."

"Thank you, officer. I will be careful. The good news is I have sold my house, and I am moving out in a month. I won't be bothered with her much longer."

While Stella Ann was not initially thrilled with the avocado green and harvest gold house they bought, she was looking forward to no longer living out of plastic storage boxes. She had been living out of blue plastic boxes for years hoping to finally land in her permanent forever home.

Lou asked Stella Ann as she helped her move, "Stella Ann, how many more times are you going to move?"

"Mama, this is it. I have no desire to ever move again. Doug will turn this place into a dream home for us, and I will be here until the day I die."

"I hope you are right, Stella Ann. I am 86 years old and don't think I have another one of your moves left in me," Lou replied. They both laughed and got back to work.

Stella Ann moved into the seventies green and gold house and lived there alone until she and Doug married. Doug continued to work in Washington, D.C. and traveled to Columbia twice a month.

She looked out the kitchen window like she did most mornings as she took her first sip of coffee. Stella Ann realized their house faced a familiar hill. On the other side of the facing hill, at the bottom, and across the highway, was the big, white, Civil War-era house where her marital nightmare started over forty years earlier. It was Hank Taber's old house and estate, long since sold and divided into subdivisions. Stella Ann thought to herself that life had a way of being enclosed in humor. She laughed aloud at the irony of her position. She was thankful to be out of the nightmare zone and on the happy side of the hill.

Doug enlisted the help of Jenny and Ron to plan an engagement proposal surprise for Stella Ann, and a lovely dinner followed. The original plan was for Doug to propose on the square at the fountain, but that plan had to be scrapped when it started raining. He proposed on the porch of the courthouse, which was a beautiful building. Doug said the most romantic and sincere things, put the ring on her finger, and gave her roses and a statue of a couple with the engagement date written on the bottom. Her family and many of her friends were there. Jenny had a professional photographer friend take pictures of the event.

The engagement dinner followed in the banquet room at The Stanley Restaurant. Jenny decorated the room with dozens of red roses, white hydrangeas, and candles, and had favors at each place. Doug gave a beautiful speech, welcomed everyone, and thanked them for sharing the occasion with them. It was a perfect evening and a beautiful proposal.

Two years after they met, they married at a wonderful venue called The Hermitage House in Columbia with their children and Doug's grandchildren fully involved and included in all the wedding plans. Landon walked Stella Ann down the aisle, Doug's son was his best man, his granddaughter was the flower girl, and his grandson was the ring bearer. Jenny agreed to read a group of special passages Stella Ann and Doug selected from the Bible, C.S. Lewis, and a favorite children's book. The minister from their new church married them, and the ceremony was beautiful.

Stella Ann shopped for months for a wedding dress appropriate for an older bride, which was no easy task. The dresses available were either too matronly looking, too girly, strapless, or had a train. She bought three dresses and ended up finding a lovely dress more suited to her taste and style at the last minute. It was a simple white silk trumpet-shaped dress with a cowl neckline, limited beading, and a shawl Stella Ann could wear over her shoulders during the wedding ceremony and tie around her waist during the reception. Stella Ann's matron of honor was Claire, who wore a beautiful navy evening dress with silver beading. Lou wore a navy cocktail pantsuit with sparkling detail under the jacket that hung perfectly on her petite frame. She looked beautiful. The men wore khaki pants, light blue shirts, burgundy ties, and sharp, double-breasted, navy Ralph Lauren jackets.

The atmosphere of the wedding weekend was one of celebration, fun, and happiness for Stella Ann and Doug, who had found love again after many years of singleness for each of them. The rehearsal dinner was held at Amber Falls Vineyard, a winery highlighting the beautiful hills of Middle Tennessee. Joining family and local friends were guests from Nashville, Chattanooga, Memphis, Knoxville, Georgia, Texas, Missouri, Colorado, Minnesota, and Wisconsin. All of Stella Ann's aunts attended, which made Lou happy, and many colleagues from both of Stella Ann's schools joined in the celebration. Stella Ann's favorite uncle, a retired minister, offered a beautiful prayer before dinner.

Her students sang "The Lord's Prayer," the school music teacher sang "Over the Rainbow" and two other songs, and a harpist played many of their favorite songs. There were lots of deep pink roses and blue and white hydrangeas decorating the inside and outside areas of the venue. There was plenty of champagne, wine, beer, great food, and a stunning four-tier wedding cake decorated with blue hydrangeas. Their first dance was to "I Cross My Heart."

Dancing and fun continued for hours. They enjoyed a bride and groom exit with oversized sparklers, which was fun. When the party neared a close, the wedding director started blowing out candles, setting off the fire alarms. Within minutes, the fire department with two trucks showed up. It was fun to get pictures of their special event with firemen and fire trucks.

Jenny, Robin, Jenny's daughter-in-law, and Jenny's sister hosted a lovely breakfast the next morning for family and out-of-town friends before everyone left for the airport or to drive home. Doug and Stella Ann left the next morning for their honeymoon.

They honeymooned in Hawaii, enjoying the beautiful beaches and sunsets, eating fabulous food, people-watching, taking a helicopter ride to see the island's tropical masterpiece, visiting the Dole pineapple plantation, partaking in a touristy luau, and renting a white Mustang convertible to go to the non-touristy part of the island.

Doug was on assignment in the New England area, where they spent most of the summer. They enjoyed whale watching in the waters off the coast of Boothbay, Maine, breakfast and a Fourth of July Festival in Bar Harbor, shopping and sightseeing in Kennebunkport, and visiting Stephen King's home in Bangor. Doug had business in Portland, so Stella Ann ventured out to shop along the port and had lunch at a wonderful gluten-free restaurant and bakery. She took a well-guided tour of Henry Wadsworth Longfellow's home and returned to the hotel for a rest before having a delicious dinner at an old library. The lighthouses and shorelines in Maine were breathtakingly beautiful. Stella Ann had never seen anything like it before.

They marveled at the Victorian opulence of the homes in Newport,

Rhode Island, and Stella Ann was captivated by what life must have been like for the kingly rich Americans who occupied such homes. She spent another day puddling around in the rain in Portsmouth while Doug was in meetings.

Boston was a historic adventure for them, and they stayed in a delightful bed and breakfast inn. She and Doug had a great weekend sightseeing and stayed over a couple of extra days for Doug to work. Stella Ann went shopping and had lunch in Boston. Later that afternoon, she went to Cambridge. She walked the campus of Harvard, enjoyed the bookstore, and bought some souvenirs. Stella Ann enjoyed soaking in the essence and history of the campus. It was like a step back in time.

One Sunday, they ventured to the small seaport town of Mystic, Connecticut, toured old ships, and learned about the art of shipbuilding. Hartford, Connecticut, was Doug's base city for his current assignment, and Stella Ann became familiar with the Uber ride system to navigate the city. She took a day to visit the Samuel L. Clemons (Mark Twain) home, which she thought was rather dark and gaudy but profoundly interesting. The Harriet Beecher Stowe house was nearby, and Stella Ann thought it to be a plain, stark contrast to the Mark Twain house.

Before it was time for Stella Ann to return to Tennessee and another school year and Doug to return to Washington, D.C., they spent time in Vermont and New Hampshire. The scenery was stunning. The summer she and Doug married was one of constant travel. They spent their first anniversary in Cabo San Lucas. After many years of never going anywhere, Stella Ann was able to contribute to summer adventure stories students and teachers shared at the beginning of school.

Three months before her June wedding, Norma called to ask if Stella Ann would forgive her for how she treated her over the years and to thank her for all she did for her family, especially Bradford. Stella Ann forgave her without hesitation. She thought she and Norma had made peace years earlier, but the request made it a formal gesture. Norma was likable and had a funny personality when she was happy. Charles, her husband, gave her the stability and loyalty Norma had desired for years. Norma and Stella Ann mended a lot of the negative rips and disagreements between them in the years after Stella Ann and Bradford divorced, but it was nice that Norma finally gave Stella Ann affirmation for being a devoted and positive addition to their family. Three weeks after Stella Ann's dream wedding, Norma died. Stella Ann was in New England, but her family paid their respects and were there to support Landon.

The rips in Stella Ann's life and heart were gradually stitched back together by the unwavering grace of God. She was safe and happy with her new husband and supportive family, and she was close to her hometown river, the Duck River. She was sharing life with someone who loved her, respected her, and wanted to be with her. In her golden years, a river of happiness and peace flowed steadily through her life. After years of adjusting and problem-solving on the riverbank, she learned she could start over, and she could return home.

EPILOGUE

Lessons

and Renewal

Life would have been easier for Stella Ann if she had listened to her parents and if she had guarded her heart. Her vulnerability and station in life got in the way and threatened to take her down. She couldn't see it at the time. It took years for Stella Ann to understand that there are people who lie and use others to their own benefit. Stella Ann was convinced academic education, religion, and Southern recipes were not the only tools a girl needed in her toolbox.

Relationship education was vital. Her reckless behavior and fearless attitude put her in the path of narcissists, pathological liars, predators, and opportunists. She came out on the positive side of all those encounters strictly by the grace and mercy of God and with a family who loved her through it all. Stella Ann learned trust is a virtue of innocence and fragility, and one needs guidance in recognizing trustworthy people as well as those who use trust to defraud and exploit. "Trust me" could be dangerous words.

There was little truth to the statement, "Honey, it is not you; it is him."

It was her, too. She contributed. She trusted beyond her better judgment to run and never return. She stayed too long and loved too much. She made numerous horrible, unhealthy choices, and she learned everyone kept secrets.

Stella Ann recognized one needed to have non-negotiable personal rules of survival in place and alternative "what if" plans in the background. If someone used the word indifferent to describe their feelings, she would believe them. Changing with the hope of getting someone to love her never worked, put her in a precarious situation, and was exhausting. Stella Ann accepted she should never expect someone else to change because it led to her own disappointment. Her worth was more valuable than either scenario. Stella Ann knew she should leave if someone threatened her. It was manipulation in the worst form. Stella Ann's experience taught her to be aware of unhealthy repetitive patterns that develop in relationships.

Desperation was typically the reason for poor choices. She knew desperation well. Not knowing how to ask for help or asking for help and not receiving it catapulted her into dark places. Stella Ann had visited those dark places many times.

It took her a long time to reconcile the junk in her life and appreciate the gifts. It took years to understand the way she was often treated was because of someone else's insecurities and compounded by her ADHD.

There was no glory or gratitude for sacrificing her own dreams for her husband's dreams. Stella Ann had a river of dreams and was frustrated and disappointed that most of those dreams never came to fruition for her. There were alternatives to her dreams that were acceptable, but alternatives left her feeling cheated and second best.

She never became a requested barroom pianist, but she played for friends at parties, helped a friend write songs, and played for school music programs. She always felt underrated as a musician, but she studied under one of the best piano professors at Gibbs Music Academy in Nashville. She didn't get to pursue art after being accepted at the Dawson School of Art and Design in Florida, but she did take painting, pottery, and ceramic classes as a hobby. She never got to be a radio personality or stand-up comic, but she made students and friends laugh and met many radio celebrities. She never finished her law school dream, but her son became an attorney. Stella Ann was never rated above a 3.5 as a competitive tennis player, but she got to enjoy over thirty years of tennis and team camaraderie. She didn't publish a book, but she wrote one. Stella Ann described herself as the "but" in a sentence, and she realized it could be an honorable place.

After years of reflection, regret, disappointment, isolation, and poor choices, life had a new meaning and purpose for her. She embraced the reality that the people and events prompting her heartache, shame, growth, tears, joy, and laughter made her a person with depth and empathy decorated with a slightly crusty and humorous edge. She could have remained stuck in a void, but she got help, asked for forgiveness, accepted the education, returned to her root values, reintroduced herself to herself, and moved forward. She realized she could go back home again. The Duck River kept calling her home, and for that, she was thankful.

Late in the journey, Stella Ann decided to be true to her core beliefs and values. She needed to use her gut and be suspicious until she no longer had to be. Prudence was a gift she should have given herself years earlier.

A raging river revealed much to Stella Ann over the years. It did not harden her heart. She believed a broken heart could heal, and a new healthy beginning could start at any time. Whether the new beginning included someone else or if it was simply the peace in accepting her own company, she was complete. She followed the rivers in her life home and moved forward with a new river of dreams. She decided to let her river of life and love flow as a clear, sparkling stream dancing in the glow of a new light.

Printed in Great Britain
by Amazon

47030136R00185